10-5-54

17974

92HC

COMPREHENSIVE
INORGANIC CHEMISTRY

COMPREHENSIVE INORGANIC CHEMISTRY

COMPREHENSIVE INORGANIC CHEMISTRY

M. CANNON SNEED

Professor of Chemistry, School of Chemistry
University of Minnesota

J. LEWIS MAYNARD

Late Professor of Chemistry, School of Chemistry
University of Minnesota

ROBERT C. BRASTED

Associate Professor of Chemistry, School of Chemistry
University of Minnesota

VOLUME THREE

THE HALOGENS
R. C. BRASTED

D. VAN NOSTRAND COMPANY, INC.

TORONTO   NEW YORK   LONDON

NEW YORK

D. Van Nostrand Company, Inc., 250 Fourth Avenue, New York 3

TORONTO

D. Van Nostrand Company (Canada), Ltd., 25 Hollinger Rd., Toronto

LONDON

Macmillan & Company, Ltd., St. Martin's Street, London, W.C. 2

PREFACE

Comprehensive Inorganic Chemistry is an eleven-volume reference work on the chemical elements and their inorganic compounds. It is comprehensive in the extensiveness of the fields covered rather than in the fullness of their treatment; hence, the volumes are offered individually as a *vade mecum* for the advanced worker—whether industrial or academic—not as an encyclopedic work. Their purpose, therefore, is to serve as a ready reference to those engaged in chemical manufacture and development and to those in advanced studies in chemistry in institutions of higher learning. To meet the requirements of these groups, emphasis has been placed largely on chemical properties and relationships and their interpretation in terms of theoretical concepts of atomic and molecular structure, the deductions from the periodic system, and the basic ideas relating to electrolytes. As a consequence, chapters on the elements are supplemented by special topics, as coordination compounds, catalysis, and reactions in nonaqueous solutions.

The various volumes of Comprehensive Inorganic Chemistry have certain usefulness in courses, especially advanced courses in colleges and universities. Nevertheless, the organization and manner of presentation of these books are not primarily pedagogic. Each chapter is essentially an independent unit, not based upon another coming before or after it. Terms are used with or without definition and statements are made with or without previous background for their understanding, for readers are assumed to be equipped with such knowledge of mathematics, physics, and chemistry to understand what is written. Indeed, the level at which the subject is presented is not too high for the average senior in chemistry or the recent graduate in this field. Notwithstanding the independence of the separate topics, there is a general unity in the treatment brought about by adhering very closely to the relationships in the periodic system and to the interpretations derived from atomic and molecular investigations. However, the transition elements, with the exception of the halogens, are treated before the regular elements.

Another feature is the presentation in tabular form of the chief physical constants of the elements. Chemical properties and the uses of the elements and their compounds are severally stressed for the most part according to their relative importance. Many inorganic compounds are not mentioned at all, and for a description of these substances the

v

literature may be consulted. From this source also may be obtained fuller treatment of the history, occurrence, physical properties, and methods of production of the elements. Selected references are given as footnotes where they are easily available when one wishes to consult the original literature. Throughout, the nomenclature used is that recommended by the committee of the International Union of Chemistry.

Many contributing authors have not only made these volumes possible, but have also added much to their usefulness and value. Such success as may come to this endeavor will in no small measure be the result of the efforts of these chemists. Acknowledgment is made to these contributors at chapter headings.

M. C. SNEED
J. LEWIS MAYNARD
ROBERT C. BRASTED

Minneapolis, Minn.
June, 1954

CONTENTS

TABLE I.1. PHYSICAL PROPERTIES OF THE HALOGENS

	Fluorine	Chlorine	Bromine	Iodine	Astatine
State (normal cond.)	Gas	Gas	Liquid	Solid	Solid
Color of vapor	Pale yellow	Greenish-yellow	Reddish-brown	Violet	—
Color of solid	Colorless	Greenish-yellow	Dark-red	Black	—
Melting point, °C	−223	−100.98[a]	−7.3	114	—
Boiling point, °C	−187	−34.05	58.78	183	—
Atomic weight	19.00	35.457	79.916	126.92	(211)[b]
Mass number of isotopes	19	35, 37	79, 81	127	211, 215, 216, 218
Atomic number	9	17	35	53	85
Heat of fusion (cal per mole)	—	1,531[a]	2,580	3,650	—
Heat of vaporization (cal per mole)	1,640	4,878	7,418	10,388	—
Density	1.108 (liq) 1.54 (at −196°C)[c]	1.557 (liq)	3.19 (liq)	4.93 (sol)	—
Solubility in H$_2$O (grams of solute per 100 g H$_2$O at 20°C)	Decomposes H$_2$O	0.732 (0.978 atm)	3.58	0.029	—
Heat of formation of hydrogen halide, 18°C, 1 atm (cal)	63,991	22,030	8,650	−5,926	—
Heat of dissociation (cal per mole)	37,700[d]	56,900	45,200	35,400	—
Dissociation constant at 1000°C	—	10^{-8}	8×10^{-3}	10^{-1}	—
Distribution ratio, CCl$_4$/H$_2$O at 0°C	—	20	27.0	85.5	—
Electron affinity, ev	4.13	3.75	3.53	3.2	—
Ionization potential of gaseous atom (volts)	17.34	12.95	11.80	10.6	—
Ionic radius of X$^-$, A	1.36	1.81	1.95	2.16	—
Dielectric constant of solid	—	2.0	3.2	4.0	—
Ionic susceptibility of X$^-$(10^6)	9.2	22.9	33.4	50.2	—

[a] L. Ziegler, Chem. Ing. Tech. 22, 229 (1950); W. F. Giauque and T. M. Powell, J. Am. Chem. Soc. 61, 1970 (1939).
[b] Most stable isotope.
[c] S. B. Kilner et al., J. Am. Chem. Soc. 74, 1086 (1952); cf. G. W. Elverum and R. N. Doescher, J. Chem. Phys. 20, 1834–1836 (1952).
[d] R. N. Doescher, J. Chem. Phys. 20, 330 (1952); cf. E. Wicke, J. Phys. Chem. 56, 358–360 (1952); see also pages 3 and 19.

INTRODUCTION

The members of the halogen family of elements are fluorine, chlorine, bromine, iodine, and astatine. They are placed in Group VIIA of the Mendeleev periodic chart and are characterized by their high electron affinity. Each of the elements has seven electrons in its outermost shell. The addition of a single electron to this orbit creates an ion which is isoelectronic with the next higher element, an inert gas. The halide ions are in general stable. The next to the outermost orbits of fluorine, chlorine, and bromine are completely filled, while the penultimate or N shell of iodine has only 18 electrons out of the maximum of 32. When the radius is compared to the size of the nuclear charge, these atoms may be considered as small. None of their seven valence electrons is easily removed from its normal state. The ease with which their atoms assume positive oxidation states increases with atomic number. For iodine, the +7 state is common (as in IO_4^-); but the assignment of a positive valence number to the halogen atoms, as in the oxycompounds, is little more than a mathematical courtesy, since the electrons are shared and not removed by the oxygen atoms.

The stability of iodine +7 in periodates is attributed to its relatively low electronegativity, whereas the double-bond repulsion factor of the chlorine is the stabilizing factor of +7 chlorine in perchlorates. Since bromine has intermediate electronegativity and double-bond repulsion, there is no marked stabilizing force to favor +7 bromine in a perbromate.[1]

The positive and negative oxidation levels assumed by the halogens in representative compounds are listed in Table I.2.

The electron affinity of the halogens decreases as the atomic number increases, in accord with the increasing number of shielding orbits and the size of the atoms. Fluorine has the greatest electronegativity of any of the elements and, therefore, is the most powerful oxidizing agent known. Iodine, on the other hand, has the lowest electronegativity among the naturally occurring halogens. The actual measured electron affinity of fluorine is 81 kcal/g atom *lower* than that of the chorine atom. Equally surprising is the fact that the measured electron affinity of the fluorine atom and the bromine atom are about the same. The reason for the large reactivity of fluorine lies in its small dissociation energy and its large electronegativity.

[1] R. deC. Ferreira, *Bull. soc. chim. France* **1950**, 135.

TABLE I.2. OXIDATION STATES OF THE HALOGENS*

Halogen	Oxidation States								
	-1	$+1$	$+2$	$+3$	$+4$	$+5$	$+6$	$+7$	$+8$
Fluorine	MF ClF	OF_2(?)	(O_2F_2)(?)	—	—	—	—	—	—
Chlorine	MCl BrCl	Cl_2O MClO	ClO	Cl_2O_3 $MClO_2$	ClO_2	Cl_2O_5 $MClO_3$	$\begin{cases} ClO_3 \\ Cl_2O_6 \end{cases}$	Cl_2O_7 $MClO_4$	(ClO_4)(?)
Bromine	MBr IBr	(Br_2O) MBrO	—	$(MBrO_2)$	BrO_2	$MBrO_3$	—	—	—
Iodine	MI	MIO	—	(MIO_2)	I_2O_4	I_2O_5 MIO_3	—	MIO_4 M_5IO_6	—
Astatine	(MAt)	(MAtO)				$(MAtO_3)$			

* Compounds whose formulas are enclosed in parentheses are not well characterized. A question mark following a compound indicates uncertainty as to the oxidation state of the halogen involved. M is hydrogen or an alkali metal.

Table I.1 shows the more common physical properties of the halogens. It can be seen that their properties change regularly when the elements are arranged in the order of their atomic numbers. The melting point, boiling point, and density for each halogen rise progressively from fluorine to iodine. The color of the elements deepens in the same order. The heats of vaporization increase with atomic number, and the heats of formation of the hydrohalogens decrease as the weight of the halogen atom increases. The hydration values (10 for Cl^- and 3.5 for I^-) for the halide ions appear to decrease with increasing atomic number, although this conclusion is based on incomplete information.[2] In view of the size of the iodide ion and its consequently low charge density, a comparatively small degree of hydration is reasonable.

The series, liquid Cl_2, Br_2, I_2, may be considered homologous in terms of $\log \eta$ (viscosity) and $1/T$ values. Thus, a straight line results when these data are plotted with an intercept at T approximately equal to $4070°K$.[3]

Table I.3 contains the standard electrode potential of each of the halogens. A large energy of hydration, typical of small ions, contributes to the large E_0 value found for fluorine.

[2] H. Spandau and G. Spandau, *Z. physik. Chem.* **192**, 211 (1943).
[3] D. A. Pospekhov, *Zhur. Priklad. Khim.* **24**, 876 (1951).

TABLE I.3. STANDARD REDOX POTENTIALS (E_0, VOLTS) AND ELECTRON
AFFINITY OF THE HALOGENS ($-\Delta E_0$) (KCAL/MOL)

$I_2 + 2e^- \rightleftharpoons 2I^- + 0.5345$	72.4 ± 1.5[a]
$Br_2 + 2e^- \rightleftharpoons 2Br^- + 1.087$	80.5 ± 0.4[b]
$Cl_2 + 2e^- \rightleftharpoons 2Cl^- + 1.3583$	85.84 ± 1.0[c]
$F_2 + 2e^- \rightleftharpoons 2F^- + 2.85$	$82(?)$[d]

[a] P. J. Sutton and J. E. Mayer, *J. Chem. Phys.* **3**, 20 (1935).
[b] P. M. Doty and J. E. Mayer, *ibid.* **12**, 323 (1944).
[c] K. J. McCallum and J. E. Mayer, *ibid.* **11**, 56 (1943).
[d] E. Wicke, *Nach. Akad. Wissensch. Göttingen* **1946**, 89; *cf. Z. angew. Chem.* **A60**, 65 (1948).

Covalent bonds between the several halogen atoms grow weaker as the size of these atoms increases. Quantitative evidence of this weakening is found in the increase in the values, from chlorine to iodine, of the dissociation constants of $X_2 \rightleftharpoons 2X$, in the increase in the dielectric constants from chlorine to iodine (no value available for fluorine), and in the decrease in the heat of fusion for each successive halogen. The dissociation energy of the fluorine molecule, $F_2(g) \rightleftharpoons 2F(g)$, has been variously reported from 63,000 cal/mol[4] from thermal conductivity measurements of fluorine at 1000° to 37.7 kcal/mol.[5] The latter value agrees well with entropy calculations but is in disagreement with flame temperature measurements.[6] A value 39.9 ± 0.08 kcal/mol is reported from effusion measurements through a nickel orifice at 10^{-4} mm pressure.[7]

In their reactions the halogens may behave as individual atoms or as if the atoms are in electromeric tautomerism:

$$:\overset{..}{\underset{..}{X}}:^- \mid \overset{..}{\underset{..}{X}}:^+ \rightleftharpoons :\overset{..}{\underset{..}{X}}^+ \mid :\overset{..}{\underset{..}{X}}:^-$$

[4] E. Wicke, *Angew. Chem.* **A60**, 65 (1948).
[5] R. N. Doescher, *J. Chem. Phys.* **20**, 330 (1952).
[6] D. Altman and M. Farber, *J. Chem. Phys.* **21**, 1118 (1953). (See page 19.)
[7] H. Wise, *J. Chem. Phys.* **20**, 927 (1952).

TABLE I.4. ISOTOPES OF FLUORINE, CHLORINE, BROMINE, IODINE, AND ASTATINE*

Isotope	Class†	Type of Decay	Half-life	Energy of Radiation in Mev	Method of Production and Genetic Relationships
$^{17}_{9}F$	A	β^+	70 s	1.72 spect	N-α-n; O-d-n; O-p-γ; F-γ-2n
^{18}F	A	β^+	112 m	0.649 spect	O-α-pn; ^{18}O-p-n; O-d-n; O-^{3}He-p; O-t-n; F-n-2n; F-d-t; F-γ-n; F-p-pn; Ne-d-α; Na-γ-αn; spall Al, Cu, Cl, Ag, Au
^{19}F; % abundance = 100					
^{20}F	A	β^-	10.7 s	5.41, no~7 β^- (lim 1%) spect	F-d-p; F-n-γ; Na-n-α
$^{33}_{17}Cl$	A	β^+	2.8 s	4.13 cl ch	S-d-n; S-p-n; Cl-γ-2n
^{34}Cl	A	β^+	33.2 m	4.5 (46%), 2.6 (28%), 1.3 (26%) spect	Al-^{12}C-αn; P-α-n; S-d-n; S-α, pn; S-p-n; S-t-n; Cl-n-2n; Cl-p-pn; Cl-γ-n; spall Fe, Cu
^{35}Cl; % abundance = 75.4					
^{36}Cl	A	β^-	4.4×10^5 y sp act	0.714 spect	Cl-n-γ; Cl-d-p
^{37}Cl: % abundance = 24.6					
^{38}Cl	A	β^-	37.29 m	4.81 (53%), 2.77 (16%), 1.11 (31%) spect	Cl-d-p; Cl-n-γ; ^{37}Cl-n-γ; K-n-α; spall Fe, Co, Cu; spall-fission Cu
^{39}Cl	A	β^-	55.5 m	1.65 (93%), 2.96 (7%) abs	A-γ-p; spall Fe, Co, Cu, As
$^{74}_{35}Br$	D	β^+, EC	35 m		Cu-C-3n
^{75}Br	B	β^+, EC	1.6 h	1.70 (46%), 0.8 (20%), 0.6 (15%), 0.3 (19%) spect	Cu-C-2n; ^{74}Se-d-n; ^{74}Se-p-γ

* From J. M. Hollander, I. Perlman, and G. T. Seaborg, *Revs. Mod. Phys.* **25** (2), 469–651 (1953).

† The degree of certainty of each isotopic assignment is indicated by a letter, according to the following code:

A = Element and mass number certain.

B = Element certain and mass number probable.

D = Element certain and mass number not well established.

E = Element probable and mass number not well established or unknown.

TABLE I.4—*Continued*

Isotope	Class†	Type of Decay	Half-life	Energy of Radiation in Mev	Method of Production and Genetic Relationships
^{76}Br	A	β^+	17.2 h	3.57 (46%), 1.7 (10%), 1.1 (11%), 0.8 (14%), 0.6 (19%) spect	As-α-3n; ^{76}Se-p-n
^{77}Br	A	EC 95%, β^+ 5%	57 h	0.336 spect	As-α-2n; ^{74}Se-α-p; ^{76}Se-d-n; parent ^{77m}Se
^{78}Br	A	β^+	6.4 m	2.4 abs	As-α-n; Se-d-n; Se-p-n; Br-γ-n; Br-n-2n
^{79}Br; % abundance = 50.52					
^{80m}Br	A	IT	4.58 h		Se-d-2n; Se-α-p; Se-p-n; Br-n-γ; Br-d-p; Br-γ-n; Br-n-2n; spall-fission Ta, Bi, U; fission Th (?)
^{80}Br	A	β^- ~92%, β^+ ~3%, EC ~5%	18 m	β^-: 1.99 (85%), 1.1 (15%) spect β^+: 0.87 spect	Se-p-n; Br-n-γ; Br-d-p; Br-γ-n; Br-n-2n; daughter ^{80m}Br
^{81}Br; % abundance = 49.48					
^{82}Br	A	β^-	35.87 h	0.465 spect, β-γ coinc	Se-p-n; Se-d-2n; Br-n-γ; Br-d-p; Rb-n-α; spall-fission Ta, Hg, Tl, Pb, Bi, U; fission U
^{83}Br	A	β^-	2.33 h	0.940 spect	Se-d-n; Rb-γ-α; spall-fission Ta, Hg, Pb, Bi, Th, U; fission Th, U, ^{233}U, Pu; daughter ^{83}Se, parent ^{83m}Kr
^{84}Br	A	β^-	30 m	4.68 (40%), 3.56 (9%), 2.53 (16%), 1.72 (35%) spect	Rb-n-α; spall-fission Bi, U; fission Th, U; daughter ^{84}Se
^{85}Br	A	β^-	3.00 m	2.5 abs	fission U; parent ^{85}Kr
^{87}Br	A	β^-, β^-n (~2% of disintegrations)	55.6 s	β^-: 2.6 (70%), 8.0 (30%) abs n (mean): 0.25 abs paraffin	fission U, ^{235}U, Pu; parent ^{87}Kr; parent ^{86}Kr
^{88}Br	A	β^-	15.5 s		fission U, parent ^{88}Kr

TABLE I.4—Continued

Isotope	Class†	Type of Decay	Half-life	Energy of Radiation in Mev	Method of Production and Genetic Relationships
^{89}Br	D	β^-, β^-n	4.51 s	n (mean): 0.43 abs paraffin	fission U, ^{235}U; parent ^{89}Kr(?), parent ^{88}Kr(?)
$^{120}_{53}$I	D	β^+	30 m	4.0 abs, spect	spall Sn (second order reaction); Sb-α-5n
^{121}I	B	β^+	1.5 h	1.2 abs, spect	spall Sn (second order reaction); Sb-α-4n, parent ^{121}Te; daughter ^{121}Xe
^{122}I	A	β^+	3.6 m	2.9 abs	Sb-α-3n; ^{122}Te-p-n; daughter ^{122}Xe
^{123}I	A	EC	13.0 h		spall Sn (second order reaction); Sb-α-2n; ^{121}Sb-α-2n; daughter ^{123}Xe
^{124}I	A	EC ~70%, β^+ ~30%	4.5 d	2.20 (51%), 1.50 (44%), 0.7 (5%) spect	spall Sn (second order reaction); Sb-α-n; Sb-α-3n; ^{121}Sb-α-n; Te-p-n; spall-fission Bi
^{125}I	A	EC (L/K 0.23)	60.0 d		Sb-α-2n; Te-d-n; spall-fission Bi; daughter ^{125}Xe; not parent ^{125m}Te (lim 0.05%)
^{126}I	A	EC ~58%, β^- ~40%, β^+(?) ~2%	13.0 d	β^-: 1.268 (27%), 0.85 (73%) spect	spall Sn (second order reaction); Sb-α-n; Te-d-n; Te-p-n; I-n-2n; I-γ-n; spall-fission Bi
^{127}I; % abundance = 100					
^{128}I	A	β^- 95.0%, EC +β^+ 5.0%	24.99 m	2.02 spect	I-n-γ; Te-d-2n; Te-p-n
^{129}I	A	β^-	1.72 × 10^7 y sp act	0.12 scint spect	fission U
^{130}I	A	β^-	12.6 h	1.03 (~60%), 0.61 (~40%) spect	Te-d-2n; Te-p-n; ^{129}I-n-γ; Cs-n-α
^{131}I	A	β^-	8.141 d	0.815 (0.7%), 0.608 (87.2%), 0.335 (9.3%), 0.250 (2.8%) spect, β-γ coinc	Te-d-n; spall-fission Th, U; fission Th, U, ^{233}U, ^{235}U, Pu; daughter ^{131}Te; parent (~1%) ^{131m}2Xe, parent ^{131m}1Xe

TABLE I.4—*Continued*

Isotope	Class†	Type of Decay	Half-life	Energy of Radiation in Mev	Method of Production and Genetic Relationships
^{132}I	B	β^-	2.4 h	2.2, 0.9 abs	spall-fission U; fission Th, U, ^{233}U; daughter ^{132}Te
^{133}I	A	β^-	20.5 h	1.3 ($\sim$91%), 0.4 ($\sim$9%) abs	spall-fission Pb, U; fission U, Pu; daughter ^{133}Te; parent ^{133}Xe; parent (2.4%) ^{133m}Xe
^{134}I	B	β^-	52.5 m	1.6 ($\sim$70%), 2.8 ($\sim$30%), hard β (weak) abs	spall-fission U; fission Th, ^{235}U, U, Pu; daughter ^{134}Te
^{135}I	A	β^-	6.68 h	0.5 (35%), 1.0 (40%), 1.4 (25%) spect	spall-fission U; fission Th, U, Pu; daughter ^{135}Te; parent ($\sim$30%) ^{135m}Xe, parent ($\sim$70%) ^{135}Xe; parent ^{135m}Xe; parent ^{135}Xe
^{136}I	D	β^-	86 s	6.5 abs	fission U, ^{233}U, Pu
^{137}I	A	β^-, β^-n ($\sim$6% of disintegrations)	22.0 s(n)	n (mean): 0.56 abs paraffin	fission U, Pu; parent ^{137}Xe
^{138}I	A	β^-	5.9 s		fission U, ancestor ^{138}Cs
^{139}I	A	β^-	2.7 s		fission U, parent ^{139}Xe, ancestor ^{139}Ba
$^{<202}_{85}$At	D	α, EC	43 s	6.50 ion ch	Bi-α-spall
$^{<203}$At	D	α, EC	1.7 m	6.35 ion ch	Bi-α-spall
^{203}At	D	α, EC	7 m	6.10 ion ch	Bi-α-10n; Au-C-6n
^{204}At	B	EC	$\sim$25 m genet		Bi-α-9n, parent ^{204}Po
^{205}At	B	α, EC	25 m	5.90 ion ch	Bi-α-8n, parent ^{205}Po; Au-C-4n
^{206}At	B	EC	2.6 h genet		Bi-α-7n, parent ^{206}Po
^{207}At	B	EC $\sim$90%, $\alpha \sim$10%	2.0 h	5.75 ion ch	Bi-α-6n; parent ^{207}Po, parent ^{203}Bi
^{208}At	B	EC	6.3 h genet		Bi-α-5n, parent ^{208}Po

TABLE I.4—*Continued*

Isotope	Class†	Type of Decay	Half-life	Energy of Radiation in Mev	Method of Production and Genetic Relationships
^{208}At	A	EC 99+%, α 0.5%	1.7 h	5.65 ion ch	daughter ^{212}Fr, parent ^{208}Po
^{209}At	B	EC ~95%, α ~5%	5.5 h	5.65 ion ch	Bi-α-4n, parent ^{209}Po, parent ^{205}Bi
^{210}At	A	EC 99+%, α 0.17%	8.3 h	5.519 (32%), 5.437 (31%), 5.355 (37%) spect	Bi-α-3n, parent ^{210}Po; parent ^{206}Bi
^{211}At	A	α 40.9%, EC 59.1%	7.5 h	5.862 spect	Bi-α-2n; spall Th, U
^{212}At	E	α	0.25 s		Bi-α-n
^{213}At‡	E	α		9.2 range emuls	descendent ^{225}Pa
^{214}At	B	α	~2 × 10^{-6} s est	8.78 ion ch	daughter ^{218}Fr
^{215}At	A	α	~10^{-4} s delay coinc	8.00 ion ch	daughter ^{219}Fr, parent ^{211}Bi; natural source, daughter ^{215}Po, parent ^{211}Bi
^{216}At	A	α	~3×10^{-4} s delay coinc	7.79 ion ch	daughter ^{220}Fr, parent ^{212}Bi (ThC); natural source, parent ^{212}Bi (ThC); daughter ^{216}Po; note ^{216}Po β-stable
^{217}At	A	α	0.018 s delay coinc	7.02 ion ch	daughter ^{221}Fr, parent ^{213}Bi
^{218}At	E	α; α 99+%, β^- 0.1%	1.5–2.0 s	α: 6.63 range	natural source, daughter ^{218}Po (RaA), parent ^{214}Bi (RaC)
^{219}At	A	α ~97%, β^- ~3%	0.9 m	α: 6.27 ion ch	natural source, daughter ^{223}Fr, parent ^{219}Em (An), parent ^{215}Bi

‡ See also page 95.

CHAPTER 1

FLUORINE

History. Fluorine is the most electronegative element known. Its extreme activity made its preparation and characterization difficult for the early investigators. It was not until 1886, sixty years after the discovery of bromine, that Moissan succeeded in isolating fluorine by electrolyzing anhydrous HF containing KHF_2. Fluorine is perhaps the least descriptive of the names of any of the halogens, being derived from the Latin word meaning "to flow," and is related to the fluxing action of calcium fluoride.

Occurrence. The great chemical activity of fluorine prevents its natural existence in the free state. Its abundance in the earth's crust (0.029 per cent) is about half that of chlorine. First evidence of any of the halogens in the sun is given by absorption lines for MgF and SrF.[1] The most important native compounds are fluorite or fluor spar, CaF_2; cryolite $3NaF \cdot AlF_3$; and fluorapatite or calcium fluophosphate, Ca_5F-$(PO_4)_3$. The first and last of these compounds are widely distributed. Calcium fluoride is mined in substantial quantities for use in the ferrous metal industry. The long chain, highly viscous, polymeric slags are broken down by the fluxing action of CaF_2 to permit a more efficient oxidation of the melt. The consumption of acid grade fluor spar has increased greatly through the years. A partial list of the uses of fluorine chemicals, illustrating their wide distribution through industry, includes acid fluorides and fluosilicates as laundry sours; cryolite as a component of the electrolyte in the manufacture of aluminum, as an insecticide, and as a constituent of enamels and glass; anhydrous hydrogen fluoride as a catalyst in the petroleum industry; Freons as refrigerants; and a number of fluorine compounds as important substances in the atomic energy program.

Greenland and Iceland supply the natural cryolite for the aluminum industry. Other fluorine-containing ores of lesser importance from an industrial standpoint are fluellite, $AlF_3 \cdot H_2O$; chiolite, $Na_5Al_3F_{14}$; pachnolite, $NaCaAlF_6 \cdot H_2O$; kryolithionite, $Li_3Na_3Al_2F_{12}$; and herderite, $CaBe$-$(FOH)PO_4$. Fluorine is found in small quantities in some of the more

[1] H. D. Babcock, *Astrophys. J.* **102**, 154–157 (1945); S. C. Ogburn, Jr., *J. Chem. Educ.* **24**, 314 (1947).

common silicates such as topaz, lepidolite, amphibole, and tourmaline. In certain localities, drinking water contains abnormally high quantities of fluoride ion. In such localities it is not unusual to find a high incidence of mottled, brittle teeth. In such places, on the other hand, the incidence of dental caries is unusually low, probably due to direct surface interaction of dissolved CaF_2 with the enamel. The mottling of teeth disappears when a change to fluorine-free water is made. The fluoride ion concentration in drinking water should not be over 1 ppm. Fluorides *naturally* occurring in the soil or in water are not a hazard from the point of view of their transfer into plants or milk. There is, however, the danger of increasing the fluorine content of foods by cooking them in such water.[2]

Superphosphates often contain enough fluorine to make them unsuitable as animal food. Superphosphate may be defluorinated by heating it in a ventilated space for a relatively short time at temperatures of 600°C and above; the fluorine content can be reduced to about 1 per cent of the amount originally present. At 800–1000°C the tricalcium phosphate formed compares favorably with bone meal as a mineral supplement for animal feeds.[3]

Preparation. Although the present method of fluorine production is not unlike that developed by Moissan, significant improvements have been made in the development of better cells, electrodes, and electrolytes.[4] One reason for the slow industrial progress in fluorine production has been the difficulty in developing an anode material capable of withstanding the action of fluorine.[5]

A nickel anode is satisfactory for fluorine production up to a cell temperature of about 150°C. Above this temperature nickel corrodes rapidly and the current efficiency drops. The German high-temperature process (240–250°C), developed during World War II, used graphite anodes. The current efficiency of these anodes at elevated temperatures is 95–98 per cent. Some cells have been in operation over a year without replacement. Carbon has been found to be more satisfactory than graphite, since the part of the carbon electrode immersed in the electrolyte retains its strength rather than spalling as graphite does. The cell itself acts as a cathode. Silver has been found to be an excellent material for the con-

    [2] H. V. Smith, M. C. Smith, and M. Vavich, *Arizona Agr. Expt. Sta.*, *Mimeographed Rept.* **77**, 6 pp. (1945).
    [3] E. J. Fox *et al.*, *Ind. Eng. Chem.* **38**, 329–334 (1946).
    [4] *Chem. & Eng. News* **24**, 2360 (1946); *Chem. & Met. Eng.* **53**, 106–108 (1946); W. C. Schumb *et al.*, *Natl. Nuclear Energy Ser. Div.* VII, 1, pp. 11–130; H. R. Leech, *Research* **5**, 449 (1952).
    [5] Symposium on Fluorine, *Ind. Eng. Chem.* **39** (3), 244–434 (1947).

struction of cells. Magnesium or a 2 per cent manganese-magnesium alloy is satisfactory and was used by the Germans in producing over 50 tons of fluorine a month.

Although the eutectic, KF·HF, has the lowest vapor pressure of any mixture of KF and HF, its melting point is too sensitive to small changes in composition to permit its use as an electrolyte. The compound KF·2HF does not have this disadvantage, but does show a sharp rise in vapor pressure with a small rise in temperature. Hydrogen fluoride used to make the electrolyte must be of the highest purity attainable by distillation. The relationship between the HF content of the electrolytic bath and its specific conductivity in the range from 90 to 100°C is shown in Table 1.1.

TABLE 1.1. SPECIFIC CONDUCTIVITY OF KF·HF ELECTROLYTES FROM 90–100°C

Weight Per Cent of HF in Electrolyte	Specific Conductivity, Ohm^{-1}		
	90°C	95°C	100°C
44.7	0.245	0.260	0.277
44.5	0.232	0.253	0.273
44.1	0.226	0.243	0.256
43.2	0.195	0.209	0.224
41.9	0.175	0.192	0.210
41.1	0.163	0.180	0.196
40.7	—	0.167	0.184
39.4	0.135	0.151	0.165
39.0	0.131	0.147	0.164
37.6	0.110	0.128	0.143
37.4	—	0.122	0.143

Some attention has been given to the operation of a room-temperature cell with an electrolyte high in HF content. All the usual materials of anode, cell, and cathode construction corrode badly, and the operating efficiency drops from a maximum of 80 per cent to 50 per cent. Electrolytes such as SbF_3, ZnF_2, PbF_2, and CdF_2 have been used with poor success.[6]

A medium-temperature process has been generally accepted in the United States as being the most efficient. The cell operates at 100°C, is constructed of mild steel, and has a carbon or a graphitized carbon anode. Nickel anodes have largely been replaced because, at a low temperature, there is substantial consumption of nickel, a large amount of sludge forms, and the current efficiency is low.

[6] W. S. Calcott and A. F. Benning, **U. S. 2,034,458**, Mar. 17, 1936.

The extremes in electrolyte composition used are from $KF \cdot HF$ to $KF \cdot 12$–$13HF$, and the extremes in temperature variation are from -80 to $250°C$. Close control of the electrolyte to $KF \cdot 1.8$–$2.0HF$ is important if polarization is to be prevented. The control is maintained by continuous observation of the specific gravity by the use of a Monel metal float so weighted that an attached stylus makes a continuous record. Table 1.2 gives the relationship between specific gravity, temperature, and mole ratio of HF to KF.

TABLE 1.2. SPECIFIC GRAVITY OF $KF \cdot HF$ ELECTROLYTES

Moles HF/Mole KF	Temperature °C	Specific Gravity
1.76_1	86.0	1.937
1.76_2	91.0	1.930
1.76_8	92.5	1.928
1.77_5	100.7	1.920
1.81_4	91.0	1.923
1.83_2	86.5	1.926
1.83_6	93.2	1.917
1.86_2	99.0	1.906
1.87_9	85.0	1.920
1.88_2	93.5	1.906

Lithium fluoride is added to lower the freezing point of the electrolytic bath so as to permit electrolysis at lower temperatures and a lower hydrogen fluoride content. Lithium fluoride is only slightly soluble in $KF \cdot HF$ at $100°C$. An ideal composition for an electrolytic bath is 82 per cent KHF_2, 3 per cent LiF, and 14.3 per cent HF. The entire role played by the LiF is not certain. It may be related to the colloidal characteristics of solid LiF, which is in excess of that actually in solution, or it may be that the wetting characteristics of the electrolyte are improved by this salt.

The operating efficiency of the cell is increased by minimizing the anodic polarization. This phenomenon is common and unpredictable. Polarization may occur at either the anode or the cathode. Several reasons suggested are (a) water in the electrolyte, (b) high current density, (c) improper control of temperature, and (d) improper electrolyte concentration.

Commercial cells operate up to approximately 2000 amps. At present, it is difficult to operate such a cell continuously, because of the need for intermittent HF replacement. The cell body is jacketed for heating and cooling. The anodes are carbon blades, arranged in parallel rows, and bolted to a heavy inverted copper channel running between rows of anodes. A typical cell may operate at 71.5 amps per sq ft at 1000 amps, and 53 amps per sq ft at 750 amps. The cathodes are parallel steel plates. The diaphragm assembly is made of six-mesh steel screen welded to a frame. Nitrogen flush lines are welded to the anode and cathode compartments. Provision is made for withdrawing electrolyte samples from both compartments, and sludge must be removed occasionally. A crackling sound often is associated with fluorine production at low current densities. This noise is due largely to combination of the hydrogen, produced at the cathode area facing the anode, with fluorine produced at the anode. In practice, it is possible to minimize this condition by placing the anode and cathode so that only the perforated portion of a diaphragm skirt is between the thin steel cylinder cathode and the carbon rod anode. Fig. 1.1 is a diagram of a 600–800 ampere high-temperature cell. The cell, which contains about 100 lb of electrolyte, is constructed of Monel metal, steel, and copper; the anodes are of carbon. The total weight of the cell is about 400 lb. Its life is estimated to be 200,000 ampere hours. Fig. 1.2 represents the carbon-anode fluorine generator, a type of 100°C cell, which is satisfactory for the large-scale production of fluorine. The anode and cathode compartments are separated to prevent gas-phase mixing by a solid metal skirt and liquid-phase mixing by a perforated Monel sheet diaphragm. Such units have been in operation for more than 5,000,000 ampere hours. This time is sufficient for the production of nearly 7000 lb of fluorine.

The fluorine issuing from the cell may contain about 5–15 per cent of HF. Fluorine free from HF may still contain about 1 per cent each of oxygen (from water in the electrolyte) and the Group 0 elements, a small amount of OF_2, and traces of a mist of fine particles of solidified electrolyte which have been swept up from the cell. The purity of the product for a particular cell reaches a maximum after some 15,000 ampere hours of operation, or after the production of about 20 lb of fluorine.

Handling of Fluorine. The sharp increase in the use of elementary fluorine by the organic chemical industries and in the atomic energy program has necessitated a comprehensive study of the compression, "bottling," storage, disposal, and physiological effects of fluorine and its compounds.

When the activity and the low critical temperature (−129°C) of fluorine are noted, the difficulties in compression and shipping become obvious. The filling of storage tanks with fluorine at moderate pressures may be accomplished by condensation with liquid nitrogen and evaporation into the containers. Labor costs and the loss of a considerable amount of nitrogen make this procedure an expensive one.

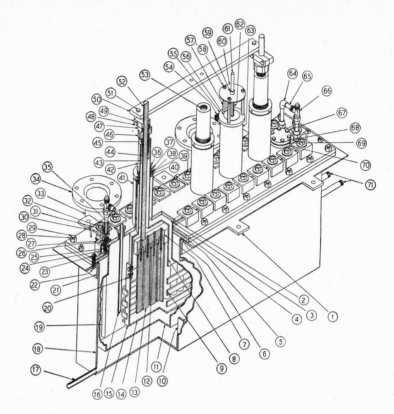

FIG. 1.1.   Construction details of 600–800 ampere cell.

From Ind. Eng. Chem. 39(3), 269 (1947).

1. Lug
2. Headplate
3. Headplate gasket
4. Clamp flange
5. Cathode box flange
6. Coolant box gasket
7. Anode bar
8. Skirt
9. Diaphragm cage bar
10. Coolant box rib
11. Cathode box
12. Copper dowel pin
13. Carbon
14. Diaphragm case bottom
15. Diaphragm case end
16. Thermocouple well
17. Coolant drain pipe
18. Coolant box
19. Regeneration tube
20. Monel bolt
21. Coolant box flange
22. Flange bolt (end)
23. Flange nut (end)
24. Headplate clamp

25. Clamp stud
26. Clamp washer
27. Clamp nut
28. Flange nut (side)
29. Flange bolt (side)
30. Packing gland
31. Packing nut
32. Packing
33. Condenser elbow
34. Condenser flange
35. Thermocouple nut
36. Diaphragm clamp ring
37. Lock ring
38. Packing
39. Cathode riser ring
40. Packing
41. Cathode tube
42. Anode tube (diaphragm riser)
43. Anode packing gland
44. Packing
45. Insulation sleeve
46. Anode packing nut
47. Spacer
48. Clamp block bolt and nut

49. Clamp block
50. Anode bus bar
51. Anode bus bar bolt and nut
52. Anode bar riser
53. Fluorine outlet fitting
54. Hydrogen outlet
55. Valve seat plate
56. Valve plunger
57. Spacer
58. Spacer nut
59. Bushing
60. Guide plate
61. Valve stem
62. Valve spring
63. Hydrogen outlet tube
64. Elbow
65. Nipple
66. Tee
67. Inspection port bolt
68. Inspection port cover
69. Inspection port gasket
70. Inspection port ring
71. Coolant overflow

The reactivity of fluorine is very much a function of temperature. Glass and many metals are not acted upon by fluorine at low temperatures (as $-187°C$), whereas at elevated temperatures they burn spontaneously. The nonreactivity of a metal surface is largely a function of the stability of the fluoride layer formed on initial contact. The successful design of compression equipment for filling tanks depends on minimizing friction of the working parts of the compressor. A special Monel metal compressor is constructed so that there are two or more pulsating

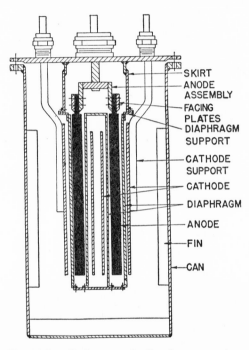

Fig. 1.2.   Carbon anode fluorine generator.
From Ind. Eng. Chem. 39(3), 259 (1947).

diaphragms (84 pulsations per minute) connected hydraulically by a liquid relatively inert to fluorine. Fig. 1.3 represents such a compressor. All necessary joints are of heavy construction and use copper or aluminum gaskets. The polymer Teflon[90] (polytetrafluoroethylene) is also used in gasket and insulation construction.

Corrosion must be minimized by reducing the hydrogen fluoride content of the fluorine. A reduction to less than 0.5 per cent is brought about by first refrigerating the mixture at $-70°C$ and atmospheric

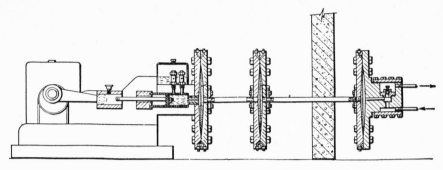

Fig. 1.3.   Fluorine gas compressor.
From Ind. Eng. Chem. 39(3), 273 (1947).

pressure, and then chemically absorbing any remaining hydrogen fluoride in NaF (Table 1.3).

Nickel and Monel metal show good resistance to fluorine attack up to 500°C and make satisfactory storage containers. Copper-nickel alloys, in which the copper content is in excess of 60 per cent, are satisfactory for containers and safe at pressures up to 200 atm. The metallic surface is protected by a coating of the inert metal fluoride.[7] Carbon steels with less than approximately 0.01 per cent silicon are resistant up to about 400°C, and stainless steels show satisfactory resistance up to 250°C. Whereas most metal fluorides formed on the surface are highly adherent and inhibit further attack, the coating on iron is a green powdery substance which affords no protection. Alloying ingredients must be considered individually. Niobium (columbium) forms a volatile fluoride, NbF_5 (bp 229°C), and thus lowers the resistance of an alloy containing the metal. Aluminum and magnesium, respectively, are resistant up to 450 and 300°C, and the corrosion is not great even beyond these temperatures. Copper is satisfactory at low temperatures, but is attacked rapidly at elevated ones. This behavior may be due to the presence of small amounts of oxygen in the fluorine. Since hydrogen fluoride is likely to be present in commercial fluorine, metals which are to be in contact with it should also be resistant to attack by HF. Nickel, nickel-base alloys, and copper show good resistance to HF up to 600°C. Inconel is less resistant than nickel or Monel metal and should not be used above 480°C.

No completely satisfactory method has been devised for the disposal of waste fluorine. Methods in current use include the reaction of the element with $CaCl_2$ or NaCl to give chlorine, which can be absorbed in

[7] H. F. Priest and A. V. Grosse, **U. S. 2,419,915**, April 29, 1947.

TABLE 1.3. RELATION OF TEMPERATURE TO VAPOR PRESSURE OF
NaHF₂ IN THE PRESENCE OF NITROGEN

Temp. °C	Vapor Pressure (mm) of HF over NaF·HF	HF in Nitrogen Volume Per Cent
25	0.01	0.001
100	1.4	0.18
200	87	11.5
250	422	55.6
275	706	93.0
278	760	100

caustic. This method is a convenient one for laboratory installations. Another method involves the intimate contact with caustic soda or lime for at least one minute. Shorter periods of time are likely to result in OF_2 formation; a spray of aqueous HF and F_2 into a tower packed with caustic is advised. Fluorine may be disposed of by burning it with hydrogen or petroleum gases. The HF which is formed creates a new corrosion problem and must in turn be absorbed. Furthermore, contact of fluorine with hydrogen brings considerable danger of an explosion. Other methods of removal involve the reaction with sulfur to form sulfur hexafluoride, SF_6, and with carbon to form carbon tetrafluoride, CF_4.

Health Hazards in Handling Fluorine and Its Compounds. The hazards involved in handling fluorine and fluorine-containing compounds are listed according to the nature of the compounds.

1. *Insoluble fluorides.* Fluor spar and cryolite are common members of this class. Because of their insolubility, they have low toxicity. They are nonirritating to the skin; but, when their dusts are inhaled in very considerable quantities, they may be absorbed slowly to produce chronic poisoning or fluorosis. Some of the symptoms reported are alopecia,[8] anorexia, vomiting, constipation, dyspnea, and rheumatic pains. The amount of this type of fluocompound that must be ingested to cause poisoning is so large as to virtually eliminate insoluble fluorides as hazardous chemicals.

2. *Soluble neutral fluorides.* The soluble nonacid-forming fluorides are widely used in the ceramic and electroplating industries. When ingested, or inhaled as a dust, they are readily absorbed. Excretion begins to take place immediately, and more than 10 mg of sodium fluoride may be ingested daily without storage or harmful effects. A lethal dose taken by mouth varies from 5 to 15 grams. It produces severe cramps and stomach and intestinal hemorrhages which precede death. The toxicity

[8] L. Spira, *J. Hyg.* **44**, 276–283 (1946).

of soluble fluorides varies greatly. Fluoborates are eliminated without toxic effect and much faster than either the fluosilicates or the fluorides.

3. *Acidic fluorine chemicals.* This class includes hydrofluoric acid, fluoboric acid, fluosilicic acid, and the general class of salts that hydrolyze to form acid solutions. All these compounds are extremely corrosive to the skin. The skin changes, resulting from contact, range from minor burns to serious ulcers which heal slowly. Hydrogen fluoride and its aqueous solution are the worst offenders of the group. Inhalation of the gas in sufficient quantities brings on a fatal lung edema. The quantity necessary to cause eye irritation is very low. It is very improbable for a lung condition to arise except by sudden inhalation of the acid from a spray or dust. A person suffering from anemia or cardiovascular disease might, however, succumb to circulatory collapse or pulmonary edema after exposure to concentrations which are not very irritating to the eyes and nose.

4. *Fluorinating agents and elementary fluorine.* The halogen fluorides and metal polyfluorides, now common as organic and inorganic fluorinating agents, and oxygen difluoride are members of this class. All of these compounds and elementary fluorine are extremely toxic. The necessary precautions include the use of protective equipment such as gauntlet-style neoprene gloves, eye shields with large visors, chemical respirators with cartridges for acid gases, acid type neoprene aprons, safety goggles, and safety shoes with neoprene soles.

5. *Organic fluorine compounds.* After the first two or three fluorine atoms have been introduced into an organic molecule, the compound becomes highly inactive. However, a fluorine compound which hydrolyzes to yield HF presents a health hazard. A chemical oddity is noted in the high toxicity of carbon tetrachloride and the complete nontoxicity of carbon tetrafluoride.[9]

Physiological Properties of Fluorine and Fluorides. Fluorine is about as toxic to insects as is HCN. Plants can stand concentrations of fluorine up to 1000 ppm without injury. No accurate tolerance limit has been established for man, but the value for HF is about 3 ppm. Solutions of HF at concentrations greater than 40 per cent and the vapors from these solutions destroy the skin on contact. A blast of fluorine on the skin causes a thermal burn not unlike that caused by an acetylene torch. If the exposure has been slight, several hours may elapse before pain is felt. In the absence of adequate treatment, necrosis and ulceration ensue. The basis for skin treatment is the infiltration of calcium

[9] H. C. Miller, *Chem. Eng. News* 27, 3854 (1949).

gluconate solution around the affected tissue. By this treatment fluoride ion is converted to insoluble calcium fluoride.

Traces of fluoride ion appear to be necessary for the maintenance of the good health of animals. Mention has already been made of the effect of the fluoride ion on tooth structure. When the fluoride ion is injected intravenously in large quantities, about 90 per cent is eliminated at once, and at least part of the remainder may be eliminated from the animal body over a long period of time. In small animals, the fluoride ion actually detoxifies As_2O_3. A quantity of from 15 to 30 mg of fluoride ion administered orally to rats is effective in detoxifying 30 mg of As_2O_3.[10]

Physical Properties. Fluorine under normal conditions is a pale-yellow gas with an irritating odor not unlike that of hypochlorous acid. At about $-252°C$ the yellow liquid becomes colorless. Inhalation of the gas is dangerous, but it does not have as adverse an action as chlorine, nor is it as poisonous as hydrogen fluoride. The atomic weight of fluorine, as obtained from a combination of density and x-ray data, is 18.9967 ± 0.0010.[11] The magnetic moment of ^{19}F is 2.626 ± 0.0001.[12]

The high values for the heat of dissociation reported prior to 1947 appear to be in error, although values in excess of 60 kcal/mol are in general agreement with the progression in this property with molecular weight of the halogens. An indication of lower values being more nearly correct is found in the work on the dissociation energy of ClF.[13] Refined techniques for the determination of lnK for $F_2 \rightleftarrows 2F$ have given the value of 37.7 ± 0.4 kcal/mol over the temperature range 759 to 1115°K.[14] A nearly identical value (37 ± 2 kcal/mol) is reported, based upon measurements of exploded hydrogen and fluorine mixtures in the presence of HF as a diluent.[15] From measurements of equilibrium pressures of fluorine at temperatures from 810 to 860°K, the dissociation energy of fluorine is reported as 31.5 ± 0.9 kcal/mol. This value agrees with the value of 31 ± 4 kcal/mol calculated by means of the Born-Haber cycle from the electron affinity value of 82 ± 3 kcal/mol at 815°K. The degree of dissociation (α) is 0.07 ± 0.04, and the dissociation equilibrium constant is calculated from these data as 0.975 ± 1.10 (10^{-3} atm). At 860°K, the values of α and K are 0.21 ± 0.05 and 10.6 ± 5.4, respectively. A possible explanation for the differences in heat of dissociation values is found in the variations of temperature in different parts of the fluorine measur-

[10] J. C. Finerty and J. D. Grace, *Science* 101, 359 (1945).
[11] D. A. Hutchinson, *Phys. Rev.* 66, 144 (1944).
[12] H. L. Poss, *Phys. Rev.* 75, 600 (1949).
[13] A. L. Wahrhaftig, *J. Chem. Phys.* 10, 248 (1942).
[14] R. N. Doescher, *J. Chem. Phys.* 20, 330 (1952).
[15] E. Wicke and H. Friz, *Z. Electrochem.* 57, 9 (1953).

ing system. The degree of dissociation as well as the equilibrium constants are not simply related to pressure differences.[16]

The surface tension of liquid fluorine at 69.2°K is 17.9 dynes/cm and 14.6 dynes/cm at 81.0°K. Density values other than the one recorded in Table I.1 are 1.639 ± 0.002 g/cc at 65.4°K and 1.509 ± 0.002 at 85.2°K. The viscosity over the temperature range 69.2 to 83.2°K is expressed by the equation $\eta = 2.43 \times 10^{-4} \exp(196/T)$.[17]

Average values of the second virial coefficient of fluorine in cc over the temperature range 180–300°K are recorded in Table 1.4.[18] The standard entropy values for F_2 and $2F$ at 1000°K are 58.50 and 88.58 cal/deg, respectively. At 900°K, the values of $S_{F_2}^\circ$ and S_{2F}° are 57.57 and 87.52 cal/deg, respectively.[19] Other physical properties of fluorine are found in Table I.1.

TABLE 1.4. VIRIAL COEFFICIENTS FOR FLUORINE

$T°K$	Value of 2nd Virial Coeff., CC
80	−385
85	−310
90	−256
95	−224
100	−202
110	−175
125	−137
150	−98
175	−67
200	−49
250	−26

The longest lived radioisotope of fluorine is ^{18}F, a β^+-emitter with a half-life of 112 min (see Table I.4 for other radio-isotopes of fluorine). Three convenient production schemes for this isotope are: $^{19}F(\gamma,n)^{18}F$, with 48–84 mev x-rays from a betatron; $^{19}F(n,2n)^{18}F$, with a cyclotron and the reaction $^7Li(d,n)^8Be$ as a source of fast neutrons; and finally $^{16}O(t,n)^{18}F$ with tritons from the reaction $^6Li(n,\alpha)T$ in a nuclear reactor. Labeled halogen fluorides (with the radioisotope 18) can be prepared by an exchange of the halogen fluoride with liquid or gaseous $H^{18}F$ or in contact with $Li^{18}F$-Al_2O_3. Radio-$^{18}F_2$ can be obtained by a gas-phase exchange reaction with $H^{18}F$ or one of the halogen 18 fluorides.

Chemical Properties and Reactions. The oxidation-reduction potential of the system, $2F^- \rightleftharpoons F_2$, is −2.85 volts, the largest negative

[16] P. W. Gilles and J. L. Margrave, *J. Chem. Phys.* **21**, 381 (1953).
[17] G. W. Elverum, Jr., and R. N. Doescher, *J. Chem. Phys.* **20**, 1834 (1952).
[18] D. White *et al., J. Chem. Phys.* **21**, 1149 (1953).
[19] R. N. Doescher, *J. Chem. Phys.* **20**, 330 (1952).

value for the transition of any simple ion to the elementary state. The corresponding oxidation-reduction potential of $2Cl^- \rightleftharpoons Cl_2$ is -1.36 volts. In agreement with the behavior of the first member of any family of regular elements, the reactions of fluorine are not strictly comparable with those of the other halogens. Only a very few substances, such as the Group 0 elements, resist the action of fluorine. The small size of the fluoride ion favors its combination with many metal ions to form stable complexes. Elements attain their highest oxidation states with fluorine because of its high electron affinity and because of the large number of fluorine atoms which may be bonded to a metal or a nonmetal.

The reactivity of fluorine is a function of temperature. At low temperatures, pure fluorine shows very little reaction with pure hydrogen. At elevated temperatures and with impure gases, there is a violent reaction. Ozone is produced only in small quantities when fluorine reacts with water and with solutions of hydroxide bases. The ozone produced by the reaction with water may be destroyed by the heat of the reaction. The OF_2 produced when fluorine reacts with basic solutions does not decompose the ozone.[20]

Much of the available information on the reactions of fluorine with simple inorganic substances is in the form of broad generalizations. In many instances, the conditions for reaction, the possible formation of intermediate compounds, and characterization of the products of a reaction need further study.[21]

1. *The hydrogen-fluorine system.* The amount of heat evolved when hydrogen and fluorine combine is so large that temperatures over 4000°C are obtained. A torch reaction is thus suggested.

Since the strength of the hydrogen to fluorine bond is great, the dissociation of hydrogen fluoride is small and thus the efficiency of the torch is high.[22] A comparison between the reactions of fluorine and oxygen with a number of reducing gases is made in the following equations:

$$H_2 + F_2 \rightarrow 2HF \text{ (gas) } + 128.0 \text{ kcal}$$
$$H_2 + \tfrac{1}{2}O_2 \rightarrow H_2O \text{ (gas) } + 57.8 \text{ kcal}$$
$$CH_4 + 4F_2 \rightarrow CF_4 + 4HF + 415 \text{ kcal}$$
$$CH_4 + 2O_2 \rightarrow CO_2 + 2H_2O + 212.79 \text{ kcal}$$
$$HC \equiv CH + 5F_2 \rightarrow 2CF_4 + 2HF + 635 \text{ kcal}$$
$$HC \equiv CH + 2\tfrac{1}{2}O_2 \rightarrow 2CO_2 + H_2O + 312 \text{ kcal}$$

[20] E. Briner and R. Tolun, *Helv. Chim. Acta* **31**, 937 (1948).
[21] E. E. Aynsley *et al.*, *J. Chem. Soc.* **1952**, 1622; M. Griffel and J. W. Stout, *J. Am. Chem. Soc.* **72**, 435 (1950); H. J. Emeléus, *Bull. soc. chim France* **1953**, 909.
[22] H. F. Priest and A. V. Grosse, *Ind. Eng. Chem.* **39**, 431–433 (1947).

TABLE 1.5. COMPARATIVE BOND STRENGTHS (KCAL PER MOL)

H—F	147.5 kcal	H—O	110.2 kcal
C—F	107	C—O	70.0
F—F	63.5	O—F	58.5
Cl—F	86.5	Cl—O	49.5

In Table 1.5 the strengths of certain fluorine and oxygen bonds are compared. It is recognized that the H—F bond is the strongest covalent bond known. The degree of dissociation at a given temperature for a fluorine compound is lower than for any corresponding oxygen compound. The emission spectrum from 0.85 to 2.75μ of the H_2—F_2 flame has been recorded with prism resolution in the fundamental as well as in the first and second overtone regions. Flame temperatures of about 4000°K have been estimated from spectroscopic data. It is not known whether there is equipartition of energy between vibrational and rotational excitation. The molecular constants are as follows: $B_0 = 20.569$ cm^{-1}, $\alpha = 0.751$ cm^{-1}, $D_0 = 2.42 \times 10^{-3}$ cm^{-1}, $\nu_1 = 3961.31$ cm^{-1}, and $\nu_2 = 7751.84$ cm^{-1}.[23]

The hydrogen-fluorine torch is made of copper or copper alloy (60 per cent copper) tubing (Fig. 1.4). Other metals are too susceptible to continued corrosion. The fluorine emerges from the inner and the hydrogen from the annular outer tube. The preferred ratios of fluorine pressure to hydrogen pressure are those in excess of 10:1; a ratio of 50:1 is very satisfactory. Temperatures in excess of 4300°K are reported for this hydrogen-fluorine flame.[24] Despite the high heat of conductivity of copper, the metal may be welded and cut with such a torch; the copper fluoride formed is self-fluxing. The high melting point of aluminum fluoride prevents aluminum from being welded. Steel, nickel, and Monel may be welded.

2. *Reaction of fluorine with metals.* All metals react with fluorine, and the rate and degree of attack are dependent on the temperature. In general, a metal tends to reach its highest oxidation state in combination with fluorine. Sulfur, selenium, silicon, carbon, and antimony ignite spontaneously in fluorine. The alkali metals potassium, rubidium, and cesium react with fluorine (free of HF) at 140–220°C to give substances higher in fluorine than is represented by the general formula MF. The limit for Rb and Cs appears to be MF_3. High fluorine activity is reported for the compounds. Lithium and sodium do not behave in this manner.[25] Iron, zinc, magnesium, manganese, nickel, aluminum, and

[23] W. S. Benedict et al., J. Opt. Soc. Amer. **43**, 1106 (1953).
[24] R. H. Wilson et al., J. Am. Chem. Soc. **73**, 5514 (1951).
[25] H. Bode and E. Klesper, Z. anorg. u. allgem. Chem. **267**, 97 (1951).

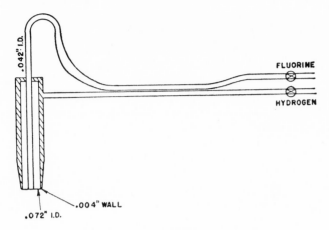

FIG. 1.4. Hydrogen-fluorine torch.
From Ind. Eng. Chem. 39(3), 433 (1947).

silver burn if the temperature is elevated. Gold and the platinum metals are attacked only at very high temperatures. Hydrocarbons burn spontaneously. Glass and asbestos burn in fluorine if they are strongly preheated. The formation of a surface coat of a metal fluoride reduces the tendency for massive metals to react completely.

As noted, the higher (though not necessarily the highest) of the normal oxidation states of an element commonly occurs in combination with fluorine. This fact is admirably illustrated in Table 1.6 which lists the binary fluorides of the elements of the first transition series.[26] These

TABLE 1.6. BINARY FLUORIDES OF THE FIRST TRANSITION SERIES

			CrF_2	MnF_2	FeF_2	CoF_2	NiF_2	CuF_2	ZnF_2
ScF_3	TiF_3	VF_3	CrF_3	MnF_3	FeF_3	CoF_3			
	TiF_4	VF_4	CrF_4						
		VF_5							

metals show their highest valences in the oxyanions they form. The dual effects of the presence of oxide ions, which are difficult to oxidize, and the formation of complex ions are both operative in stabilizing high oxidation states. It would be expected that fluocomplexes could be prepared in which the central metal atoms would show their highest oxidation states. That this is not always the case is illustrated by the data given in Table 1.7.

[26] R. N. Haszeldine and A. G. Sharpe, *Fluorine and Its Compounds*, p. 48, Methuen and Co., Ltd., London, 1951.

TABLE 1.7. HIGHEST OXIDATION STATES OF THE FIRST TRANSITION SERIES
OF ELEMENTS IN FLUOCOMPLEXES AND OXYCOMPLEXES

Element	Maximum Oxidation State in Fluocomplex	Maximum Oxidation State in Oxycomplex
Sc	3	—
Ti	4	4
V	5	5
Cr	4	6
Mn	4	7
Fe	3	6
Co	4	4
Ni	5	3
Cu	3	3
Zn	2	2

The fluocomplexes of the elements vanadium through copper have been prepared[27] by fluorination of mixtures of potassium chloride and the chloride of the appropriate metal. In each case the molar ratio of potassium chloride to transition metal chloride was varied until a homogeneous product was obtained. Each product has been characterized by analysis, weight change during fluorination, and by x-ray, as well as by chemical analysis.

Red potassium hexafluonickelate(IV), $K_2[NiF_6]$ prepared in the described manner is isomorphous with potassium hexafluosilicate. It is subject to hydrolysis and is reduced by hydrogen according to the equation

$$K_2[NiF_6] + H_2 \rightarrow K_2[NiF_4] + 2HF$$

With copper a pale green complex of the composition $K_3[CuF_6]$ is obtained. This compound is also decomposed by water. Hydrogen reduction produces copper(I) fluoride.[28]

Cobalt forms a bright blue complex, potassium heptafluocobaltate(IV). This substance is isomorphous with $K_3[ZrF_7]$, is fairly stable toward hydrogen reduction, but, at 450° is slowly converted to $K_3[CoF_6]$. Only a small portion of the available fluorine is released when $K_3[CoF_7]$ reacts with water.

Fluorination of iron salts produces only the stable hexafluoferrate(III) complex which is identical with the product prepared by normal wet methods.

The only product obtained by the dry method with manganese is potassium hexafluomanganate(IV), $K_2[MnF_6]$.

[27] W. Klemm and E. Huss, *Z. anorg. u. allgem. Chem.* **258**, 221 (1949).
[28] Klemm and Huss, *loc. cit.*

The preparation of chromium complexes by the dry method is complicated by the formation and volatilization of chromium(V) fluoride. With the molar ratio of 2KCl to 1CrCl₃, the amount of chromium lost by volatilization is, however, a minimum. A yellow potassium hexafluochromate(IV) is found in the solid residue. Potassium hexafluochromate(IV) is isomorphous with potassium hexafluomanganate(V). When heated in the presence of hydrogen, the chromium disproportionates with the result that volatile chromium(V) fluoride sublimes, leaving green potassium hexafluochromate(III)

$$2K_2[CrF_6] \rightarrow CrF_5 + K_3[CrF_6] + KF$$

The above reaction also occurs in a nitrogen atmosphere, although it does not proceed to completion even at 300°.

There are similarities between the vanadium reactions and those of chromium.[29]   At reaction temperatures in excess of 100°C vanadium(V) fluoride sublimes.   The best results for the preparation of high oxidation state vanadium fluocomplexes are obtained by subjecting the green potassium pentafluovanadate(III) to fluorination.   The nearly colorless product of the reaction has the composition represented by $K_2[VF_6]$. Potassium pentafluovanadate(III) is prepared by the addition of potassium fluoride to a solution of vanadium(III) fluoride in anhydrous hydrogen fluoride.   The potassium, as well as the barium and silver salts of hexafluovanadate(V) ion, have been prepared by the reaction of vanadium(III) chloride and potassium chloride in anhydrous bromine trifluoride.   Potassium hexafluovanadate(V) may also be prepared by the reaction of potassium fluoride with vanadium(V) fluoride in a sealed tube.   These salts fume in air, liberating hydrogen fluoride and vanadium(V) oxide.   The compound $K[VF_6]$ is decomposed *in vacuo* at 330°.[30]

Two fluocomplexes of tetravalent manganese are known.[31]   The reaction of bromine trifluoride with potassium permanganate produces pink potassium pentafluomanganate(IV).   The x-ray pattern of this compound shows no potassium fluoride, manganese(III) fluoride, or potassium hexafluomanganate(IV).   The complex, $K[MnF_5]$, reacts with water liberating manganese(IV) oxide, hydrogen fluoride, and potassium fluoride.   A yellow product, potassium hexafluomanganate(IV), is prepared by the reaction of potassium permanganate with bromine trifluoride in the presence of potassium chloride.   The yellow

[29] W. Klemm and E. Huss, *Z. anorg. u. allgem. Chem.* **262**, 25 (1950).
[30] H. J. Emeléus and V. Gutmann, *J. Chem. Soc.* **1949**, 2979.
[31] A. G. Sharpe and A. A. Woolf, *J. Chem. Soc.* **1951**, 798.

product is identical with $K_2[MnF_6]$ prepared by wet methods. It is of interest to note that the chromate ion with bromine trifluoride produces only mixed oxyfluocomplexes.[32]

Some thermodynamic data on the fluocomplexes of the first transition series of elements permits some conclusions as to relative stability and reasons for certain of the complexes not containing the metal in the maximum oxidation states.

Calculation of the heats of reaction for the following instances are reported:[33]

$$3KF + VF_3 \rightarrow K_3[VF_6]$$
$$2KF + VF_4 \rightarrow K_2[VF_6]$$

and

$$KF + VF_5 \rightarrow K[VF_6]$$

Calculations indicate that, on the basis of electrostatic relationships, the complex of tetravalent vanadium should be the most stable of the three while $K[VF_6]$ should be relatively easy to decompose into VF_5 and KF. Experimental data confirm the calculations.

Failure to prepare fluocomplexes in which chromium, manganese, iron, cobalt, and nickel exhibit their maximum known valences might be surprising except for the fact that stabilization of high oxidation states by fluoride ion is not as common as is stabilization by certain other ligands (as bidentate ions and organic molecules). The bonds formed between metal ions and fluoride ions are essentially ionic; thus the stable electronic configurations attainable by the central atom do not involve filling of its electronic orbitals with electrons contributed by coordinating ligands. The stable configurations are, on the contrary, the same as those associated with the gaseous atoms; that is to say, those with completely filled, half-filled, and empty electron shells.[34]   The stability of the $[FeF_6]^{-3}$ and $[CoF_7]^{-4}$ ions is more easily explained on such a basis. Since there must be an upper limit to the number of electrons which may be removed from such atoms as chromium, manganese, and nickel and placed on associated fluorine atoms, this fact may explain the absence of fluocomplexes of these metals in their highest oxidation states.

The reason for the higher valencies of metal atoms in oxycomplexes than those found in fluocomplexes is related to the binegative charge on the oxide ion, favoring a higher positive charge on the central metal atom

[32] Sharpe and Woolf, *loc. cit.*
[33] W. Klemm, *Naturwissenschaften* **37**, 175 (1950).
[34] Klemm and Huss, *loc. cit.* ref. 29.; L. Pauling, *Nature of the Chemical Bond*, p. 70, Cornell University Press, Ithaca, New York, 1948.

from purely electrostatic and space considerations. Electronegativity differences between the average values for the first transition series metals and that for oxygen indicate that the corresponding bonds should be about 55 per cent ionic. It is therefore reasonable to expect the formation of bonds in which electron-sharing plays an important part so that an upper limit on the oxidation state of the transition element need not be expected on the basis of electrostatic considerations.[35]

The fluoaluminum complexes represented by $[AlF_n]^{3-n}$ (where n is 1 to 6) have been studied in terms of the heats of the successive reactions noted below.[36] The heats and equilibrium constants permit the calculation of the entropies indicated for each step. $Al^{+3} + F^- \rightarrow [AlF]^{+2}$, $\Delta S = 32$; $[AlF]^{+2} + F^- \rightarrow [AlF_2]^+$, $\Delta S = 26$; $[AlF_2]^+ + F^- \rightarrow AlF_3$, $\Delta S = 18$; $AlF_3 + F^- \rightarrow [AlF_4]^-$, $\Delta S = 18$; $[AlF_4]^- + F^- \rightarrow [AlF_5]^{-2}$, $\Delta S = 5$; $[AlF_5]^{-2} + F^- \rightarrow [AlF_6]^{-3}$, $\Delta S = -3$.

TABLE 1.8. COMPARATIVE HEATS OF REACTION

Reaction	ΔH, $BTU/Lb\ Mol\ Reactant$
$F_2 + 2NaI \rightarrow 2NaF + I_2$	$-240,000/F_2$
$Cl_2 + 2NaI \rightarrow 2NaCl + I_2$	$-105,000/Cl_2$
$F_2 + Ni \rightarrow NiF_2$	$-283,000/F_2$
$Cl_2 + Ni \rightarrow NiCl_2$	$-135,000/Cl_2$
$-C-H + F_2 \rightarrow -C-F + HF$	$-184,000/F_2$
$-C-H + Cl_2 \rightarrow -C-Cl + HCl$	$-42,000/Cl_2$
$2H + F_2 \rightarrow 2HF$ (gas)	$-600,000/F_2$ or H_2
$4H + O_2 \rightarrow 2H_2O$ (gas)	$-970,000/O_2$
	$-485,000/H_2$
$S + 3F_2 \rightarrow SF_6$	$-161,000/F_2$
$2S + 3O_2 \rightarrow 2SO_3$	$-115,000/O_2$

3. *Comparative heats of reaction of fluorine.* Table 1.8 offers a comparison of some heats of reaction of fluorine, chlorine, and oxygen. The values of ΔH are given in Btu/lb mol of reactant.[37]

4. *Nitrogen-oxygen-fluorine compounds.* Three known (1954) nitrogen-oxygen-fluorine compounds are NOF, NO_2F, and NO_3F. Nitrosyl fluoride, NOF, is formed by the direct fluorination of NO or by the reaction between nitrosyl chloride and silver fluoride. Nitroxyl fluoride, NO_2F, is formed by the action of nitrogen dioxide on fluorine. Fluorine

[35] Pertinent information on the fluocomplexes of the first transition series is from the *Reports of the Inorganic Seminar*, University of Illinois, 1952–53.

[36] W. M. Latimer and W. L. Jolly, *J. Am. Chem. Soc.* **75**, 1548 (1953).

[37] R. Landau and R. Rosen, *Ind. Eng. Chem.* **39**, 281 (1947).

nitrate, NO_3F or FNO_3, results from the action of fluorine on 100 per cent nitric acid. Fluorine nitrate has a pungent odor not unlike oxygen difluoride. The nitrate is unstable and explosions are common in its preparation. It is moderately soluble in water, with which it reacts slowly, liberating oxygen. In a basic solution NO_3F undergoes the following reaction:

$$NO_3F + 2OH^- \rightarrow \tfrac{1}{2}O_2 + F^- + NO_3^- + H_2O$$

The oxidizing action of the fluorine atom is obvious from the reaction of NO_3F with iodide ion:[38]

$$NO_3F + 3I^- \rightarrow I_3^- + F^- + NO_3^-$$

The configuration assigned to the molecule is[39]

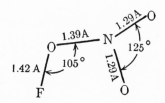

5. *Chlorine-oxygen-fluorine compounds.* Perchloryl fluoride or fluorine chlorate, ClO_3F, has been prepared by the electrolysis of a 10 per cent sodium perchlorate-anhydrous hydrofluoric acid solution with nickel anodes and also by the action of chlorine(VII) oxide on anhydrous hydrofluoric acid. A compound of similar formula is also reported,[40] prepared by the action of fluorine on an alkali chlorate at low temperature. On the basis of chemical reactions, however, the latter compound is probably a chloryl oxyfluoride, O_2Cl—O—F. Perchloryl fluoride is a colorless gas somewhat resembling OF_2 in behavior. The vapor pressure curve follows the equation

$$\log P = 7.7183 - 1088.67 \cdot (1/K)$$

The boiling point, calculated from the equation, is $-48.1°C$. In a strongly acid solution, the compound reacts with iodide ion according to the equation

$$ClO_3F + 8I^- + 6H^+ \rightarrow Cl^- + F^- + 4I_2 + 3H_2O$$

[38] G. H. Cady, *J. Am. Chem. Soc.* 56, 2635 (1934).
[39] L. Pauling and L. O. Brockway, *J. Am. Chem. Soc.* 59, 13 (1937).
[40] H. Bode and E. Klesper, *Z. anorg. u. allgem. Chem.* 266, 275 (1951).

It is reported that the compound is thermostable even to the temperature of the softening of glass.[41]

An analogous perchlorate, ClO_4F, is formed along with OF_2 when gaseous fluorine reacts with perchloric acid. The compound has a freezing point of $-167.3°C$ and a boiling point of $-15.9°C$. It possesses a sharp, irritating, acid-like odor, is highly reactive, and explodes readily. Its reactions with iodide ion and with hydroxide bases are represented as follows:[42]

$$2I^- + ClO_4F \rightarrow I_2 + ClO_4^- + F^-$$

$$2ClO_4F + 4OH^- \rightarrow O_2 + 2ClO_4^- + 2F^- + 2H_2O$$

6. *Nitrogen-fluorine and carbon-fluorine compounds.* Nitrogen trifluoride, NF_3, is produced in the electrolysis of NH_4HF_2. At the same time, small amounts of NF_2, NHF_2, and NH_2F are also formed.

Fluorine reacts vigorously with finely divided carbon to give mainly carbon tetrafluoride; however, the fluorocarbons C_2F_6, C_3F_8, and C_4F_{10} are reported as also being formed. Carbon tetrafluoride yields C_2F_4 and C_2F_6 in a carbon arc flame. The absorption spectrum of CF_4 gas, thermally decomposed under equilibrium conditions in a graphite furnace, shows the bands of CF_2 at a temperature of approximately $1900°K$ and bands attributed to CF at a temperature of approximately $2400°K$. These temperatures are as would be expected from the use of 170 kcal/mol for the heat of sublimation of graphite and when f values of about 10^{-3} for both CF_2 and CF bands are assumed.[43] The C—F distance in CF_4, based upon electron diffraction studies with 0.0594 A wavelength electrons, is 1.31_7 A.[44]

The heat of formation of CF_4 is 231 ± 3 kcal, based on the following reactions:[45]

$$C(graphite) + 2F_2 \rightarrow CF_4$$

and $4K + CF_4 \rightarrow C(graphite) + 4KF + 307 \pm 3$ kcal

An active form of charcoal, as Norite, reacts with fluorine at 420–550°C to give the compound CF. Fluorine appears to enter into the carbon lattice to some extent. The polymer $(CF)_x$ is formed by the reaction of fluorine on graphite in the presence of HF, which lowers the reaction temperature from 420–550°C to 250–360°C. The formation of

[41] A. Engelbrecht and H. Atzwanger, *Monatsh.* 83, 1087 (1952).

[42] G. H. Rohrback and G. H. Cady, *J. Am. Chem. Soc.* 69, 677 (1947).

[43] J. L. Margrave and K. Wieland, *J. Chem. Phys.* 21, 1552 (1953); P. Venkateswarlu, *Phys. Rev.* 77, 676 (1950).

[44] C. W. W. Hoffman and R. L. Livingston, *J. Chem. Phys.* 21, 565 (1953).

[45] H. v. Wartenberg and G. Riteris, *Z. anorg. Chem.* 258, 356 (1949).

the same polymer $(CF)_x$, at the anodes in the production of fluorine, is one of the causes for the increased drop in potential across the cell, during the electrolysis. When the current is stepped up to 40–50 volts, the polymer is removed. The band spectrum of CF has been reported in two band systems.[46]

The compound C_4F, also formed from graphite and a mixture of fluorine and hydrogen fluoride, is highly stable. It is not decomposed by acids, alkalies, or mild heating. No fluoride ion is detectable after heating the solid with sodium hydroxide or with reducing agents as Fe(II) salts. Concentrated sulfuric acid decomposes C_4F very slowly. On strong heating, C_4F deflagrates. X-ray examination shows that the fluorine atoms lie between the planes of the carbon atoms.

In the fluorocarbons, the C—C distance varies inversely with the total fluorine content. The axis distances in the hexagonal lattice are compatible with the assumption of tetrahedral coordination of carbon atoms. Lattice distances make it doubtful that there is any ionic contribution of the atoms.[47] It may be that the compound C_2F is an intermediate between CF and C_4F.[48]

7. *Carbon-oxygen-fluorine and trifluoromethyl compounds.* Carbonyl fluoride, COF_2, is formed from CO and AgF_2, but not, as might be expected, by the treatment of $COCl_2$ with HF.[49] The heat of formation of COF_2 has been determined from the following sequence of reactions:

1. $ClF_3 + 3NaCl \rightarrow 3NaF + 2Cl_2 + 86.8 \pm 0.3$ kcal (exothermic)
2. $\frac{1}{2}Cl_2 + \frac{3}{2}F_2 \rightarrow ClF_3 + 28.4 \pm 0.3$ kcal
3. $COF_2 + H_2O \rightarrow 2HF$ (aq) $+ CO_2 + 26.73 \pm 0.2$ kcal

and from the known values for the heats of formation of HF and CO_2. The heat of formation of COF_2 is, then, $C + \frac{1}{2}O_2 + F_2 \rightarrow COF_2 + 150.35 \pm 0.5$ kcal. This value is slightly higher than a previously reported one of 142 kcal:

$$F_2 + CO \rightarrow COF_2 + 115 \text{ kcal}$$

$$COF_2 + 4KOH \rightarrow 2KF + K_2CO_3 + 2H_2O + 95 \pm 1 \text{ kcal}$$

and

$$F_2 + C(\text{diamond}) + \frac{1}{2}O_2 \rightarrow COF_2 + 142 \text{ kcal}[50]$$

[46] E. B. Andrews and R. F. Barrow, *Proc. Phys. Soc.* **64A**, 481 (1951); *Nature* **165**, 890 (1950).

[47] W. Rudorff and G. Rudorff, *Z. anorg. Chem.* **253**, 281 (1947).

[48] W. Rudorff and G. Rudorff, *Chem. Ber.* **80**, 413 (1947).

[49] K. Wiechert, *Z. anorg. Chem.* **261**, 310 (1950); D. F. Smith et al., *Phys. Rev.* **83**, 485 (1951).

[50] H. v. Wartenberg, *Nach. Akad. Wiss. Göttingen, Math.-physik, Klasse* **1946**, 89.

Trifluoromethyl hypofluorite, CF_3OF, is prepared by fluorinating CO or methyl alcohol in the presence of AgF_2. The compound F_2CO is an intermediate. The usual fluorinating agent, CoF_3, is not effective in this reaction. The hypofluorite is a gas with an odor like that of F_2 or OF_2. In the liquid state it has a pale straw color. It boils at $-95°C$ under one atm and is stable up to $450°C$. It is a strong oxidizing agent.

The spectrum of CF_3OF is of interest because of the CH_3OH analogy. The infrared absorption of a sample containing small amounts of CF_4, F_2CO, and HF has been reported over the range 2 to 25μ. Interpretation of the spectrum has been made in terms of the contributions of the impurities. The C—O—F chain is assumed to be bent. The remainder of the molecule is probably of a tetrahedral nature resembling methyl alcohol. If the F atom of the OF group is located on one of the planes of symmetry of the CF group, the molecule would have but one plane of symmetry, the C—O—F plane, and would belong to the point group C_s. This point group appears to be logical. It is convenient to consider the CF_3OF molecule in so far as its vibrations are concerned as a five-point system, the OF group being a single particle. This "hypofluorite" group would have but small effect upon the vibrations which belong to the trifluoromethyl and trifluoromethoxy groups. The fundamental (including double degenerate modes) frequencies expected of CF_3OF have, in nine of the possible twelve frequencies expected for an asymmetric molecule with a C_s point group, been identified.[51]

The trifluoromethyl group is of particular interest because of its unusually high electronegative character. A large number of trifluoromethyl metallic and metalloidal compounds have been prepared and their properties studied. The gas, trifluoroiodomethane, CF_3I, is an important intermediate in the preparation of other trifluoromethyl compounds. The parent compound is prepared by treating carbon tetraiodide with iodine pentafluoride. A mixture of other fluoroiodomethanes is produced along with the desired trifluoromethyl iodide.[52] The lead, silver, sodium as well as potassium salts of trifluoroacetic acid react with iodine to give trifluoromethyl iodide.[53]

In certain respects, the $CF_3\cdot$ group behaves as a halogenoid.[54] The reaction of CF_3I with ethylene results in $CF_3CH_2CH_2I$; thus, addition

[51] K. B. Kellogg and G. H. Cady, *J. Am. Chem. Soc.* **70**, 3986 (1948); E. A. Jones and P. J. H. Woltz, *J. Chem. Phys.* **20**, 1768 (1952).
[52] A. A. Banks, H. J. Emeléus, and R. N. Haszeldine, *J. Chem. Soc.* **1948**, 2188.
[53] J. Sheridan and W. Gordy, *Phys. Rev.* **77**, 292 (1950).
[54] Material on trifluoromethyl compounds is, in part, from Seminars, Inorganic Chemistry, University of Illinois, 1953–54.

across the double bond must have taken place.[55]   On the other hand, a displacement type reaction is reported in which CF_3I reacts with methyl acetylene to give methyltrifluoromethyl acetylene,[56] $CH_3C \equiv CCF_3$.

The reaction of CF_3I with potassium hydroxide takes place by the "positive iodine" mechanism, fluoroform being obtained instead of the expected alcohol. The postulated mechanism involves heterolytic cleavage of the carbon to iodine bond.[57]

$$K^+ + \overset{\frown}{OH^- + I} : \overset{\frown}{CF_3} \to [CF_3^- + K^+ + HOI] \to CF_3H + KOI$$
$$ {}_{+\delta} {}_{-\delta}$$

It has not been possible to carry out nucleophilic substitution of the I of CF_3I by such groups as OH^-, CN^-, NH_2^-, and NO_2^-. The majority of the reactions investigated in this region involve homolytic rather than heterolytic cleavage of the carbon-iodine bond with the formation of $CF_3 \cdot$ free radicals.

Four resonance forms contribute to the stability of CF_3I.

$$\begin{array}{cccc}
\overset{F^+}{\underset{|}{\overset{||}{F-C-I}}} & \overset{F}{\underset{|}{\overset{|}{F-C=I^+}}} & \overset{F}{\underset{|}{\overset{|}{F-C-\,I^+}}} & \overset{F}{\underset{|}{\overset{|}{F-C^+\,I^-}}} \\
F^- & F^- & F & F \\
(A) & (B) & (C) & (D)
\end{array}$$

The forms (A), (B), and (D) appear to contribute to a lesser degree than does (C).   The C—I bond is thus weaker than the C—F bond.

A large number of trifluoromethyl sulfur compounds are reported. A substance of the formula CF_3SF_5 is formed by the treatment of CH_3SH with CoF_3 at 250°C. The same compound is formed by the direct fluorination of CH_3SH in a nitrogen atmosphere in presence of copper turnings and AgF.   The compound $CSHF_7$ is reported as a secondary product.   The substance CF_3SF_5 (mp -86.9 ± 0.2°C, bp -20.4°C) is relatively inert.   It reacts with alkali metals only at red heat and not at all with 6M NaOH.   In a spark discharge, CF_4 and SF_4 are formed.[58]

*Bis*trifluoromethyldisulfide is prepared by heating sulfur to 260°C with CF_3I.   Among the products identified are $(CF_3)_2S_2$, $(CF_3)_2S_3$,

[55] R. N. Haszeldine and H. J. Eméleus, *Research* 1, 715 (1948).

[56] B. Bak *et al.*, *J. Chem. Phys.* 21, 1612 (1953).

[57] J. Banus, H. J. Eméleus, and R. N. Haszeldine, *J. Chem. Soc.* 1951, 60; Haszeldine and Eméleus, *loc. cit.*

[58] G. A. Silvey and G. H. Cady, *J. Am. Chem. Soc.* 72, 3624 (1950).

$(CF_3)_2S_4$, and CSF_2. A more convenient preparation of $(CF_3)_2S_2$ involves the fluorination of CS_2 with IF_5.[59]

The compound $(CF_3)_2S_2$ changes to the monosulfide, $(CF_3)_2S$, in the presence of ultraviolet light. The mechanism of the photolysis is postulated as a homolytic cleavage of the sulfur-sulfur bond to give to $CF_3S\cdot$ radicals. Evidence of the presence of these radicals is indicated by the smooth formation of CF_3—S—Hg—CF_3 when mercury is present during the photolysis. A tentative mechanism is represented by the following equations:

$$CF_3S_2CF_3 \rightarrow 2CF_3S\cdot$$

$$CF_3S\cdot + CF_3S_2CF_3 \rightarrow CF_3SCF_3 + CF_3SS\cdot$$

$$CF_3SS\cdot \rightarrow CF_3 + S, etc.$$

$$2CF_3SS\cdot \rightarrow CF_3SSSSCF_3$$

$$CF_3S\cdot + CF_3SSSSCF_3 \rightarrow CF_3SCF_3 + CF_3SSSS\cdot$$

$$2CF_3SSSS\cdot \rightarrow CF_3S_8CF_3, etc.$$

Arsenic derivatives in high yields are formed when CF_3I is heated to 220–240°C in the presence of arsenic

$$CF_3I + As \xrightarrow[\leftarrow]{220-240°C} As(CF_3)_3 + AsI(CF_3)_2 + AsI_2CF_3 + AsI_3$$

The high yield of the *tris* compound is attributed to disproportionation reactions.[60] If AsI_3 is added to the original reaction mixture, the percentage yields of iodotrifluoromethyl arsines are increased. A main point of difference between methyl and trifluoromethyl derivatives of arsine lies in their respective hydrolytic reactions. The methyl group is stable toward dilute alkaline hydrolysis, whereas the trifluoro compounds hydrolyze to liberate fluoroform quantitatively.[61] In contrast to the methyl arsines, the fluoro compounds fail to yield quaternary compounds. The more negative trifluoro group attached to arsenic makes this atom more resistant to oxidation than the arsenic in methyl derivatives. *Tetrakis*-trifluoromethyldiarsine, prepared by the action of mercury on *bis*trifluoro-methyliododiarsine, is stable to water, but with alkali at room temperature it gives fluoroform in about 75 per cent yield. The remainder of the trifluoromethyl groups are converted to fluoride and carbonate ions.

The iodine in trifluoromethyliododiarsines is replaceable with hydrogen by reaction with such reducing agents as $LiAlH_4$ and zinc-hydrochloric acid.

[59] R. N. Haszeldine *et al.*, Abstracts, Am. Chem. Soc. Meeting, Chicago, Sept., 1953.
[60] H. J. Emeléus *et al.*, *J. Chem. Soc.* 1953, 1552.
[61] G. R. A. Brandt *et al.*, *J. Chem. Soc.* 1952, 2552.

Phosphine derivatives as *tris*fluoromethylphosphine are formed when CF_3I reacts with white phosphorus at 220°C:[62]

$$CF_3I + P(\text{white}) \rightarrow (CF_3)_3P + (CF_3)_2PI + CF_3PI_2 + I_2PPI_2 + PI_3$$

*Tris*trifluoromethylphosphine is a colorless, spontaneously flammable liquid (bp 17°C). Iodine atoms in the derivatives just noted are very reactive. The yield of these iododerivatives is increased by recycling the $(CF_3)_3P$ and unreacted CF_3I with phosphorus and PI_3. As is the case with the arsines, no quaternary compounds of the phosphines have been isolated. A difference between the trialkyl and trifluoromethyl derivatives is found in their respective rates of reaction with chlorine. Alkyls react explosively, whereas trifluoromethylphosphine reacts smoothly at low temperature:

$$(CF_3)_3P + Cl_2 \xrightarrow{\;-40°C\;} (CF_3)_3PCl_2$$

Oxidative hydrolysis of trifluoromethylphosphorus iodide or chloride yields trifluoromethylphosphonic acid, $CF_3PO(OH)_2$, whose k_1 and k_2 values are 6.8×10^{-2} and 1.8×10^{-4}, respectively.[63]

One of the few alkyl compounds in which stable P—P bonds exist is prepared by the action of mercury on *bis*trifluoromethyliodophosphine at room temperature. The resulting compound is *tetrakis*trifluoromethyldiphosphine, $(CF_3)_2P—P(CF_3)_2$. The trifluoromethyl groups attached to the metalloid (phosphorus) atoms appear to stabilize the atom.

Pure trifluoronitrosomethane, CF_3NO, is prepared by the irradiation of a mixture of CF_3I and NO in the presence of mercury.[64] The compound may be oxidized to CF_3NO_2 by treatment with CrO_3.

Table 1.9 includes the boiling and melting points of a number of trifluoromethyl derivatives.

8. *Sulfur-fluorine compounds.* The direct action of crude burning sulfur with a current of fluorine gas results in the formation of stable sulfur hexafluoride, SF_6, and some S_2F_2, S_2F_{10}, SF_4, and SF_2. Also present as impurities are hydrogen fluoride, oxygen, oxygen difluoride, and moisture. The lower fluorides are in general toxic and corrosive. They can be pyrolyzed to SF_6. Any unpyrolyzed sulfur fluorides can be separated from sulfur hexafluoride by absorbing them in water and caustic. Activated alumina is also effective in removing the lower fluorides by adsorption. The S_2F_{10} molecule is suggested as being made up of two octa-

[62] F. W. Bennett *et al.*, *J. Chem. Soc.* **1953**, 1565.
[63] R. N. Haszeldine *et al.*, Abstracts, Am. Chem. Soc. Meeting, Chicago, Sept., 1953.
[64] R. N. Haszeldine, *J. Chem. Soc.* **1953**, 2075.

TABLE 1.9. BOILING AND MELTING POINTS OF SOME
TRIFLUOROMETHYL COMPOUNDS

Compound	Mp (°C)	Bp (°C)	Compound	Mp (°C)	Bp (°C)
CF_3I		−22.5	$(CF_3)_3P$		17
$(CF_3)_2S_2$		35	$(CF_3)_2PI$		73
CF_3SF_5	−86.9	−20.4	CF_3PI_2		69/29 mm
$(CF_3)_2S$		−22	$(CF_3)_4P_2$		84
$(CF_3S)_2Hg$	37.5		$(CF_3)_2Hg$	163	
			CF_3HgI	112.5	
$(CF_3)_3As$		33.3*	CF_3HgCl	76	
$(CF_3)_2AsI$		92	CF_3NO		−84
$(CF_3)_4As_2$		106–7	CF_3NO_2		−20
$(CF_3)_2AsH$		19			

* Calculated from vapor pressure data.

hedral SF_5 groups joined by a S—S bond. The evidence for such a structure lies in the comparison of theoretical and experimental radial nuclear charge density distribution curves. The S—F distance is 1.56 ± 0.02 A and the S—S distance is 2.21 ± 0.03 A. Hindered rotation would be expected about the S—S axis.[65]

The hexafluoride (mp = −50.8°C, T_c = 45.6°C, P_c = 540 psi) is about as inert chemically as nitrogen. It resembles nitrogen trifluoride and carbon tetrafluoride in this respect. It is colorless, tasteless, non-combustible, and gaseous under normal conditions. Even at temperatures at which soft glass becomes fluid, SF_6, is stable. Along with the Freons, it has potentialities as a high voltage insulator. Under the stress of a spark discharge, however, there is some decomposition to the lower fluorides of sulfur and to elemental sulfur.[66] When this decomposition is made to occur in a gold-lined cell provided with KBr windows, it is possible to study the decomposition by infrared spectroscopy. The chief products identified are SF_2 and S_2F_2. The mechanism of the decomposition at low voltages is proposed as

$$e^- + SF_6 \rightarrow (SF_6{}^-)^* \rightarrow SF_6{}^- + h\nu$$
$$\rightarrow SF_5{}^- + F$$
$$\rightarrow SF_5 \cdot + F^-$$
$$\rightarrow SF_5 \cdot + F \cdot + e^-$$

Recombination steps would then be expected to follow.[67]

[65] R. B. Harvey and S. H. Bauer, *J. Am. Chem. Soc.* **75**, 2840 (1953).
[66] W. C. Schumb *et al.*, *Ind. Eng. Chem.* **41**, 1348 (1949).
[67] D. Edelson *et al.*, *Ind. Eng. Chem.* **45**, 2094 (1953).

Sulfur monofluoride, S_2F_2, does not react with such reducing agents as aluminum powder, silicon, zinc, or potassium up to 100°C. With strong oxidizing agents, such as peroxides and permanganate, there is a reaction at room temperature with the former and at 100°C with the latter.[68]

9. *Fluorination of CoF₂*. The direct fluorination of cobalt(II) fluoride is important because of the need for cobalt(III) fluoride in organic fluorinations. Cobalt(II) fluoride is slowly heated in a reactor to about 200°C in a current of dry nitrogen to remove traces of moisture, and then fluorine is added to give the desired conversion:

$$2CoF_2 + F_2 \xrightarrow{\ 250°C\ } 2CoF_3 + 58 \text{ kcal}$$

A more probable value for the heat of reaction is 56 ± 2.0 kcal.[69] If hydrated cobalt(II) chloride, $CoCl_2 \cdot 6H_2O$, is used as a starting material, it is first dried at 100°C, and then heated with hydrogen fluoride. The conversion to CoF_2 is considered complete when it is no longer possible to detect HCl fumes. Conversion to the trivalent state follows according to the preceding equation.

10. *Phosphorus- and antimony-fluorine compounds*. Direct union of fluorine with phosphorus and antimony gives PF_3 and SbF_3, respectively. Prolonged treatment of these elements with fluorine favors complete oxidation to PF_5 and SbF_5. The trifluoro compounds are useful fluorinating agents. Antimony trifluoride is effective in fluorinating BCl_3 with $SbCl_5$ as a catalyst. When $PSBr_3$ is fluorinated by SbF_3, the compounds PSF_2Br (bp 35.5°C) and $PSFBr_2$ (bp 125.3°C) are produced along with some PSF_3 (p. 37). The compound PSF_2Br is unusually resistant to hydrolysis.[70] The mixed phosphorus halides, PF_2Cl and $PFCl_2$, are formed by heating PCl_3 with PF_3. The Schwartz reaction is also used to produce these mixed halides. Phosphorus trichloride is fluorinated by SbF_3 in the presence of $SbCl_5$ as a catalyst. The pressure is maintained at 250 mm and the temperature at 39°C for several hours. A typical analysis shows the presence of $PFCl_2$ (58 per cent), PF_2Cl (19 per cent), and PF_3 (22 per cent). When a gas-solid reaction between PCl_3 vapor and hot CaF_2 takes place, the formation of $PFCl_2$ is favored. The compound $PFCl_2$ is stable when stored under pressure in a sealed tube. It is absorbed rapidly in sodium hydroxide solution, and heat is evolved. The normal boiling point is 13.85°C, and the melting point is −144.4°C. The latent heat of evaporation is 5950 cal/mol. The critical temperature is

[68] L. M. Dubnikov and N. I. Zorin, *J. Gen. Chem.*, *U.S.S.R.* **17**, 185 (1947).
[69] R. S. Jessup *et al.*, *J. Res. Natl. Bur. Standards* **44**, 457 (1950).
[70] H. S. Booth and G. F. Spencer, *J. Am. Chem. Soc.* **65**, 1834, 1836 (1943).

TABLE 1.10. SOME FLUORINE-CONTAINING OXYHALIDES OF SULFUR

Name	Formula	Melting Point, °C	Boiling Point, °C
Thionyl fluoride	SOF$_2$	-110	-43.8
Sulfuryl fluoride	SO$_2$F$_2$	-120	-52
Sulfuryl chlorofluoride	SO$_2$FCl	-124.7	7.1
Thionyl chlorofluoride	SOClF	-139.5	12.3
Sulfuryl bromofluoride	SO$_2$BrF	-86	40
"Thionyl tetrafluoride"	SOF$_4$	-107	-48
Pyrosufuryl fluoride	S$_2$O$_5$F$_2$	-48	51

189.88°C, and the critical pressure is 48.99 atm. The compound PF$_2$Cl hydrolyzes less rapidly than PFCl$_2$. Its (PF$_2$Cl) normal boiling point is -47.3°C, melting point -164.8°C, critical temperature 89.17°C, critical pressure 44.6 atm, and latent heat of evaporation 4200 cal/mol. Analogous bromides, PFBr$_2$ and PF$_2$Br, have been prepared by similar methods.[71] Phosphorus(III) fluoride reacts with POCl$_3$ to give a mixture of POF$_3$, POF$_2$Cl, and POFCl$_2$. The oxybromides are similarly formed from PF$_3$ and POBr$_3$.

Certain physical data are reported for POF$_3$ as well as for its thio-analog PSF$_3$: the bond distances in A are P—O $= 1.48$, P—F in POF$_3$ $= 1.52$, P—S $= 1.86$, and P—F in PSF$_3$ $= 1.53$; dipole moments[72] relative to COS are 1.69 $\pm$ 3 per cent for POF$_3$ and 0.633 $\pm$ 3 per cent for PSF$_3$. The short bond distances make reasonable the assumption that $3d$ orbitals are involved and that there is an appreciable triple bond character to the phosphorus bonds.[73]

11. *Sulfur-oxygen-fluorine compounds.*[74] A number of fluorine-containing oxyhalides of sulfur have been prepared and studied. Table 1.10 includes several of these compounds with their melting and boiling points.[75]

Thionyl fluoride, SOF$_2$, is prepared by reacting thionyl chloride with antimony(III) fluoride in the presence of SbCl$_5$ as a catalyst. The SOF$_2$ is a relatively stable compound which hydrolyzes slowly in water and does not attack glass below 400°C. Dilute alkali solutions rapidly attack the compound.

[71] H. S. Booth and A. R. Bozarth, *J. Am. Chem. Soc.* **61**, 2927 (1939); H. S. Booth and S. G. Frary, *ibid.* **61**, 2934 (1939).

[72] R. Shulman *et al.*, *Phys. Revs.* **78**, 293 (1950).

[73] N. J. Hawkins and V. W. Cohen, *J. Chem. Phys.* **20**, 528 (1952).

[74] Reference material from University of Illinois Seminar Reports, 1952–53.

[75] H. Jonas, *Z. anorg. u. allgem. Chem.* **265**, 273 (1951); H. C. Miller and F. J. Grall, *Ind. Eng. Chem.* **42**, 2224 (1950).

Sulfuryl fluoride, SO_2F_2, can be obtained in fair yields by decomposing barium fluosulfonate. Sulfuryl fluoride is stable even to molten sodium. The vapor pressure of SO_2F_2 follows the relation log $p = 7.593 - 1023/T$. The vapor pressures of $SOCl_2$ and SO_2F_2 are sufficiently different at $-145°$ to permit efficient separation by distillation.[76]

Sulfuryl fluoride has been prepared by the direct fluorination of alkali metal sulfates, sulfites, and thiosulfates. The reaction

$$2F_2 + Na_2SO_4 \rightarrow 2NaF + SO_2F_2 + O_2$$

is 40 per cent complete at 300° in 40 min but only 2 per cent complete at 100° in the same length of time.

The rate of the reaction represented by the equation

$$2F_2 + 2Na_2SO_3 \rightarrow Na_2SO_4 + SO_2F_2 + 2NaF$$

is appreciable at 100°C; however, since SO_2F_2 is a dense gas, fluorine will not react beyond this first step unless it is heated to 200°C to permit the further reaction of the element with Na_2SO_4.

The reaction between fluorine and sodium thiosulfate begins at $-80°C$ and is vigorous to the point of incandescence at 15°C. At $-40°C$, free sulfur is produced (about 3 per cent) followed by its conversion to SF_6 and SOF_2. The following reaction accounts for 57 per cent of the products:

$$8F_2 + 2Na_2S_2O_3 \rightarrow Na_2SO_4 + 2NaF + SO_2F_2 + 2SF_6$$

Some free sulfur is also formed. Another reaction,

$$6F_2 + 2Na_2S_2O_3 \rightarrow 4NaF + 2SO_2F_2 + 2SOF_2$$

accounts for 30 per cent of the products. A third reaction,

$$8F_2 + 2Na_2S_2O_3 \rightarrow 4NaF + 3SO_2F_2 + SF_6$$

accounts for 13 per cent of the products.[77]

Sulfuryl chlorofluoride, SO_2ClF, is prepared in good yields from sulfuryl chloride and $SbCl_3$ in the presence of $SbCl_5$. The compound is intermediate in stability between SO_2Cl_2 and SO_2F_2. It hydrolyzes slowly in water and very rapidly in dilute alkali. It does not react with glass, mercury, or common metals at room temperature.[78]

Thionyl chlorofluoride, $SOClF$, is prepared by fluorinating $SOCl_2$ with SbF_3 using antimony pentachloride as a catalyst. This method is

[76] J. Neudörffer, *Compt. rend.* **236**, 706 (1953).
[77] M. Picon and L. Domange, *Compt. rend.* **236**, 704 (1953).
[78] H. S. Booth and C. V. Herrmann, *J. Am. Chem. Soc.* **58**, 63 (1936).

FLUORINE 39

essentially the same as that used to prepare SOF_2. Fractional distillation
of the reaction products yields approximately 50 per cent SOF_2, 20 per
cent $SOClF$, and 5 per cent SO_2; the remaining 25 per cent is unreacted
thionyl chloride.[79] Better yields of $SOClF$ are obtained by reacting
$SOCl_2$ with iodine pentafluoride and then fractionally distilling the product. The purest SOF_2 distills over the temperature range -36 to
$-22°C$. From -22 to $10°C$ $SOClF$ and SOF_2 both distill together, and
nearly pure $SOClF$ distills between 10 and $18°C$. The vapor density of
$SOClF$ is 103.2 g/22.4 l. The vapor pressures follows the equation log
$p = 7.83 - 1409/T$. The density is expressed by the equation $D =
1.576 - 0.00224t$ The boiling point is $12.3°C$.[80]

It has been predicted[81] that $SOClF$ is actually a mixture of two stere-
oisomers; hence its abnormally low melting point as compared with $SOCl_2$
and $SOClF$. No other inorganic thionyl compound has been prepared
(1954) with two different substituents.

Thionyl chlorofluoride at $0°C$ is a colorless volatile liquid. It reacts
only very slightly with dry glass or quartz at room temperature. Moisture catalyzes the reaction to form SiF_4, SO_2, and HCl.

Sulfuryl bromofluoride, SO_2BrF, is prepared either by the reaction of
trichloromethanesulfuryl chloride with BrF_3 or by reacting a mixture of
BrF_3, Br_2, and SO_2. The second method is said to give nearly quantitative yields.[82] Sulfuryl bromofluoride is a colorless, choking gas. Its
vapor density is 162.6/22.4 l. Its vapor pressure follows the equation
log $p = 8.02 - 1010/T$. Its density is expressed by the equation $D =
2.75 - 0.00298t$. The density of the solid at liquid air temperature is
3.16 g/cc. The melting point is $-86 \pm 0.5°C$, and the boiling point at
1 atm is $40.0°C$. At room temperature the compound is somewhat more
reactive than $SOClF$, attacking glass but not quartz. On hydrolysis,
HBr, HF, and H_2SO_4 are formed. The vapor of SO_2BrF is moderately
stable, decomposing slightly at $320°C$ and completely at $340°C$ to SO_2,
SO_2F_2, and Br_2.

"Thionyl tetrafluoride" is prepared by reacting SOF_2 and elemental
fluorine in the presence of platinum gauze at $150°C$. Fractionally distilling the product mixture gives reasonably pure SOF_4 in the temperature
range -49 to $-48°C$. Over the range -52 to $-49°$ a mixture of SF_6,
SO_2F_2, and SOF_4 is distilled. The vapor density is 122.5 g/22.4 l. The
vapor pressure follows the equation, log $p = 7.76 - 1092/T$. The

[79] H. S. Booth and F. C. Mericola, *J. Am. Chem. Soc.* **62**, 640 (1940).
[80] J. Jonas, *Z. anorg. u. allgem. Chem.* **265**, 273 (1951).
[81] Jonas, *loc. cit.*
[82] Jonas, *loc. cit.*

density is expressed by $D = 1.653 - 0.00360t$. The melting and boiling points are, respectively, $-107 \pm 0.5°$ and $-48.5°C$ at 1 atm. At room temperature, SOF_4 is a colorless pungent gas. It reacts violently with water and dilute alkali with the formation of SO_2F_2 and HF. Reaction with mercury gives SOF_2 and Hg_2F_2 at a slow rate.[83]

Pyrosulfuryl fluoride, $S_2O_5F_2$, may be prepared by a variety of methods. Nonaqueous fluorides of metals or metalloids reacting with SO_3 or with SO_3-yielding compounds at elevated temperatures under pressure yield fluosulfonates which decompose to $S_2O_5F_2$. Another method is the antimony pentafluoride reaction with SO_3. The reaction products are refluxed and the $S_2O_5F_2$ is separated by distillation. A third method is to heat NaF to 150°C with SO_3 to give $NaSO_3F$ and SO_3—NaF addition products. Thermal decomposition of the mixture gives $S_2O_5F_2$, which is distilled off. The pyrosulfuryl fluoride is useful as a solvent.[84]

The potassium salt of pyrofluosulfonic acid, $K[S_2O_6F]$, has been prepared by the reaction of SO_3 with potassium fluoride. Finely ground and well dried KF is allowed to react with SO_3 under anhydrous conditions at room temperature. The reaction mixture is liquefied by heating it to 35°C for 12–124 hours, depending upon the amount of surface area of the KF. The excess of SO_3 is removed by allowing the reaction mixture to stand over concentrated sulfuric acid at room temperature at 13 mm pressure. Transparent prismatic crystals of potassium monofluopoly-sulfate crystallize from the reaction liquor. The crystals effloresce slowly at room temperature and rapidly at 35°C to give a white opaque solid with the empirical composition of $KF \cdot 2SO_3$. The compound has an appreciable vapor pressure of SO_3. Heating at 100°C brings about the formation of potassium fluosulfonate in four hours. The x-ray pattern verifies the fact that the compound is KS_2O_6F and not KSO_3F. The most probable structure is one in which an OH group of pyrosulfuric acid has been replaced by an atom of fluorine. In contrast to this structure, an analogous compound, NaS_2O_6Cl, appears to have a S—Cl—S linkage.[85]

12. *Fluosilicon and some fluorine-alkylhalide compounds.* Complete fluorination of the general type of compound, $RSiCl_3$ (R is an alkyl radical), may be accomplished by using SbF_3. Intermediates expected are $RSiCl_2F$ and $RSiClF_2$; however, it is difficult to control the conditions of this reaction so that anything but the completely fluorinated silane is

[83] Jonas, *loc. cit.*
[84] E. Hayek, Austrian **173,679**, Jan. 10, 1953.
[85] H. A. Lehmann and L. Kolditz, *Z. anorg. u. allgem. Chem.* **272**, 69 (1953).

formed.[86] The mono-, di-, and trifluorosilanes can be produced by fluorination with CaF_2 powder at 200°C under 700–750 mm pressure in a rotary copper tube. The factors which favor intermediate chlorofluorides of alkyl silanes are: (1) keeping the temperature and pressure as low as possible, consistent with a smooth but rapid reaction; (2) using a catalyst such as $SbCl_5$, which lowers the threshold temperature of fluorination; (3) adding the fluorinating agent slowly with stirring; and (4) "forcing" the reaction by taking out the fluorination products in the vacuum line as fast as they are formed. The last procedure (4) has been used successfully to prepare iso-$C_3H_7SiF_3$ (70–75 per cent yield), iso-$C_3H_7SiF_2Cl$ (8–10 per cent yield), and iso-$C_3H_7SiFCl_2$ (17–20 per cent yield).

13. *Reaction of fluorine with RMX_n type compounds.* Alkyl chalcogenides of the type RMX_3, R_2MX_2, and R_3MX (in which R is an alkyl or aryl radical, M is S, Se, or Te, and X is a halogen other than fluorine) are best fluorinated by the use of AgF_2. Substituted halides are generally rather resistant to conversion into fluorides. The halides of bivalent sulfur and selenium are the most reactive, although C_6H_5SCl and other similar aryl substituted compounds are not readily fluorinated. The mono- and disubstituted tetrahalides of the tellurium(IV) atom are moderately reactive as indicated by the ready formation of $(CH_3)_2TeF_2$ and $(C_6H_5)_2TeF_2$, with AgF_2 as a fluorinating agent. The mono- and disubstituted tetrahalides of sulfur and selenium are resistant to fluorination. The trisubstituted tetrahalides (R_3SX) are salt-like in their behavior with AgF:

$$[(CH_3)_3S]^+ I^- \xrightarrow{AgF} (CH_3)_3SF + AgI$$

The Fluorination of Hydrocarbons. Two mechanisms by which fluorine may react are represented by

$$MF + :\overset{..}{\underset{..}{F}} \,\Big|\, \overset{..}{\underset{..}{F}}: \rightarrow MF_n(\text{carrier}) \rightleftharpoons MF_nF^-(\text{ionic}) + :\overset{..}{F}^+$$

or

$$:\overset{..}{\underset{..}{F}} \,\overset{|}{\smash{\overline{}}}\, \overset{..}{\underset{..}{F}}: \xrightarrow[\text{light (h}\nu)]{\text{heat and/or}} 2 :\overset{..}{F}. \text{ (atomic)}$$

The very considerable positive charge on the fluorine nucleus makes the formation of a positive ion unlikely, particularly in reaction with non-polar carbon compounds. Fluorine would probably react according to

---

[86] H. S. Booth *et al., J. Am. Chem. Soc.* **68**, 2650 (1946).

the second mechanism; that is, in the active atomic state. The nature of such reactions with hydrocarbons would be rapid and difficult to control. Methods for controlling the rate of reaction between fluorine and carbon compounds are:

1. Diluting the fluorine with an inert gas.
2. Bringing about the reaction in an inert solvent.
3. Using fluorides of high-oxidation-level metals as CoF_3 or AgF_2 as fluorinating agents.
4. Using vapor phase reaction with the meshes of a metal packing, such as copper.
5. Reacting the fluorine only with relatively inert compounds.
6. Fluorinating in an electrolytic cell, using a mixture of HF and the compound to be fluorinated as an electrolyte.

The most frequently used method is some modification of (3); however, a combination of (1) and (4) is effective in hydrocarbon fluorination. Vapors of the substance to be fluorinated and fluorine, each diluted with nitrogen, are mixed at 150–325°C over a catalyst of copper turnings coated with a thin layer of silver fluoride. Method (6) shows promise in its versatility. Actually elementary fluorine is neither produced nor employed. In most cases the compound to be fluorinated acts as the electrolyte in the cell; however, for hydrocarbons a third substance, to impart conductivity, must be added. The products are isolated from the cell gases or may be drained from the bottom of the cell.[87]

A series of perfluorocarbons (completely fluorinated hydrocarbons) were manufactured (1950) at costs ranging from $3.50 to $4.50 per pound for hexane derivatives, and $16 to $18 per pound for fluorinated petroleum derivitives. These compounds are not in direct competition with ordinary oils, greases, and solvents except when very special properties are required. Under conditions in which other solvents, lubricants, or liquids would be attacked by strong oxidizing acids or by high temperatures, the perfluorocarbons are very inert. They do not burn, are stable to 400°C, and do not act with sulfuric acid, nitric acid, nitrating mixtures, or strong oxidizing agents. None of the substances—CrO_3, H_2SO_3, $KMnO_4$, Cl_2, $SOCl_2$, HF, or NaOH—has any action. Perfluorocarbons are attacked by sodium and potassium at 200°C, and by fluorine at a somewhat lower temperature. Decomposition takes place at a dull red heat. They all have low indices of refraction, high specific gravities, and low boiling points compared with compounds of similar molecular weight. They

[87] J. H. Simons *et al., J. Electrochem. Soc.* 95 (2), 47 (1949); J. H. Simons, *Fluorine Chemistry*, Academic Press, Inc., New York, 1950.

are usually slightly soluble in nonpolar solvents and insoluble in polar solvents.

Some of the typical compounds which are available are:

Perfluoromethyl hexane, C_7F_{14} (bp 76°)
Perfluorodimethyl hexane, C_8F_{16} (bp 102°)
(isomeric mixtures of 1,3 and 1,4)
Monochloropentadecafluorodimethylcyclohexane,
$C_8F_{15}Cl$ (bp 129°) (an isomeric mixture)

Other fluorinated high-molecular-weight compounds classed as kerosenes and oils are $C_{12}F_{26}$, $C_{14}F_{30}$, $C_{20}F_{42}$, $C_{21}F_{44}$ (approximate composition). All of them have electrical properties which make them ideal transformer liquids.

The lower members in general are miscible with such solvents as $CHCl_3$, CCl_4, petroleum ether, and ethyl ether. The higher members are insoluble in most all ordinary solvents. Trifluorochloroethylene, C_2F_3Cl, serves as a solvent for almost all the perfluorocarbons.

Perfluorocarbons have many other uses. In high-ultraviolet transmission experimentation, these compounds are unique since they do not absorb down to 1650 A. Therefore, C—H bands of a solute are observable. Their use in the lubricant field has already been mentioned. They serve as plasticizers for the perfluoroethylene polymers. The use of these polymers in corrosion resistant apparatus has been impeded by the inability to fabricate them and maintain their resistance to attack. A choice of perfluorocarbons is possible, depending on the temperature range desired: −25 to 125°F, 50 to 250°F and 150 to 400°F. When highly corrosive conditions exist within a mechanism or machine, the use of perfluorocarbons as lubricants may be a necessity regardless of cost.

When metal fluorides such as CoF_3 and AgF_2 are used in fluorination, the general reaction is assumed to be

$$—CH_2— + 4CoF_3 \rightarrow —CF_2— + 2HF + 4CoF_2$$

followed by

$$2CoF_2 + F_2 \rightarrow 2CoF_3$$

Some specific examples are:

$$C_7H_{16} + 32CoF_3 \rightarrow C_7F_{16} + 32CoF_2 + 16HF + 1000 \text{ kcal}$$
$$C_6H_6 + 18AgF_2 \rightarrow 18AgF + C_6F_{12} + 6HF$$

When fluorine is substituted for hydrogen in a hydrocarbon, the change in boiling point is small as compared to that resulting from a similar substitution by chlorine.   A monofluoro compound of this type is likely to be unstable, while a more highly fluorinated one is apt to be comparatively stable.

Other metal fluorides have been examined as possible substitutes for CoF_3 and AgF_2.   Manganese(III) fluoride shows some promise from the standpoint of yields and the ease with which it is regenerated from MnF_2. Compounds of higher viscosity are obtained than when CoF_3 is used. Cerium(IV) fluoride, CeF_4, gives high yields of compounds boiling between 147 and 216°C (at 10 mm pressure).   This fraction represents the most useful of the products obtainable in the lubrication field.   Metal fluorides which show little or no promise in practice are PbF_4, BiF_5, HgF_2, and the fluorides of chlorine.   In general, all metals with oxidation reduction potentials below that of manganese form fluorides which should be active fluorinating agents.   There does not appear to be any quantitative relationship between the reactivity of the various metal fluorides and their crystal structures, or their solubilities in organic solvents.[88]

Perfluoro- or fluorochlorocarbons are polymerized to obtain high viscosity oils, greases, and waxes as well as plastics.   The steps involved in the formation of such products are:

$$CF_3—CFCl_2 \xrightarrow[\text{alcohol}]{\text{Zn}} CF_2{=}CFCl$$

(monomer preparation and dechlorination)

$$CF_2{=}CFCl \xrightarrow[\text{CHCl}_3]{\text{peroxide}} R(CF_2—CFCl)_nR|$$

(polymerization of chlorotrifluoroethylene)

$$R(CF_2—CFCl)_nR' \xrightarrow{CoF_3} R(CF_2—CF_2)_nR'$$

(fluorination of crude polymer)

The variations in viscosity for various polymers may cover a range of from 301 centistokes at 100°F to 11 centistokes at 210°F.

A new phase of the plastics industry has been opened with the introduction of perfluoro- and perfluorochloropolymers.   Two major polymers (1953) on the market are Teflon,[89] polytetrafluoroethylene, and KEL-F[90] polychlorotrifluoroethylene.   Both polymers are analogs of polyethylene (polythene), in which all hydrogen atoms have been replaced by halogen atoms.   The high resistance to attack by chemical agents (other than fused alkali metals, fluorine, and certain aromatics) is due to the shielding

---

[88] C. I. Tewksbury and H. M. Haendler, *J. Am. Chem. Soc.* **71**, 2336 (1949).

[89] Trade-mark used exclusively by the E. I. du Pont Company for this polymer.

[90] Trade-mark used exclusively by the M. W. Kellogg Company for this polymer.

of the carbon atoms by the halogen atoms in closely packed structures. Both Teflon and KEL-F are able to withstand temperatures ranging from − 100° to over 350°F (500°F in the case of Teflon). Transitions of polytetrafluoroethylene polymer have been studied as a function of temperature and pressure. The results indicate the existence of three polymorphic forms with high-pressure (5000 atm) and low-pressure transitions. Increasing temperatures cause a decrease in the high-pressure transition and an increase in the low-pressure transition. A triple point is indicated at about 70°C.[91]

The fluoroplastics have high electrical resistance, low dielectric loss factor, and zero water absorption. Uses of the plastics are extensive in the electrical industry. Included among the major uses are coatings for magnet wire, insulation for coaxial cable, and supports for radar and FM antennas. Since virtually nothing will stick to either Teflon or KEL-F, these polymers are used on conveyor belts bearing sticky materials, on machinery for heat-sealing plastic films, and on rollers and other components of bread-making machinery.

Molding and forming the polymer powder of Teflon requires high pressure (about 2000 psi) and temperatures about 620°F, at which the crystalline material is transformed into a gel. By the use of aqueous dispersions containing 50 per cent solids, fluoroplastic thin films may be formed. Thick films of sheets are formed by bonding thin films. The fluoroplastic dispersions are used to coat glass fabrics to prevent cracking during creasing operations.

Among the many fluorinated organic compounds reported are trifluoromethyl isocyanate, CF_3NCO, and a number of fluorimido and -amido compounds. The isocyanate is prepared by the action of sodium azide on trifluoromethyl carbonyl chloride, CF_3COCl, in a benzene reaction medium. The reaction between mercury(II) fluoride and methyl-cyanide results in the formation of a mixture of fluorimido and -amido compounds: $CH_3CF:NF$, $CH_3CF_2NF_2$, $CH_2:C:NF$, and $CH_2:CFNF_2$.[92]

The Freons[93] are chlorofluorocarbons which have found extensive use as solvents, refrigerants, and inert dispersing agents. Dichlorodifluoro-methane, CCl_2F_2, is known as Freon-12. It is prepared in a liquid phase reaction in the presence of $SbCl_5$, or in the vapor phase in the absence of catalysts according to the reaction represented as

$$CCl_4 + 2HF \rightarrow CCl_2F_2 + 2HCl$$

[91] C. E. Weir, J. Research Natl. Bur. Standards 50, 95 (1953); H. S. Kaufman, J. Am. Chem. Soc. 75, 1477 (1953).

[92] W. Hückel, Nachr. Akad. Will. Gottingen. Math.-physik. Klasse, 1946, No. 1, 55–56.

[93] Freon is a brand name (or trade-mark) used by the E. I. du Pont Company.

A vapor-phase tube reaction with activated charcoal makes possible a continuous process. The same compound is also prepared by flowing a mixture of 4 parts of methane, 60 parts of chlorine, and 70 parts of HF (by weight) through a steel-jacketed tube over activated carbon, impregnated with CrF_3, at 340°C. With a 3-minute contact time the product is substantially all CCl_2F_2. Freon-12 has been used in air-conditioning systems in submarines, battleships, hospital ships, and aircraft carriers; it is also used in the aerosol type insecticidal bombs. Freon-22, CHF_2Cl, boils at −41.44°F (−40.8°C). This nontoxic and nonflammable refrigerant has been used in the refrigeration equipment of cold rooms to simulate arctic conditions, in stratosphere chambers, and in the production of low temperatures in wind tunnels.

Although relatively inert, Freon-12 has been used to convert tungsten(IV) oxide to a mixture of WOF_4, $WOCl_4$, and some WCl_6 by passing the gas over WO_2 at 525°C in a nickel reactor. The main reaction is represented by the equation[94]

$$2WO_2 + 2CCl_2F_2 \rightarrow WOF_4 + WOCl_4 + 2CO$$

The presence of CCl_2F_2 as well as other halogenated hydrocarbons is detected by passing the air containing these impurities into a burner fitted with a sodium-chloride-coated wire located in the flame. The halogenated hydrocarbons cause the faintly yellow flame to brighten to a brilliant yellow color.[95]

[94] A. D. Webb and H. A. Young, *J. Am. Chem. Soc.* **72**, 3356 (1950).
[95] P. J. Bendt, **Brit. 678,806**, Sept. 10, 1942.

CHAPTER 2

CHLORINE

History. Carl Scheele first prepared chlorine in 1774 by the reaction between hydrogen chloride and manganese dioxide. In accordance with the accepted view at that time that all acids contained oxygen, chlorine was thought to be an oxyacid of hydrogen chloride and was named *oxymuriatic acid*. This view was strengthened by the investigations of Berthollet in 1785. The oxygen evolved when chlorine reacts with water was erroneously attributed to oxygen in combination with chlorine. Gay-Lussac, Thénard, and Davy were all unable to decompose chlorine. Davy gave the name chlorine to Scheele's oxymuriatic acid because of its greenish-yellow color. The group name *halogen* comes from the salt-forming tendency of the individual members.

Occurrence. It is estimated that about 0.045 per cent of the earth's crust is combined chlorine. None of the halogens occur free in nature due to their high combining power. The largest source of chlorine is the sea, which is about 3 per cent sodium chloride (with other chlorides also present in smaller proportions). Isolated bodies of water in arid regions are frequently found to be high in chlorine content. The Great Salt Lake of Utah is 23 per cent sodium chloride. Brines, such as those found in Michigan, are rich in other halide salts as well as sodium chloride. The rock salt deposits near Syracuse, New York, and the Stassfurt deposits in Germany provide other sources of the halogens, particularly sodium chloride. The underground rock salt may either be mined or pumped to the surface as a saturated solution. Industrially unimportant with regard to chlorine content or as a source of chlorine, are the ores of certain heavy metals which occur as chlorides (e.g., $AgCl$, $CuCl$, $PbCl_2$). It is probable that the magnesium in bittern, brines, and sea water has resulted originally from the dissolution of magnesium chloride.

The majority of chlorine and bromine present in sedimentary and volcanic rocks is substituted for OH groups in hydroxide-bearing minerals. This fact can be shown for hornblendes, micas, clay minerals, and aluminum hydroxide. In volcanic rock, both elements are present in the trapped fluids. In sedimentary rocks, part of the chlorine and bromine can be leached out. Chlorine and bromine in sea water are probably of volcanic origin, but the weathering of volcanic rocks does not contribute

47

these elements to the sea water. Sedimentary rocks contain the same amount of chlorine but less bromine than volcanic rocks.[1]

Sodium Chloride. Special consideration is given to sodium chloride because of its importance in chemical industry. Some 7,000,000 tons of salt are converted annually to sodium carbonate by methods which have replaced the now obsolete but historically important LeBlanc process for making sodium carbonate. Sodium chloride and sodium carbonate act as the foundation of the alkali industry. The conversion of sodium chloride into chlorine, and subsequently into bleaching powder by Tennant in 1799, was a synthetic process only slightly less important than that of LeBlanc. After 1823 the production of bleaching powder, alkalies, and chlorine began in earnest.

The vast ramifications of the sodium chloride industries become evident when the total yearly tonnage consumed is noted to be over 160,000,-000 tons. The graph of consumption versus year is an accurate barometer of general business activity. Chemicals which were considered waste and nuisance by-products of the sodium chloride industry in the past have since become highly useful. Hydrogen chloride, sodium hydrogen sulfate, sodium sulfate, chlorine, bleaches, and sodium hydroxide all account for substantial tonnages of the sodium chloride consumed.

The ammonia process for the conversion of sodium chloride to sodium carbonate was developed by Solvay, a Belgian chemist, in 1868. By 1880 the Solvay process was in serious competition with the LeBlanc process, and by 1920 the latter was considered uneconomical. A factor that contributed to this situation was the cheap production of electric power which led, in turn, to cheap chlorine, bleaching powder, and sodium bicarbonate. Hydrogen chloride is produced by reactions that are essentially the first two steps of the LeBlanc process.

The marked increase in sodium chloride consumption at the outbreak of World War II was accounted for by the need for the large production of phosgene, chloropicrin, arsenic(III) chloride, mustard gas, nitrophenol, picric acid, and antiknock fuels. The soda ash used in soap and subsequent glyceryl nitrate production also requires large tonnages of sodium chloride.

In peacetime, as well as in wartime, sodium chloride is vital because of its use in the production of plastics, drugs, deodorants, rayon yarns, casehardened steels, insecticides, degreasers, films, tetraethyl lead, and rubber. The chemical and metallurgical industries of the United States use

[1] W. Behne, *Geochim. et Cosmochim. Acta* **3**, 186 (1953).

annually 11,000,000 tons of sodium chloride. The United States production is about 43 per cent of the world total.

Other chemicals, largely sodium salts, whose preparation depends upon sodium chloride as a raw material are $NaNO_2$, $NaNH_2$, $NaCN$, $NaBO_3 \cdot 4H_2O$, and sodium silicates.

Preparation of Chlorine. The methods of preparing chlorine may be roughly classified into those which have little or no commercial applications and those which are used commercially or have commercial potentialities.

1. *Noncommercial methods.* Heavy metal chlorides, particularly those in which the metal exists in a high oxidation level, are susceptible to thermal decomposition. In such compounds the metal to chlorine bond is weak. The free energy of formation of the salt is relatively small. The following equations represent certain of these decompositions:

$$PtCl_4 \xrightarrow{374°C} PtCl_2 + Cl_2$$

$$PtCl_2 \xrightarrow{582°C} Pt + Cl_2$$

$$2AuCl_3 \xrightarrow{175°C} 2AuCl + 2Cl_2$$

$$2AuCl \xrightarrow{185°C} 2Au + Cl_2$$

$$CuCl_2 \xrightarrow{350°C} 2Cu_2Cl_2 + Cl_2 \text{ (rapid at 500°)}$$

$$PbCl_4 \longrightarrow PbCl_2 + Cl_2$$

Certain laboratory preparations are of interest. Chlorine may be obtained from hydrogen chloride by the use of manganese dioxide. The reaction probably proceeds in several steps:

$$MnO_2 + 4HCl \rightarrow MnCl_4 + 2H_2O$$
$$MnCl_4 \rightarrow MnCl_2 + Cl_2$$
$$MnO_2 + 8HCl \rightarrow 2MnCl_3 + Cl_2 + 4H_2O$$
$$2MnCl_3 \rightarrow 2MnCl_2 + Cl_2$$

The over-all reaction follows:

$$MnO_2 + 4HCl \rightarrow MnCl_2 + Cl_2 + 2H_2O$$

Hydrogen chloride may be produced within the system by mixing $NaCl$ and H_2SO_4, or HCl (gas) may be passed over the MnO_2 in a heated system. Among other effective oxidizing agents are dichromates (if the HCl is reasonably concentrated), permanganates, lead dioxide, and sodium bismuthate:

$$14H^+ + Cr_2O_7^= + 6Cl^- \rightarrow 2Cr^{+3} + 3Cl_2 + 7H_2O$$
$$16H^+ + 2MnO_4^- + 10Cl^- \rightarrow 2Mn^{++} + 5Cl_2 + 8H_2O$$
$$4H^+ + PbO_2 + 2Cl^- \rightarrow Pb^{++} + Cl_2 + 2H_2O$$
$$6H^+ + BiO_3^- + 2Cl^- \rightarrow Bi^{+3} + Cl_2 + 3H_2O$$

When hydrogen chloride, produced by the action of sulfuric acid with sodium chloride, was considered a drug on the market, several commercial processes were developed for the conversion of HCl to chlorine. The Weldon process utilized the oxidizing action of pyrolusite on HCl to generate chlorine. Manganese(II) chloride is partially oxidized by air in the presence of calcium oxide:

$$124MnCl_2 + 160CaO + 49O_2 \rightarrow$$
$$36(CaO,2MnO_2) + 26(MnO,MnO_2) + 124CaCl_2$$

The manganese not changed to manganese dioxide must be replaced by fresh pyrolusite.

Procedures useful for the preparation of radiochlorine from $H^{36}Cl$ involve treatment of a $K^{36}Cl-H_2SO_4$ solution with 2–3 equivalents of $K_2S_2O_8$ or the addition of the peroxydisulfate to $0.5M$ $H^{36}Cl$. An inert gas is bubbled through the reaction mixtures and the temperature is maintained between 70 and 75°C. The chlorine so produced may be obtained carrier free by freezing it out in a trap cooled with liquid nitrogen. The oxygen evolution is extremely slow in the temperature range mentioned.[2]

2. *Commercial methods.* These methods are divided into two classes: nonelectrolytic and electrolytic.

a. Nonelectrolytic. During the period 1940–45, when heavy demands were being made on the chlorine industry[3] and on all electric power, the acute need for chlorine revived the interest in the Deacon process. This process involves the air oxidation of HCl in the presence of certain catalysts. In conjunction with the need for chlorine there was also revived interest in the Hargreaves process for the production of HCl:

$$4NaCl + 2SO_2 + 2H_2O + O_2 \rightarrow 2Na_2SO_4 + 4HCl$$

A variety of catalysts have been suggested for the air oxidation of HCl. They include chromium(VI) oxide, manganese(IV) oxide, and uranium(VI) oxide on carriers of silica gel, titania, kieselguhr, or pumice.

[2] F. Brown *et al.*, *Can. J. Chem.* **31**, 768 (1953).
[3] J. Gordon, *Chem. Eng.* **60** (50), 187 (1953).

A 77 per cent yield of chlorine is possible with chromium(VI) oxide; the latter is regenerated by air oxidation. Chromium(III) oxide supported on titania gel is effective at a reaction temperature of 650–850°F. The catalyst may be reactivated by passing air over it at 800–900°F for a time approximately equal to that of the HCl contact. Copper(I) chloride acts as a catalyst in a slightly different fashion. When CuCl is heated in air, the following reactions occur:

$$4CuCl + O_2 \rightarrow 2Cu_2OCl_2$$
$$Cu_2OCl_2 + 2HCl \rightarrow 2CuCl + H_2O + Cl_2$$

The cycle is completed by the chemical reduction of Cu_2OCl_2 to CuCl in the presence of HCl. The original Deacon-Hurter process involves the use of $CuCl_2$ as a catalyst rather than of CuCl. A mixture of HCl and O_2 (4 volumes to 1 volume) is passed over pumice stone saturated with $CuCl_2$, at a temperature below 400°C. The reaction, $4HCl + O_2 \rightleftharpoons 2Cl_2 + 2H_2O$, is reversible and the purity of the chlorine is highly dependent on the use of the optimum temperature.[4] At about 400°C an 80 per cent yield may be expected. The yields of chlorine are increased if anhydrous oxygen and HCl (1 volume to 4 volumes) free of diluent gases are passed over a solid catalyst of a compound of copper and vanadium. The gaseous effluent mixture, composed of chlorine, water, hydrogen chloride, and oxygen is dried over sulfuric acid and circulated over a similar catalyst under oxidizing conditions. Compounds of potassium, bismuth, antimony, beryllium, or magnesium may be added to the catalyst with beneficial effects.[5] A $CuCl_2$ catalyst is promoted by the addition of $PbCl_2$. The unreacted HCl may be separated from chlorine by scrubbing the gaseous mixture with a HCl solution.[6] At a time when favorable prices existed for chlorine, it was possible for these processes to compete with the electrolytic ones.[7]

A modified Deacon process[8] uses hot dry air to oxidize mixtures of hydrogen chloride, organic chlorides, and hydrocarbons in the presence of a combustion catalyst as copper(II) chromite. Unchanged HCl is absorbed in constant-boiling HCl and may be recovered by heating the solution. The HCl-free effluent mixture is suitable for the chlorination of hydrocarbons.

A solid reactant of $FeCl_3$, KCl, and $CuCl_2$ (as a promoter) supported on 6–20 mesh silica fire brick is efficient in the Deacon process for air

[4] C. W. Arnold and K. A. Kobe, *Chem. Eng. Progress* **48**, 293 (1952).
[5] F. W. De John, **U. S. 2,330,114**, Sept. 21, 1944.
[6] D. D. Luter, Jr., **U. S. 2,448,255**, Aug. 31, 1948.
[7] A. M. Thomsen, **U. S. 2,415,152**, Feb. 4, 1947.
[8] **U. S. 2,395,314**, Feb. 19, 1946.

oxidation of hydrogen chloride. Even though the HCl gas is contaminated with methane there is no adverse effect on the solid reactant.[9]

Chlorine without caustic is produced by the action of sulfur trioxide on sodium chloride.[10] At 40–100°C, sulfur trioxide reacts with NaCl to form sodium chlorosulfonate. At 150°C the chlorosulfonate reacts with sulfur trioxide to form $Na_2S_2O_7$ and sulfur pentoxydichloride, SO_5Cl_2. The latter is unstable above 200°C and forms SO_3, SO_2, and chlorine. If the sodium chlorosulfonate is formed at lower temperatures and then heated to about 230°C, it decomposes to $Na_2S_2O_7$, NaCl, SO_2, and Cl_2. The mixture of $Na_2S_2O_7$ and NaCl when heated to 400°C decomposes into Na_2SO_4, Cl_2, and SO_2. The over-all reaction may be represented by the following system:

$$2NaCl + SO_2 + O_2 \rightarrow Na_2SO_4 + Cl_2$$

or

$$Na_2S_2O_7 + 2NaCl + \tfrac{3}{2}O_2 \xrightarrow{\ 325\text{–}600°C\ } 2Na_2SO_4 + SO_2 + Cl_2$$

$$2SO_2 + O_2 \xrightarrow[\text{catalyst}]{V} 2SO_3$$

$$SO_3 + Na_2SO_4 \xrightarrow{\ 400\text{–}600°C\ } Na_2S_2O_7$$

A suitable separation of SO_2 from Cl_2 is necessary if a suitable grade of chlorine is to be expected. If an SO_2-Cl_2 mixtures is brought into contact with $ZrCl_4$ at a low temperature (0–10°C), the SO_2 forms an addition compound with the zirconium salt and pure chlorine passes on.[11] When SO_2 and Cl_2 exist in nearly equimolecular mixtures, fractionation at 7 atmospheres (absolute) gives an azeotropic distillate and a residue rich in SO_2. The former is distilled at 20 atmospheres (absolute) to produce a residue rich in chlorine and also a second azeotropic mixture. The latter is returned to the first distillate in a ratio of three parts to one part of a fresh 1:1 mixture of SO_2 and Cl_2. The chlorine can eventually be freed from the SO_2 in this way.[12] Sulfur dioxide may also be separated from chlorine by passing the gaseous mixture through $SbCl_3$ to yield $SbCl_5$ and a gas stream of SO_2. The $SbCl_5$ is then heated above 140°C to liberate chlorine and form $SbCl_3$.[13]

[9] D. J. Pye and W. J. Joseph, U. S. 2,577,808, Dec. 11, 1951.
[10] R. K. Iler, U. S. 2,445,117, July 13, 1948; 2,375,000, May 1, 1945.
[11] A. W. Hixson and R. Miller, U. S. 2,340,961, Feb. 8, 1944.
[12] H. C. Carlson, U. S. 2,381,876, Aug. 14, 1945.
[13] K. W. Geubert, U. S. 2,639,976, May 26, 1953.

Solvents may be used which preferentially dissolve chlorine and not certain other diluent gases. Among the solvents suggested are $C_2H_2Cl_4$, C_2HCl_5, and CCl_4.

The direct oxidation of HCl by concentrated nitric acid results in the formation of chlorine and nitrosyl chloride:[14]

$$3HCl + HNO_3 \rightarrow Cl_2 + NOCl + 2H_2O$$

The HCl and HNO_3 may be generated by the addition of concentrated sulfuric acid to an alkali or alkaline earth chloride and nitrate. Nitric acid added to an MnO_2 and HCl mixture increases the efficiency of chlorine production:

$$MnO_2 + 2HNO_3 + 2HCl \rightarrow Mn(NO_3)_2 + 2H_2O + Cl_2$$

When heated, the $Mn(NO_3)_2$ yields MnO_2 and N_2O_4. The latter is converted to nitric acid and recyclization is possible:

$$Mn(NO_3)_2 \rightarrow MnO_2 + N_2O_4$$
$$N_2O_4 + (O) + H_2O \rightarrow 2HNO_3$$

The thermodynamics of the following reactions indicate that large-scale production of chlorine could be carried out below 300°C:

(I) $3NaCl + 4HNO_3 \rightarrow 3NaNO_3 + Cl_2 + NOCl + 2H_2O$

(II) $NOCl + \frac{1}{2}O_2 \rightarrow NO_2 + \frac{1}{2}Cl_2$

(III) $NO + \frac{1}{2}Cl_2 \rightarrow NOCl$

(IV) $NO + \frac{1}{2}O_2 \rightarrow NO_2$

The oxidation of nitrosyl chloride to chlorine should be conducted in nitric acid of at least 70 per cent concentration. Reaction (III) is repressed (decreased in rate) by high temperature, whereas reaction (IV) increases with increase in temperature. Reaction (IV) is about 1000 times faster at room temperature than reaction (III); but, as the temperature rises, the rates become more nearly alike.[15]

The system Cl_2-NOCl has been studied over the entire concentration range 9 to 81 mol per cent chlorine as well as the properties of the two individual pure liquids at temperatures from $-57.5°$ to $-5°C$. The boiling point of the mixtures varies smoothly from $-35°C$ (for chlorine) to $-5°C$ (for NOCl). There is, thus, no evidence of compound formation between the two pure components over this temperature range.[16]

---

[14] The processes involving the interaction of nitric acid and alkali chlorides accounted for only about one per cent of the U. S. chlorine in 1951. Unfortunately the by-product, an alkali nitrate, has but few industrial uses.

[15] N. N. Drozin and I. S. Golinker, *J. Applied Chem.*, *U.S.S.R.* 22, 475 (1949).

[16] D. A. Epshtein and S. V. Mikhaleva, *Doklady Akad. Nauk S.S.S.R.* 78, 71 (1951).

Sodium chloride, which may be converted to chlorine and sodium nitrate in a continuous process, is brought in contact with gaseous anhydrous NO_2, Cl_2, and $NOCl$ (Reactions I–IV). The solid $NaCl$ after absorbing NO_2 is brought into contact with nitric acid. Thus, a solution of $NaCl$, $NaNO_3$, and an approximately equimolecular mixture of Cl_2 and $NOCl$ is formed. The Cl_2 is separated from $NOCl$ by fractional distillation. Cyclization is achieved by using the $NaNO_3$ and $NaCl$ thus formed (from $NaCl$ and NO_2) to absorb chlorine and $NOCl$, and to form more $NaCl$.[17] The separation of NO_2 and water vapor from the chlorine generated from nitric acid and sodium chloride is accomplished by preferential absorption of NO_2 and H_2O on "glaucosil."

Bleaching powder acts as a source of active chlorine in solution. If concentrated HCl is added to calcium hypochlorite, the following reaction occurs:

$$Ca(OCl_2) + 4HCl \rightarrow 2Cl_2 + CaCl_2 + 2H_2O$$

Calcium chlorite, $Ca(ClO_2)_2$, may serve as a source of pure chlorine (as well as oxygen). A catalyst of cobalt and iron salts, in a ratio of $3:2$ in water, is mixed with $Ca(ClO_2)_2$ and then dried. The mixture, when heated with additional $Ca(ClO_2)_2$ to 70 to 100°C, gives off oxygen. When CaO is added to the mixture, chlorine and oxygen are given off without heating.[18]

b. Electrolytic (caustic) methods for the production of chlorine. The production of caustic chlorine has become one of the foremost electrolytic industries in the United States. The by-products, hydrogen and sodium hydroxide, provide a very favorable economic balance.[19]

The variations in the types of cells used in the electrolytic decomposition of brine are related to the separation of the anode and cathode compartments, as well as the nature of the cathode. The mercury cells are becoming increasingly important in the United States.

It is essential that the chlorine generated at the anode not be allowed to come in contact with the sodium hydroxide produced at the cathode. The half reactions for the decomposition of brine are

$$(2OH^- + 2H^+) + 2e^- \rightarrow H_2 + 2OH^- \quad \text{(cathode)}$$

and

$$2Cl^- \rightarrow Cl_2 + 2e^- \quad \text{(anode)}$$

[17] H. W. Plucker, Ger. **708,461**, June 12, 1941; R. C. H. Chuffart, U. S. **2,225,685**, Oct. 24, 1941.

[18] V. M. Gallok, *Zhur. Priklad. Khim.* **24**, 798 (1951).

[19] W. C. Gardiner, *J. Chem. Ed.* **30** (3), 116 (1953).

In the Hooker "S" type cell (Fig. 2.1) the sodium and hydroxide ions remain in the cathode compartment. Evaporation of the catholyte yields caustic soda. Chlorine is collected from the indicated openings at the top of the cell, and hydrogen is removed from the cathode compartment. In order to avoid the danger of an explosion, the apparatus is designed so that the chlorine and hydrogen do not mix. To prevent the mixing of chlorine (in solution) and caustic by normal diffusion, the perforated cathodes are covered with a diaphragm. Other diaphragm-type cells in use are the Nelson (Fig. 2.2) and Allen-Moore cells which, like the Hooker cell, are rectangular. The Vorce (Fig. 2.3) and Wheeler cells are cylindri-

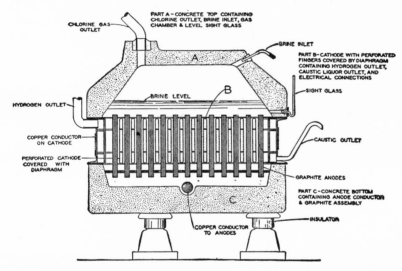

FIG. 2.1. Hooker "S" cell for the production of chlorine.

cal. In Britain the cylindrical Gibbs cell uses the diaphragm principle. The anodes are carbon rods separated from the iron cathode by an asbestos diaphragm. The purity of the sodium hydroxide produced in these diaphragm cells is not as high as that obtained from the Castner-Kellner cell, and the product must be purified by recrystallization.

At the close of hostilities of World War II, highly efficient German mercury chlorine-cells of several designs were in operation.[20] These cells turned out sodium hydroxide of 50 per cent concentration, and thus expensive evaporation equipment was made unnecessary.

[20] *Chem. & Eng. News* **23**, 2364 (1945); **24**, 1708 (1946). See also R. M. Hunter, *Chem. & Met. Eng.* **52**, No. 10, 104–6, 112 (1945).

The Castner-Kellner mercury type cell (Fig. 2.4) utilizes a different principle in the cathode design. Brine is decomposed in a cell or compartment between a graphite anode and a mercury cathode. As the electrolysis proceeds, sodium amalgam is formed at the cathode, and chlorine is withdrawn without contamination with hydrogen. A three-compartment cell may be used with a flow of mercury on the floor of the cell; the flow is brought about by means of an eccentric. The end compartments contain strong brine, while the center compartment (the denuding cell) contains water or dilute sodium hydroxide. The mercury acts as

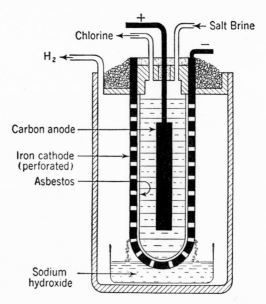

FIG. 2.2.   Diagram showing the cross-section of the Nelson electrolytic cell.

the cathode in the brine cells, but is made the anode in the denuding cell (short circuited to an iron or graphite cathode). The sodium amalgam is decomposed by the water or dilute caustic. Sodium hydroxide of 30–50 per cent concentration and high purity is produced in the center cell. Hydrogen discharge in the Castner cell takes place to an appreciable extent if one or more of the following conditions obtain: sodium ion concentration reaches too low a level, the temperature is too high, the sodium concentration in the amalgam becomes too great, or impurities are present which might be electrolytically deposited on the mercury surface. The efficient operating current density for the cell is up to 3 amperes. The

Castner type cell has a fundamental disadvantage of about 0.78 volt over the diaphragm type cell.[21]

The Italian de Nora cell[22] also uses flowing mercury as a cathode in the electrolytic decomposition of brine to form chlorine, sodium hydroxide, and hydrogen. The de Nora unit (see Fig. 2.5) consists of a long, narrow, steel trough lined with chemically resistant stone as contrasted to rubber-lined steel units used in the Mathison E-8 cell (see Fig. 2.6).

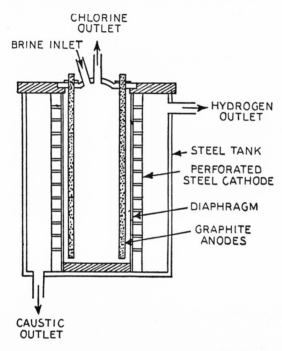

FIG. 2.3. Vorce cell for the production of chlorine.

Blocks of graphite (anodes) are suspended in the trough and supported by hard-rubber covers which form a gas-tight seal. Mercury flows along the bottom of the trough.

Brine, prepared from rock salt and free of such impurities as iron, magnesium, and calcium, is fed into the cell, flows on top of the mercury cathode, and is decomposed by a current of 30,000 amperes. The chlorine generated is trapped above the brine and beneath the hard-rubber covers.

[21] W. C. Gardner, *Chem. & Met. Eng.* **52** (7), 110 (1945).
[22] R. L. Kenyon and P. Gallone, *Ind. Eng. Chem.* **45**, 1762 (1953); H. J. Sanders *et al.*, *ibid.*, 1824 (1953).

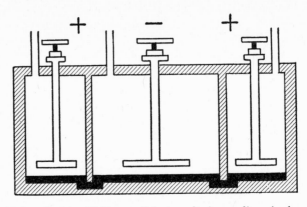

FIG. 2.4.   Castner-Kellner cell for producing sodium hydroxide.

As in the Castner-Kellner cell, sodium formed in the electrolysis dissolves in the mercury forming an amalgam.   The chlorine is withdrawn from the cell, cooled to −40°, dried, and liquefied under pressure.   The amalgam is passed into small steel towers packed with graphite lumps.   Water sprayed into the tower reacts with sodium to form hydrogen and sodium hydroxide.

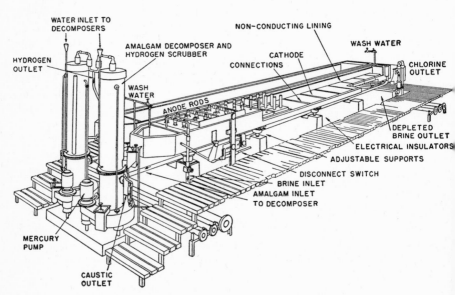

FIG. 2.5.   Perspective view of two de Nora cells.
From Ind. Eng. Chem. 45(6), 1164 (1953).

Each de Nora cell is capable of producing one ton of chlorine, 1.7 tons of 70 per cent sodium hydroxide, and 10,000 cubic feet of hydrogen per day from 1.7 tons of salt and 3,100 kilowatt-hours of electric current.

There are variations in the mercury cells used in the United States. The Mathieson E-8 cell (see Fig. 2.6) pipes the mercury to a decomposer cell where the mercury-sodium amalgam is decomposed. The amalgam serves as the anode which is short-circuited to graphite, which serves as the cathode. The formation of this couple between the amalgam and the graphite accelerates the conversion of metallic sodium to sodium hydroxide and hydrogen. The sodium hydroxide resulting is of 50 per cent concentration and of sufficient purity to be used directly by the viscose industry. A single Mathieson E-8 cell is capable of producing 2000 lb of chlorine, 2250 lb of 50 per cent caustic and 10,000 cu ft of hydrogen per day.

The chlorine produced in 1953 exceeded 2,750,000 tons. The mercury cells produced approximately 14.5 per cent, diaphragm cells 78.6 per cent, fused salt methods 5.7 per cent, and chemical (noncaustic) about 1.2 per cent. In the three-year period from 1950 to 1953, the amount of chlorine produced by mercury cells nearly tripled.

The problems inherent in the construction of electrodes for brine electrolysis are far from solved. The life of the carbon electrodes may be extended by pretreating them with linseed and/or oiticica oil, followed by heating them in an air current to about 260°C for 15 hours. Small amounts of drier may be added to the oil.[23] A superior electrode results if a metal base, such as iron, is provided with an adherent layer of magnetite in which there is embedded a discontinuous deposit of a noble metal, such as Au, Pt, Ir, or Rh. In this electrode, both the noble metal and the magnetite are exposed. The magnetite coating must be of sufficient thickness to hold the noble metal in place.[24]

Electrolytes other than brine may be used in the electrolytic production of chlorine. In the Downs cell, a fused mixture of NaCl and Na$_2$CO$_3$ is electrolyzed. The latter salt is added to reduce the melting point of the bath from 801°C (mp of NaCl) to 600°C. Graphite anodes and iron or copper cathodes are used in the cell construction. The primary products are sodium metal and chlorine. Chlorine is piped from the anode compartment, which is separated from the cathode by a wire gauze partition. Practically all the sodium metal in the United States is produced by this method.

[23] E. F. Kiefer and W. G. Krellner, **U. S. 2,368,306**, Jan. 30, 1945.
[24] R. O. Lowry, **U. S. 2,305,539**, Dec. 15, 1943.

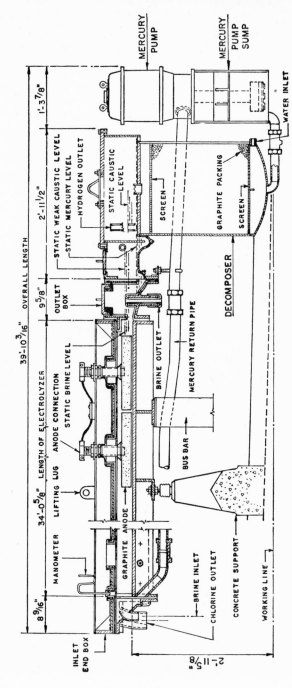

LONGITUDINAL SECTION OF MATHIESON MERCURY CELL

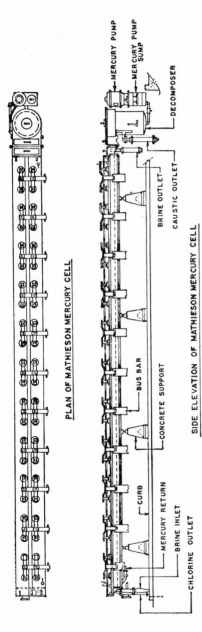

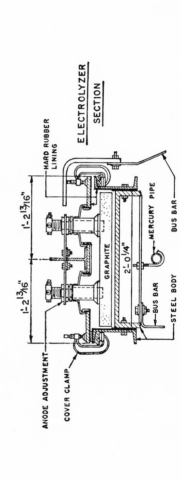

FIG. 2.6. Engineering drawing of Mathieson E-8 mercury cell. *From Ind. Eng. Chem.* 45(9), 1831 (1953).

A multi stage electrolytic process for the production of chlorine from HCl has been developed which yields over 99 per cent chlorine. A chloride of a multivalent metal (e.g., $CuCl_2$) in an HCl solution whose concentration must not exceed 25 per cent is used as an electrolyte. Chlorine is liberated during the electrolysis of the $CuCl_2$. The partially spent electrolyte is removed through the electrolytically active portion of the porous cathode, which forms one wall of the cell. The copper(I) chloride, formed by electrolytic reduction, is oxidized to $CuCl_2$ by air and returned to the cell.[25]   At a cathode density of 108 amps/sq ft, a current efficiency of over 85 per cent is obtained.

The electrolytic production of magnesium from anhydrous $MgCl_2$ accounts for a large tonnage of chlorine. The anode gas contains HCl as well as Cl_2. One way of purifying the chlorine produced by this method involves washing the mixture with dilute HCl and absorbing the nearly pure Cl_2 in a calcium carbonate suspension. This slurry is then treated with either HCl or H_2SO_4 to free the chlorine.[26]   In localities where cheap hydrogen is available, the chlorine is economically converted to HCl if the latter is an essential raw material.

Physical Properties of Chlorine.   At ordinary temperatures, chlorine is a greenish-yellow gas with a characteristic suffocating odor. The liquid also has a greenish-yellow color. The refractive index is low. The covalent nature of liquid chlorine is indicated by its nonconducting property. The liter density of 3.214 g is proof of its diatomic nature. The K equilibrium values for the system $Cl_2 \rightleftharpoons 2Cl$ at the temperatures 298.1, 500, 1000, 2000, and 3000°K are 1.17×10^{-37}, 1.97×10^{-20}, 1.46×10^{-7}, 0.519, and 87.6, respectively.[27]   The gas may be condensed to a liquid under one atmosphere pressure at a temperature of -34.6°C. The critical temperature and pressure are, respectively, 144°C and 76.1 atm.

The entropy of the ideal gas at the boiling point (239.05°K) is 51.56 cal deg^{-1} mol^{-1}. This value corresponds well with the value 53.290 cal deg^{-1} mol^{-1} calculated from spectroscopic data.[28]   The entropy of the ideal gas at 298.10°K is 53.32 cal deg^{-1} mol^{-1}. The vapor pressure of liquid chlorine is represented by the following equation for the range from the triple point, 172.12°K to 240°K: $\log_{10} P_{(inter. cm)} = -1418/T - 0.01206T + 1.34 \times 10^{-5}T^2 + 9.91635$. The observed triple point pressure is 1.044 cm.[29]

[25] F. S. Low, **U. S. 2,468,766**, May 3, 1949.
[26] A. P. Julien and J. K. Farrel, **U. S. 2,398,891**, April 23, 1946.
[27] K. V. Butkov, *Rec. trav. chim.* 67, 551, (1948).
[28] R. H. Sherman and W. F. Giauque, *J. Am. Chem. Soc.* 75, 2007 (1953).
[29] W. F. Giauque and T. M. Powell, *J. Am. Chem. Soc.* 61, 1970 (1939).

Precision x-ray photographs of solid chlorine ($-160°C$) indicate unit cell dimensions of $a = 6.29$, $b = 4.50$, and $c = 8.21$ A. There are four molecules per unit cell giving a calculated density of 2.03. The observed density agrees well with the calculated value. The space group is D_{2h}^{18}-C_{mca}. The bond distance within the molecule is 2.02 A, and the shortest nonbonded distance is 3.34 A. The structures of all the halogens are very similar.[30]

The solubility of chlorine in water is between that of the slightly soluble gases, such as oxygen and hydrogen, and the exceedingly soluble gases, such as HCl and NH_3. Its fairly low solubility in water is partially attributable to the lack of polarity of the molecule. About 2.15 volumes of chlorine dissolve in one volume of water at 20°C. In view of the slow reaction between chlorine and water to form hypochlorous acid and hydrogen chloride, as well as the secondary decomposition of the HClO to HCl and O_2, exact measurements of solubility are difficult. When chlorine is passed into water at 0°C, the amount of gas which dissolves is increased because of the formation of hydrates. Both the hexahydrate, $Cl_2 \cdot 6H_2O$ (pale green crystals), and the octahydrate, $Cl_2 \cdot 8H_2O$, may be separated from an aqueous solution. The composition of the latter has been determined by calculating the heats of dissociation in gaseous chlorine and ice, and in gaseous chlorine and water.[31]

The Hydrolysis of Chlorine. Two mechanisms have been proposed to explain the action of chlorine on water:[32]

$$(1) \quad Cl_2 + H_2O \rightleftharpoons HClO + H^+ + Cl^-$$

and[33]

$$(2) \quad Cl_2 + OH^- \rightarrow HClO + Cl^-$$

The kinetic equation of (2) is $-d[Cl_2]/dt = K_1[Cl_2][OH^-] - K_2[HClO] \times [Cl^-]$. Little or no activation energy is required according to scheme (2) and a reaction is possible every time there is a collision. A rate constant of 5×10^{14} is in accord with this conclusion.[34] The thermodynamic quantities for (2) are found in Table 2.1.

It is difficult to reconcile the K values based on (2) with other experimental evidence which shows the reaction constant increasing with decreasing hydroxide concentration. This decrease in hydroxide concentration is in conformance with mechanism (2).

[30] Robert L. Collin, *Acta Cryst.* **5**, 431 (1952).
[31] I. Harris, *Nature* **151**, 309 (1943).
[32] J. C. Morris, *J. Am. Chem. Soc.* **68**, 1692 (1946).
[33] E. A. Shilov and S. N. Solodushenkov, *J. Phys. Chem. U.S.S.R.* **21**, 1159 (1947).
[34] Morris, *loc. cit.*

TABLE 2.1. THERMODYNAMIC QUANTITIES FOR THE REACTION
$Cl_2 + OH^- \rightleftharpoons HClO + Cl^-$

Temperature °C	$K_{eq.} \times 10^{-10}$	$-\Delta F°$	$-\Delta H°$	$\Delta S°$
0	13.77	13,920	7040	25.2
15	7.02	14,310	7820	23.8
25	4.25	14,530		22.5

Chemical Properties of Chlorine. In its normal chemical reactions, chlorine behaves as an electron acceptor. As noted in Table I.2, a variety of compounds of chlorine exist in which the apparent oxidation state is positive. There are no simple salts in which a positively charged chlorine exists. Rather, the positively charged halogen usually is either combined with oxygen or with fluorine. Oxygen and chlorine have the common property of accepting electrons; however, the affinity is more marked in the case of chlorine.

1. *Action of chlorine with hydrogen.* Hydrogen is readily oxidized by chlorine to form hydrogen chloride. A jet of hydrogen burning in air continues to burn in a chlorine atmosphere:

$$H_2 + Cl_2 \rightarrow 2HCl + 44,061 \text{ cal}$$

Enclosed mixtures of hydrogen and chlorine undergo combination if exposed to high energy light. The fact that the combination continues after the first exposure to light indicates a chain reaction. The chains start from the wall of the vessel. In the absence of oxygen the chains extend over the whole volume of the container. In the presence of oxygen the reaction takes place in a thin layer (0.8 mm) adjacent to the walls of vessel.[35] Although a small amount of water is necessary to initiate a chain (10^{-6} mm partial pressure), it retards the reaction once it has begun. The amount of moisture needed to initiate the reaction appears to be a function of the wave length of light. Combination may begin to take place with dry gases if the intensity of the light is sufficiently high. If the gases are free from such impurities as ammonia or nitrogenous materials (likely to be present from water), the photochemical combination of hydrogen and chlorine takes place without any induction period. The chain reaction is most simply represented as follows:

$$Cl_2 + h\nu \rightleftharpoons 2Cl$$
$$Cl + H_2 \rightleftharpoons HCl + H$$
$$H + Cl_2 \rightleftharpoons HCl + Cl$$

[35] A. M. Markevich, *Zhur. Fiz. Khim.* **22**, 941 (1948).

Combinations in which the activated atoms combine, or react with impurities within the system, disrupt the chain.

The exchange reaction betweeen HCl and Cl_2 in the gas state is
heterogeneous at room temperature. A slow homogeneous exchange
takes place and a rapid photochemical exchange reaction then occurs.
The photochemical exchange occurs through [Cl] atoms. These atoms
then exchange rapidly and heterogeneously with both HCl and Cl_2.[36]

2. *Action of chlorine with metals.* The reaction of chlorine on the
alkali and alkaline-earth metals is rapid; the rate is determined largely by
the temperature, the state of subdivision, and the purity (freedom from
oxide coating). Finely divided antimony and thin sheets of preheated
copper burn spontaneously in a chlorine atmosphere. Sheet steel ignites
after a 30-minute exposure to commercially dry chlorine gas at 251°C.[37]
Multivalent metals usually show their higher oxidation states in reacting
with chlorine:

$$2Fe + 3Cl_2 \rightarrow 2FeCl_3$$

$$Cu + Cl_2 \rightarrow CuCl_2$$

$$2Au + 3Cl_2 \rightarrow 2AuCl_3$$

$$Pt + 2Cl_2 \rightarrow PtCl_4$$

$$Sn + 2Cl_2 \rightarrow SnCl_4$$

If a high temperature is attained either from the heat of reaction or
from external sources, a higher chloride may decompose to form a lower
one. Whether or not a metal attains its maximum oxidation level in the
presence of excess chlorine may depend upon the mole ratio of chlorine as
well as the size of the positive ion. Small, highly positive metals are able
to accommodate only a limited number of anionic groups. Thus, an
element (whether it be a metal or nonmetal) may attain a higher oxidation
level in direct combination with fluorine than it can with chlorine. This
behavior is particularly evident in the platinum-metal triads.[38]

3. *Action of chlorine on nonmetals.* The high degree of activity of
chlorine is well exhibited in its tendency to react with the free halogens of
higher atomic number. A number of chlorine fluorides are formed in
which the chlorine has an apparent positive oxidation state. In combination with bromine and iodine, the chlorine is negative (see chap. 8).

[36] W. H. Johnston and W. F. Libby, *J. Am. Chem. Soc.* **73**, 854 (1951).

[37] G. Heinemann, F. G. Garrison, and P. A. Haber, *Ind. Eng. Chem.* **38**, 497 (1946).

[38] W. Klemm, *FIAT Rev. German Sci.*, 1939–1946, Inorganic Chemistry, Pt. III,
1948 (2–3).

With phosphorus, a vigorous reaction occurs, the final product depending on the mole ratio of the reactants:

$$P_4 + 6Cl_2 \rightarrow 4PCl_3$$
$$P_4 + 10Cl_2 \rightarrow 4PCl_5$$

Arsenic resembles antimony in its reaction with chlorine, since both the tri- and pentachlorides are known. With oxygen a number of chlorides are possible; however, few, if any, are best prepared by direct combination.

The reaction of sulfur with chlorine results in the formation of SCl (mp 151°K), S_2Cl_2 (mp 191°K), and S_2Cl_3 (mp 145°K). The exact composition of the last of these compounds is uncertain. There is no evidence for the formation of S_3Cl_4.[39] Sulfur monochloride, S_2Cl_2, is catalytically converted to SO_2Cl_2 by two moles of oxygen and one mole of chlorine. The S_2Cl_2 (liquid) and chlorine gas are sprayed by nozzel into the top of a quartz vessel. Oxygen is introduced at the bottom. The catalyst is activated charcoal.[40]

4. *Action of chlorine with compounds.* A reaction between chlorine and a halide occurs if the halogen in combination is less electronegative than chlorine. Two simple displacement reactions are represented by

$$2Br^- + Cl_2 \rightarrow Br_2 + 2Cl^-$$
$$2I^- + Cl_2 \rightarrow I_2 + 2Cl^-$$

A hydrohalide (HBr or HI) acts more rapidly than one of its salts. The second reaction provides a simple test for the presence of an iodide. If the reaction takes place in the presence of starch, a deep blue starch-iodine complex is formed. Also classed as displacements are the reactions between alkanes and chlorine when the former are allowed to burn in an atmosphere of chlorine. The general reaction may be represented as

$$C_nH_{(2n+2)} + (n + 1)Cl_2 \rightarrow (2n + 2)HCl + nC$$

Unsaturated hydrocarbons, such as turpentine, burn readily in chlorine:

$$C_{10}H_{16} + 8Cl_2 \rightarrow 10C + 16HCl$$

When saturated hydrocarbons are exposed to chlorine in the presence of sunlight, a reaction, difficult to control, takes place, in which the hydrogen atoms are replaced stepwise until a completely chlorinated carbon compound is formed. This type of reaction is represented by the chlorination

[39] G. H. Whiting, *J. Appl. Chem.* 2, 390 (1952).
[40] K. Wintersberger and G. K. Koudela, Ger. 801,637, Jan. 18, 1951.

f methane:

$$CH_4 \xrightarrow{Cl_2} HCl + CH_3Cl \xrightarrow{Cl_2} HCl + CH_2Cl_2 \xrightarrow{Cl_2} CHCl_3 + HCl$$
$$\downarrow Cl_2$$
$$HCl + CCl_4$$

Chlorine reacts with certain metal oxides (often only in the presence of arbon for a complete reaction) to yield the anhydrous chlorides. A eaction which has become important in the production of magnesium netal is represented as

$$MgO + Cl_2 \rightarrow MgCl_2 + \tfrac{1}{2}O_2$$

The reaction temperature must be 1000°C or higher. The addition of arbon favors a lower temperature and prevents the formation of a nagnesium chloride layer on the surface of the oxide.[41]

Iron(III) oxide is converted to the chloride according to the reaction:

$$2Fe_2O_3 + 6Cl_2 \rightarrow 4FeCl_3 + 3O_2$$

The K equilibrium value for the reaction increases from 4×10^{-12} to $\times 10^{-4}$ over the temperature range of 700 to 1000°C. In contrast, the K equilibrium value for the chlorination of WO_3

$$2WO_3 + 2Cl_2 \rightarrow 2WO_2Cl_2 + O_2$$

changes from 1.3×10^{-6} to 5×10^{-1} over about the same temperature range. A means of separating iron from tungsten is suggested by his difference.[42]

The chlorine-iron(III) chloride system has been studied in detail. When $FeCl_3$ crystals are grown from the gas phase with sufficient chlorine present to prevent the independent formation of $FeCl_2$, the $FeCl_3$ crystals contain some $FeCl_2$ in solid solution. At 290°C the $FeCl_3$ phase is homogeneous from $FeCl_{3.000}$ to $FeCl_{2.9975}$. The $FeCl_2$ content increases with increasing temperature at constant chlorine pressure but decreases with increasing chlorine pressure at constant temperature.[43]

Chlorides of the alkaline earths may be obtained from their sulfates by direct chlorination in the presence of carbon.

$$2CaSO_4 + 6C + 3Cl_2 \rightarrow 2CaCl_2 + S_2Cl_2 + 4CO + 2CO_2$$

[41] H. A. Doerner and W. F. Holbrook, *U. S. Bur. Mines Rept. Investigation* **3833** (1945).

[42] P. Galmiche, *Ann. chim.* **3** (12), 243 (1948).

[43] H. Schäfer and L. Bayer, *Z. anorg. u. allgem. Chem.* **272**, 265 (1953).

This reaction is essentially complete (96 per cent) in 15 minutes. A two-step reaction actually takes place. The first step is the reduction of the calcium sulfate by carbon to calcium sulfide, and the second step is the reaction of chlorine on calcium sulfide to form calcium chloride and sulfur monochloride.

Sulfamic acid is totally decomposed by chlorine (or sodium hypochlorite) in an alkaline medium. Free nitrogen is produced along with chlorinated sulfamates ($ClNHSO_3Na$ and Cl_2NSO_3Na), which are very unstable. In an acid solution, the chlorination results in a trichlorosulfonic acid of undetermined structure which decomposes into NCl_3 and H_2SO_4.[44] Chlorine reacts with CO and SO_2 to form carbonyl chloride (phosgene), and sulfuryl chloride, SO_2Cl_2, respectively.

Chlorine reacts with water in addition to dissolving in this solvent. The solution, then, has the properties not only of chlorine but also of hydrochloric acid, hypochlorous acid, and atomic oxygen. Its oxidizing action is illustrated by the following equations:

$$H_2S + Cl_2 \rightarrow 2HCl + S$$
$$2KI + Cl_2 \rightarrow 2KCl + I_2$$
$$2H_2O + Cl_2 + SO_2 \rightarrow H_2SO_4 + 2HCl$$

In the presence of sunlight, the oxidizing action of chlorine on water favors the formation of chloric acid and additional oxygen:

$$2H_2O + 2Cl_2 \rightarrow 4HCl + O_2$$
$$5Cl_2 + 5H_2O \rightarrow HClO_3 + 9HCl + O_2$$

Gaseous chlorine reacts with hydrogen sulfide to form sulfur dichloride, SCl_2, and, in the presence of excess hydrogen sulfide, sulfur monochloride, S_2Cl_2.[45]

Chlorine reacts with calcium phosphate and charcoal at 750°C to give phosphorus oxychloride, $POCl_3$ (mp 1.25°C and bp 105.8°C). Purification of the compound for solvent study purposes requires the complete elimination of water. Water reacts with $POCl_3$ to give phosphoric acid and hydrogen chloride, thereby raising the conductivity of the $POCl_3$ solvent. Metallic sodium may be added, if the water content is small, and the resulting mixture distilled with great caution at atmospheric pressure.[46]

[44] V. V. Korshak *et al.*, *J. Gen. Chem. U.S.S.R.* **18**, 753 (1948).
[45] P. W. Schenk and S. Sternes, *Monatsh.* **80**, 117 (1949).
[46] V. Gutmann, *Monatsh. Chem.* **83**, 164 (1952); H. P. Cady and R. Taft, *J. Phys. Chem.* **29**, 1057 (1925).

Chlorine reacts with silver nitrate in the presence of pyridine to form an addition compound represented by the formula $ClNO_3 \cdot 2C_5H_5N$. The system must be dry for the successful preparation of the compound. It melts with decomposition at 73–78°C. Other halogens react similarly to form $BrNO_3 \cdot 2C_5H_5N$, $BrNO_3 \cdot C_5H_5N$ and $INO_3 \cdot C_5H_5N$.[47]

Uses of Chlorine. The estimated consumption of both liquid and gaseous chlorine in 1953 was more than 2.7 million tons. Chemical manufacture, chiefly organic processes, dominates the chlorine consumption picture. Prior to 1930, water purification and pulp and paper placed the largest demands on chlorine. The 1912 typhoid fever epidemic at Niagara Falls established chlorine in the field of water sterilization. Changes in the percentage consumption of chlorine through various outlets are illustrated by the increased use by the chemical industries from 30 per cent in 1930 to 40 per cent in 1937 to 80 per cent in 1951. The chlorination of olefins, paraffins, and the production of ethylene glycol were important factors in this growth. The uses for pulp and paper and sanitation are of secondary importance, accounting for about 18 per cent of the total consumption in 1951.

During the war years (1941–45), as well in the year 1947, the supply of chlorine was insufficient for the demands. The difficulties in transporting chlorine were not solved until late in 1947. The production of chlorine doubled from 1940 to 1944, whereas the total number of tank cars needed for distribution was only 50 per cent more for 1947 than for the 1940 figure.

The demand for high-grade caustic and hydrogen has stimulated the production of electrolytic chlorine. The magnesium plants in the southwest are substantial chlorine producers. Much of the chlorine is recycled, however, to produce hydrogen chloride for the conversion of magnesium oxide to the chloride. The abundance of limestone, salt (from brines and tide water), and gaseous fuel has made the southwestern section of the United States an important center for the caustic industry.

[47] M. J. Ouchakow and W. O. Tschistow, *J. Gen. Chem.*, *U.S.S.R.* 1, 63, 1258 (1931); *ibid.* 3, 2142 (1936).

CHAPTER 3

BROMINE

History. The discovery of bromine is credited to A. J. Balard in 1826 He obtained it from the mother liquor of the Montpellier bitterns, which are high in magnesium bromide. There is no question but that the element had been prepared by Joss and Liebig prior to Balard's discovery however, neither of these investigators recognized the elemental nature of their product. Balard thought it was selenium, and Liebig assumed that his product was a "chloride of iodine." The name bromine is derived from the Greek word meaning odor or stench.

Occurrence. Brines, bitterns, sea water, and saline deposits (from evaporation of inland seas), regardless of their location, all contain bromides derived originally from the dissolution of alkali, alkaline earth and magnesium salts. The bromide content is much smaller than the chloride content in all of these sources; however, a high percentage of conversion to elemental bromine (over 90 per cent) is possible by modern technology. Average sea water contains about 0.015 per cent bromine. Such bodies of water as the Great Salt Lake of Utah, the Dead Sea, and Searles Lake of California contain much higher concentrations of bromine. The Stassfurt deposits of Germany formerly provided a large percentage of the world's supply of bromine. In the United States prior to 1930, most of the bromine was derived from the Michigan, Ohio, Kentucky, and West Virginia well brines. Certain forms of marine plant life contain a small percentage of combined bromine. The dibromo-indigo of Tyrian purple comes from a shell fish.

Preparation. All methods of bromine production depend on the oxidation of the bromide ion. There are no naturally occurring oxygen salts of bromine which act as a source of the element. Manganese dioxide in the presence of sulfuric acid oxidizes the bromide ion to bromine:

$$Mn O_2 + 4H^+ + 2Br^- \rightarrow Br_2 + Mn^{++} + 2H_2O$$

Concentrated sulfuric acid is a sufficiently good oxidizing agent itself to oxidize the bromide ion to bromine. For this reason the usual displacement of the more volatile hydrohalide from its salt by sulfuric acid cannot be used for the preparation of anhydrous hydrogen bromide:

$$2H^+ + H_2SO_4 + 2Br^- \rightarrow Br_2 + SO_2 + 2H_2O$$

70

Bromine is liberated from a solution of its salts by the treatment with chlorine. Oil-field brines are sufficiently high in bromide ion content to make their industrial processing feasible:

$$Br^- + Cl_2 \rightarrow 2Cl^- + Br_2$$

This reaction is the basis for the bromine industry which utilizes sea water (or bitterns) as a source of the bromide ion. In 1924 the production of free and combined bromine amounted to about 1000 tons; by 1931 the production was about five times this tonnage, and the production of bromine (1954) is about 45 times the 1924 figure. The demand for bromine is closely allied to antiknock fuel consumption. The original objection to lead tetraethyl as an antiknock agent resulted from the objectionable deposit left after combustion. The formation of this lead deposit is prevented by the introduction of ethylene dibromide, $C_2H_4Br_2$.

One of the first processes for the extraction of bromine involved the oxidation of brine by elementary chlorine and the precipitation of tribromoaniline:

$$3Br^- + 3Cl_2 + C_6H_5NH_2 \rightarrow C_6H_2Br_3NH_2 + 3H^+ + 6Cl^-$$

The relative expense of aniline and the inefficiency of bromine production based on chlorine consumption stopped the use of this procedure. The Ethyl-Dow Corporation now processes sea water at the Freeport, Texas, plant with the ultimate object of converting all bromine produced to ethylene dibromide. The original plant at Cape Fear, North Carolina, was shut down in 1945. From about 1934 to 1937, the extraction of bromine from sea water involved the absorption of liberated bromine in sodium carbonate to form mixed crystals of sodium bromide and sodium bromate. The equations representing the process are

$$2Br^- + Cl_2 \rightarrow Br_2 + 2Cl^-$$
$$3Br_2 + 3CO_3^= \rightarrow 5Br^- + BrO_3^- + 3CO_2$$

and

$$5Br^- + BrO_3^- + 6H^+ \rightarrow 3Br_2 + 3H_2O$$

The raw brine was acidified and treated with enough chlorine to liberate approximately 98 per cent of the bromine and to oxidize any iodide to the iodate. A 75–100 per cent excess of chlorine was usually used. The pH of the brine was adjusted with sulfuric acid to a value between 1 and 4. This adjustment was necessary due to the high alkalinity of sea water from carbonates and bicarbonates. In even weakly alkaline solutions, the bromine liberated by the chlorine was converted to products which prevent liberation of bromine. Even in a neutral solution, some bromine was auto-oxidized and reduced to bromide ion and bromate ion:

$$3Br_2 + 3H_2O \rightarrow 6H^+ + 5Br^- + BrO_3^-$$

The reaction, $Cl_2 + 2OH^- \rightarrow ClO^- + H_2O + Cl^-$, was also inhibited at a low pH. In such a reaction, chlorine otherwise available for bromide oxidation was lost. Sulfuric acid favored the elimination of bromine from the brine solution. The back pressure of carbon dioxide which was formed on acidification of brine inhibited the normal absorption of bromine in sodium carbonate solution. It was advantageous to blow the carbon dioxide out of the system prior to the chlorination of brine.

All the plants for obtaining bromine from sea water built in the United States since 1937 utilize the sulfur dioxide process for the concentration of bromine. In the sulfur dioxide process, the screened sea water is mixed with chlorine and sulfuric acid. Bromine in a very dilute form is blown out by air in a tower. The dilute bromine gas is mixed with sulfur dioxide in a mixing chamber. Water is added to the mixture in an absorber to give a solution of hydrobromic acid and sulfuric acid

$$SO_2 + 2H_2O + Br_2 \rightarrow 2HBr + H_2SO_4$$

Chlorine and steam are then blown into the HBr-H_2SO_4 solution in a steaming out tower. Bromine in a highly concentrated form is condensed to the liquid state. The liquid bromine is reacted directly with ethylene to form ethylene dibromide.[1]

Some other methods have been offered for the isolation of bromine from the chlorinated brine. The latter is pumped to the top of an absorption tower, treated with an upward current of air, and the resulting mixture of bromine and air is scrubbed with iron(II) bromide. Bromine is liberated from the resulting iron(III) bromide by a second chlorination and is then cooled to condense it. The iron(III) chloride is reduced to iron(II) chloride by direct treatment with scrap iron. The reduced salt is also used to obtain iodine from the chlorinated brine by reducing the iodate (and iodite) to free iodine. The latter is recovered in a sodium carbonate solution.[2]

If bromine vapor (from the brine process) containing approximately 1 per cent chlorine is bubbled through iron(III) bromide solution, the chlorine is retained; and bromine with a greatly reduced (0.025 per cent) chlorine content is obtained as a condensate. Further purification of bromine is possible by allowing an iron(III) bromide and bromine mixture

[1] P. Hart, *Chem. Eng.* **54**, 102 (1947); R. Bock, *Chem.-Ing.-Tech.* **25**, 245 (1953); S. B. Heath, **U. S. 2,143,223** (1939); G. W. Hooker, **U. S. 2,143,224** (1939).

[2] J. Cranston, **U. S. 2,412,390**, Dec. 10, 1946.

to stand for about three days. At the end of this time the bromine layer shows a tenfold reduction in its chlorine content.[3] Purification of bromine from chlorine by fractional distillation is possible, since all the dissolved chlorine is found in the first 1 to 4 per cent of the distillate.

The recovery and purification of bromine from a natural saline solution at 20–30°C are achieved by first introducing the solution into a condensing tower packed with Raschig rings. The bromide solution, which collects at the bottom of the tower, is then piped to the top of a steaming-out tower. Steam and chlorine are admitted to the bottom of the tower. The bromide ion is converted to bromine by the combined action of the chlorine and steam and is then removed from the solution. The bromine is separated from the chlorine in a condensing tower in which the chlorine is dissolved in a counter current of a bromide solution. The condensed bromine is collected at the bottom of the tower.[4]

An alternate method for the liberation of bromine from bromide solution is by electrolysis. Synthetic brines ($2M$ in NaCl and $0.005M$ in KBr) may be electrolyzed with graphite electrodes at a pH of 0, 25°C, and 0.3 amp/cm^2 current density. Complete recovery of the bromine is achieved without oxidation of the chloride ion. The redox potential of the system is 0.982 volts.[5]

The Deacon process of air oxidation is adaptable to the conversion of hydrogen bromide to bromine. A cerium(IV) oxide catalyst supported on pumice or other refractory material at 800–1000°C is used. The bromine is separated from the reaction gases by fractionation and scrubbing with sodium bromide solution.[6]

An application of a laboratory procedure for the preparation of bromine by concentrated oxidizing acids may have commercial potentialities. Bromine and iodine are liberated from brines containing sulfuric acid by controlled reaction with nitric acid. The following equations describe the sequence of reactions:

$$3HBr + (H_2SO_4) + HNO_3 \rightarrow Br_2 + NOBr + 2H_2O + (H_2SO_4)$$
$$NOBr + H_2O \rightarrow HBr + HNO_2$$
$$HNO_2 + HNO_3 \rightarrow 2NO + H_2O + O_2$$
$$4NO + 3O_2 + 2H_2O \rightarrow 4HNO_3$$
$$2HNO_3 + 3SO_2 + 2H_2O \rightarrow 3H_2SO_4 + 2NO$$

[3] C. M. Antonena, *Bol. inform. petrol.* 25, No. 285, 11 (1948).

[4] I. A. Kenaga, U. S. 2,359,221, Sept. 26, 1944.

[5] J. J. Ronco, *Lab. ensayo materiales e invest. technol.*, Buenos Aires, Ser. II, No. 19 (1947).

[6] M. Mugdon, Brit. 585,728, Feb. 21, 1947.

Chlorine is used to complete the liberation of bromine. The system is heated to vaporize the bromine which is finally condensed or it may be absorbed in caustic.[7]

Physical Properties. Bromine is a mobile, dark red liquid with a pungent odor and a density of 3.19 at 0°C. The color at $-252°C$ is a deep orange. Contrary to some previous reports, it does not appear possible to obtain colorless bromine even at this low temperature. Spectrophotometric examination shows that the absorption band never shifts to a point where the liquid may be assumed to be colorless.[8] The solubility of bromine is low in water and high in nonpolar solvents (CCl_4, CS_2). This behavior is in agreement with the covalent nature of the bond. Bromine solutions may be made by shaking the liquid with 5 per cent aqueous potassium bromide. Absorption measurements in the visible region of the spectrum show that bromine is not solvated. The displacement noted in such associated solvents as ethanol and concentrated sulfuric and phosphoric acids is ascribed to the effect of the semi-rigid cage of solvent molecules surrounding each bromine molecule rather than to actual solvation. In normal solvents, such as hexane, the displacement of the absorption continuum at 4150 A is slightly toward the red; however, in other normal solvents it may be toward the violet. The displacement is marked toward the violet in associated solvents.[9]

Some information is available on bromine as a solvent. The equivalent conductance of tetrabutylammonium bromide dissolved in bromine increases from 0.05 to a maximum of 15.75 at 2.01N concentration. The equivalent conductance for trimethyl ammonium bromide increases from 0.01 to 13.92 at 1.13N concentration. At 0.036N the bromide salt conducts 30 times as well as the chloride salt in liquid bromine. There must be a high degree of dissociation of the ammonium salts at high concentrations considering the high viscosity of the solutions.[10]

Vapor density measurements below 750°C prove the diatomic nature of the molecule. The equilibrium constants for the reaction $Br_2 \rightleftarrows 2Br$ at 298.1, 500, 1000, 2000, and 3000°C are 4.74×10^{-29}, 2.22×10^{-15}, 3.27×10^{-5}, 4.934, and 304, respectively. Values for PV at temperatures from 87.7 to 112.4°C at one atmosphere range from 28.85 to 31.11. The compressibility factor to be applied in the above temperature range in the perfect gas law is 0.992–3.[11]

[7] J. J. Grebe *et al.*, **U. S. 2,371,886**, March 20, 1945.
[8] K. Clausius, *Z. Naturforsch.* **2B**, 244 (1947).
[9] N. S. Bayliss *et al.*, *Australian J. Sci. Research*, Ser. A, 1, 472 (1948).
[10] G. W. Moessen and C. A. Kraus, *Proc. Natl. Acad. Sci.*, *U. S.* 38, 1023 (1952).
[11] J. A. Lasater *et al.*, *J. Am. Chem. Soc.* 72, 1845 (1950).

Bromine is absorbed on graphite, and some information on the electron accepting properties of bromine are indicated by gram susceptibility studies of the graphite in presence of adsorbed bromine. Using Peierls' theory of diamagnetism of free electrons in the solid and Wallaces' results concerning the bond structure of graphite, it is possible to relate magnetic susceptibility with the change in the number of electrons in the Brillouin zones. The gram susceptibility of graphite at room temperature drops from -5.3×10^{-6} to -4.2×10^{-6} at a concentration corresponding to 7.6×10^{-3} bromine atoms per atom of carbon. A further drop in gram susceptibility to -3×10^{-8} is noted at a concentration of 0.10 atom of bromine per carbon atom. These data are in accord with the general electron accepting property of bromine.[12]

The only two isotopes of bromine which have been reported are ^{79}Br and ^{81}Br. For every 100 atoms of the former there are 97.9 ± 0.4 atoms of the latter. The natural abundance ratios of these isotopes may also be represented as $^{79}Br : {}^{81}Br :: (50.51 \pm 0.06) : (49.49 \pm 0.06)$. Use of the packing fraction -7.4 gives a chemical atomic weight of 79.91. The international value is listed as 79.916. It is doubtful that the fifth significant figure in the international value is warranted.[13] On electrical bombardment of bromine vapor the following ionic species are noted: Br_2^+, Br^+, and Br^{+2}.[14]

Bromine is an active corrosive poison. It is very irritating to the mucous membrane of the eyes, nose, and throat. Direct contact of the liquid with the skin destroys the tissues and causes sores which are slow to heal. The frequency with which the liquid is used makes it potentially more dangerous than chlorine. The volatility and more active nature of bromine make the hazards of handling it many times those of iodine. A bromine content of over 50 mg per cent in the serum of the body is considered abnormal.

Chemical Properties. The chemical properties of bromine approximate those of chlorine, but, as is indicated by the differences in electrode potentials, bromine is a less active oxidizing agent. All active metals react to form bromides. Potassium burns readily, but sodium must be heated to about 200°C before a reaction of equal intensity takes place. Hydrogen burns in bromine vapor less vigorously than in chlorine.

The noble metals are oxidized by bromine at elevated temperatures. Silver is stable in bromine vapor unless some impurity is present on the surface to break up the silver bromide film that is formed.

---

[12] R. Smoluchowski, *Revs. Mod. Phys.* **25**, 178 (1953).
[13] J. R. White and A. E. Cameron, *Phys. Rev.* **74**, 991 (1948).
[14] D. Williams and P. Yuster, *Phys. Rev.* **69**, 556 (1946).

The nonmetals, as phosphorus (red) and arsenic, burn in bromine vapor when they are finely divided; the products are PBr_3, PBr_5, and $AsBr_3$. Antimony forms the tribromide, $SbBr_3$. Within a period of an hour there is complete exchange of bromine atoms between bromine and antimony(III) bromide. This exchange has been proved by the use of radiobromine.[15]

A number of other exchange reactions using radiobromine have been studied, namely, those of CBr_4, $SiBr_4$, $SnBr_4$ and the systems CBr_4-$AlBr_3$* and $SiBr_4$-$AlBr_3$*. The exchange of bromine atoms between elemental radiobromine and carbon tetrabromide is 10 per cent complete at 100°C in three hours. There is no exchange at room temperature. With silicon tetrabromide and radiobromine there is no exchange in four hours at temperatures up to 100°C. The exchange between radio-bromine and tin(IV) bromide is complete at 20°C in one hour. There is complete exchange between CBr_4 and $AlBr_3$* at 50° but no exchange between bromines of $SiBr_4$ and $AlBr_3$*. The lack of exchange in this last reaction is attributed to the possibility of partially double bonds between silicon and bromine using d orbitals of silicon. The normal polarity of the Si-Br bond is weakened. The weight of the ionic state is decreased, and therefore the exchangeability is decreased.

The radius of the silicon atom is favorable to 4 coordination with bromine atoms resulting in close packing. This situation would not be true for 4-coordinated carbon (as in CBr_4). The smaller size of carbon would result in a looser packing. The large size of the tin atom permits higher coordination than 4. A higher tendency toward exchange of coordinated atoms would be expected.[16]

The reaction of bromine with sulfur in the presence of water provides a method for the production of hydrobromic acid:

$$3Br_2 + S + 4H_2O \rightarrow 6HBr + H_2SO_4 + 110 \text{ kcal}$$

A two-step mechanism has been suggested for this reaction. The first step involves the reaction of sulfur and bromine to form SBr, and the second step is the reaction of SBr with water and more bromine to form sulfuric acid and HBr. The final product contains 42.1 per cent HBr, 8.5 per cent sulfuric acid, and about 1 per cent free bromine. Distillation yields 48 per cent HBr, while some sulfuric acid and HBr remain in the residue.[17] In a large-scale production of HBr, proportionately less water is needed than for a small-scale one. The system must be cooled toward

[15] R. Muxart, *Compt. rend.* **224**, 1107 (1947).
[16] Ya A. Fialkov and Yu P. Nazarenko, *Doklady Akad. Nauk S.S.S.R.* **73**, 727 (1950).
[17] B. R. Dishon and F. Goldschmidt, *J. Soc. Chem. Ind.* **66**, 444 (1947).

he end of the reaction to prevent the decomposition of HBr by the ulfuric acid.[18]

An aqueous solution of bromine is much more stable than one of chlorine. The reactions

$$H_2O + Br_2 \rightarrow H^+ + Br^- + HBrO$$

and

$$2HBrO \rightarrow 2H^+ + 2Br^- + O_2$$

are catalyzed by sunlight. When saturated bromine water is cooled, red crystals of the octahydrate, $Br_2 \cdot 8H_2O$, separate. This substance is stable below 6.2°C.

Bromine reacts with oxalic acid at high hydrogen ion concentration and under the catalytic effect of the Mn(III) ion to form carbon dioxide and the bromide ion.[19] The industrial use of ethylene dibromide in antiknock fuels has already been mentioned. An efficient mixture which gives low chamber residues and long life to valves is attained by mixing 104 volumes of ethylene dichloride with 320 of ethylene bromide and 1000 of tetraethyl lead. Halogenated alkanes are highly stable, and their use in fire extinguishers is common. A mixture of C_2H_5Br (70–90 parts), CH_3Br (5–10 parts) and CH_2ClCH_2Br (5–20 parts) is an effective fire extinguisher when it is applied as a fine spray.[20]

[18] R. Block et al., ibid. 66, 115 (1947).
[19] H. Taube, J. Am. Chem. Soc. 70, 3928 (1948).
[20] I. G. M. Timpson, U. S. 2,389,652, Nov. 27, 1945.

CHAPTER 4

IODINE

History. Iodine was first prepared in 1812 by the French chemist Courtois. After seaweed or kelp (*Laminaria digitata* or *L. stenophylla*) had been ashed and the soda removed, it was noted by Courtois that sulfuric acid reacted with the hot mother liquor to liberate the new element in the form of its violet vapor. Based upon the Greek word for the violet color of the vapor, Gay Lussac named the new substance iodine.

Occurrence. Most of the iodine produced in the world, excluding the United States, is obtained from Chilean saltpeter. It contains from 0.05 to 0.1 per cent of iodine in the form of iodates of sodium and calcium. Chile formerly held a monopoly on the world's supply of iodine. California oil-well brines contain from 10 to 135 ppm of iodine and produce annually about 500,000 pounds of the element.[1]

In addition to seaweeds, a number of other types of marine life, such as oysters, sponges, and certain fishes, concentrate iodine in their systems. The greatest concentration of iodine in the human body is found in the thyroid gland.

Preparation. The processing of kelp for its iodine content is still carried out in certain locations off the coasts of France, Ireland, and Scotland. The ashes from the carbonized kelp are heated with water and the solution concentrated to permit the crystallization of such salts as sodium chloride, potassium chloride, and their carbonates and sulfates. The mother liquor, containing soluble iodides, is treated with an oxidizing mixture of manganese dioxide and sulfuric acid in cast-iron or duriron vessels fitted with lead covers. The manganese dioxide is added a little at a time until iodine vapor is no longer noted. Delivery pipes from these retorts may act as the condensers, or the vapors may be led into a train of earthenware receivers called *aludels*, in which condensation takes place. About 12 pounds of iodine may be obtained from a ton of kelp.[2] This weight represents about a 50 per cent yield. The following equation represents the reaction:

$$2NaI + MnO_2 + 3H_2SO_4 \rightarrow MnSO_4 + 2NaHSO_4 + I_2 + 2H_2O$$

[1] *State of California, Div. Mines, Dept. Natural Resources, Mineral Industry of California in 1947*, p. 12.
[2] French 893,656; 894,635; 897,641; 897,870.

The same equation also represents a laboratory preparation of iodine, in which the source of iodine may be any alkali or alkaline-earth metal iodide.

Iodine is also displaced from solutions of iodides by chlorine. This process is essentially the same as that employed for the preparation of bromine. The quantity of chlorine used is critical since, if insufficient chlorine is used, there is not only a loss of available chlorine but some of the iodine dissolves in the brine through the reaction, $I_2 + I^- \rightarrow I_3^-$. If too much chlorine is used, iodine is lost through the reaction, $I_2 + Cl_2 \rightarrow 2ICl$, or through the formation of IO_3^-.

Iodates such as those occurring naturally in Chile saltpeter are reduced by sulfites. The over-all reaction is:

$$2IO_3^- + 2HSO_3^- + 3SO_3^= \rightarrow 5SO_4^= + I_2 + H_2O$$

Actually several steps are involved; namely, the reduction of the iodate to iodide by sulfite,

$$3SO_3^= + IO_3^- \rightarrow I^- + 3SO_4^=$$

the conversion of the iodide in an acid solution to hydrogen iodide, and the oxidation of hydrogen iodide by the iodate,

$$IO_3^- + 5I^- + 6H^+ \rightarrow 3I_2 + 3H_2O$$

No iodine is produced in the system as long as there is any sulfite present, since the latter ion reacts rapidly with iodine to form iodide ions and sulfate ions. The iodine is precipitated, filtered, dried, and purified by sublimation.

Recently the interest in freeing iodine from oil-well brines has been revived. Some iodine was produced from this source as early as the World War I period. In the past, low tariff barriers on iodine from Chile have generally been unfavorable to production in the United States.

Two processes are currently used for the recovery of iodine from oil-field brines. The first of these processes, developed in 1931, is described by the following sequence of equations:

$$Ag + 2HNO_3 \rightarrow AgNO_3 + NO_2 + H_2O$$
$$NaI + AgNO_3 \rightarrow AgI + NaNO_3$$
$$2AgI + Fe \rightarrow FeI_2 + 2Ag$$
$$2FeI_2 + 3Cl_2 \rightarrow 2FeCl_3 + 2I_2$$

The rise in the price of silver to $0.64 an ounce and a reduction in the price of iodine brought the resumption of active research on a second process, first developed in 1928. Over 90 per cent of the domestic iodine is produced by this process at Seal Beach, California. Two additional plants, one at Venice and one at Inglewood, California, utilize the *blowing-out process* for the production of concentrated liquor which is then shipped via rubber lined tank trucks to the Venice plant for final processing. The iodine content of typical California oil field brines ranges from 35 to 70 ppm. Brines, containing 35–80 ppm of iodine, are first subjected to a "clean-up" operation which removes residual oil. Clariflocculation removes residual organic matter whose presence in later steps would cause as much as a 10 to 20 per cent loss of iodine. Sulfuric acid is then added to the clear brine to lower the pH from 7.5 to 3.5. Any barium sulfate is filtered off. Chlorine is added and the iodine formed is stripped countercurrently by air. The blown-out iodine is absorbed in an aqueous solution of hydrogen iodide and sulfurous acid. Water and sulfur dioxide are added continuously to the absorbing solution. The stripped air is recycled to absorb more iodine. A portion of the acid absorbent is treated with chlorine and the crude iodine is filtered off. By heating the crude iodine with concentrated sulfuric acid, a final product of 99.8 per cent purity is possible.[3]

Brines may also be treated with a nitrite as an oxidizing agent:

$$2I^- + 2NO_2^- + 4H^+ \rightarrow I_2 + 2NO + 2H_2O$$

This procedure is adaptable to the treatment of the solution obtained on extracting seaweed after its fusion with a mixture of NaOH, Na_2CO_3, K_2CO_3, and KNO_3.

The purification of iodine from the last traces of such impurities as iodine monochloride or iodine monobromide is difficult. Resublimation of iodine over potassium iodide removes most of the impurities. Further purification may be accomplished by forming a heavy-metal insoluble iodide (AgI or CuI), reducing the iodide with hydrogen to the metal and hydrogen iodide, and then oxidizing the HI with nitrite. Direct oxidation of the metal iodide to the metal oxide and iodine is possible.

Physical Properties. Iodine is a black solid with a slight metallic luster. When sublimed it crystallizes only in the rhombic form. There is inconclusive evidence for a transition point at 46.5°C. Some information regarding allotropic modifications of iodine is available from a study of the photoelectric constants of the solid. Three distinct and reproducible types of photoelectric response have been noted for solid iodine, depending upon crystal variations. The amorphous, monoclinic, and rhombic forms have work functions of 6.8, 5.4, and 2.8 ev and thresholds of 1880, 2050, and 2360 A, respectively. The energy gaps of the crystalline modifica-

[3] F. G. Sawyer *et al.*, *Ind. Eng. Chem.* **41**, 1547 (1949).

tion are 0.6 and 2.5 ev. An apparently amorphous form of iodine has been reported as being prepared by rapid condensation of vapor at liquid air temperature. On standing at liquid air temperature, or on warming, the brownish-red, transparent, amorphous film changes to monoclinic according to its photoelectric behavior. Actually there is no electron diffraction evidence for this amorphous structure. The monoclinic and rhombic forms of iodine have the same color. A black, microcrystalline surface of iodine has been observed to change its behavior on standing for several hours at liquid air temperature or on being warmed to room temperature. This change has been attributed to the metastability of the monoclinic form with respect to the orthorhombic crystal.[4] The quadrupole resonance frequency ν_1 measured at room temperature and ν_2 from 85°C to liquid air temperature gives values of $\nu_1 = 642.8$ Mc and ν_2 334.0 Mc by extrapolation to 0°K. The moment Q is calculated to be -0.69×10^{-24} sq cm.[5]

The cubic coefficient of expansion of I_2 is 264×10^{-6}, and the density by x-ray measurements at 18°C is 4.9520 g/ml.[6] Other physical properties are noted in Table I.1. It has been reported that ^{129}I exists in an abundance of less than 3 ppm relative to that of ^{127}I.[7]

Iodine is less soluble in water than are bromine and chlorine. This slight solubility is in accordance with the strong covalent bond between the iodine atoms.

The reaction, $I_2 \rightarrow 2I$, is accompanied by the absorption of 28,500 calories. This same amount of heat is liberated when two gram-atoms of iodine combine. Photoelectric observations have been made of the rate of the homogeneous 3-body recombination of iodine atoms by flash photolysis of molecular iodine in the gas phase and applied to the measurements of the rate of recombination of iodine atoms in the nonpolar solvents n-heptane and carbon tetrachloride. The values of k at room temperature for the equation $I + I \rightleftarrows I_2$, $d(I_2)/dt = k(I_2)$ are 2.2×10^{10} M/sec for n-heptane and 0.72×10 M/sec for carbon tetrachloride. The recombination of iodine atoms in the presence of rare gases has been studied by flash techniques. The recombination is proved to follow a trimolecular rate law over wide ranges in pressure. Absolute values for the rate constants have not been obtained, however, due to the inadequacies of existing theories of such combinations. The kinetic theory expression of trimolecular collisions is inadequate in its simplest form and

[4] D. C. West, *Can. J. Phys.* **31**, 691 (1953).
[5] T. Kamei, *J. Phys. Soc. Japan* **7**, 649 (1952).
[6] M. Straumanis and J. Sauka, *Z. physik. Chem.* **B53**, 320 (1943).
[7] M. Blau *et al.*, *Phys. Rev.* **78**, 860 (1949).

requires a special interpretation when applied to the measurement collision duration.[8]

Iodine is readily soluble in carbon tetrachloride, carbon disulfide, and in other organic solvents. Iodine dissolves readily in an aqueous concentrated KI solution with the formation of the complex ion, I_3^-. Aqueous hydrogen iodide, likewise, is a suitable solvent for iodine (Table 4.1).[9]

TABLE 4.1. THE SOLUBILITY OF IODINE IN AQUEOUS HYDROGEN IODIDE

Solubility (kg/l)	Concentration of HI (aq) (Per Cent)
5.22	66.7
4.72	64.0
3.47	54.4
2.84	50.2
2.28	45.9

Color and Nature of Iodine Solutions. Solutions of iodine are generally brown or violet. Intermediate tints of violet-red to reddish-brown have been observed, but they are due to impurities. Iodine gives a violet solution with chloroform. When alcohol is added to this solution, there is a progressive change from violet to reddish-violet, to red, and finally to brown. In general, hydrocarbons, alkyl halides (other than iodides), nitro compounds, and carbon disulfide give violet solutions of iodine, while brown solutions result with iodides, alcohols, ethers, ketones, acids, esters, nitriles, and certain sulfur-containing solvents.

Physicochemical evidence has shown that iodine in brown solution is chemically combined with solvent molecules, and this iodine is in equilibrium with the free iodine.[10] When brown solutions are formed, the solvent seems to be capable of furnishing a pair of electrons for a coordinate covalent bond. It will be noted that the carbonyl group is common to some of the solvents in the list. When coordinated to the carbonyl group, the iodine appears to be more reactive than when in the free dissolved condition, as in the violet solutions.

In many cases, brown solutions become violet when they are heated, and violet solutions become brown when cooled. Such is the case for the violet solution of iodine in paraffin oil.[11] The generalization is not followed for the brown solution of iodine in ethyl ether, for the color shows

---

[8] R. Marshall and N. R. Davidson, *J. Chem. Phys.* **21**, 2086 (1953); M. I. Christie et al., *Proc. Roy. Soc.* (London) **216A**, 152 (1953)

[9] C. F. Powell and I. E. Campbell, *J. Am. Chem. Soc.* **69**, 1227 (1947).

[10] J. Kleinberg and A. W. Davidson, *Chem. Revs.* **42**, 601 (1948).

[11] P. Waentig, *Z. physik. Chem.* **68**, 513 (1909).

no tendency to become violet even up to the critical temperature of the solvent.

Table 4.2 gives the solubility of iodine in 95 per cent ethanol from 0°C to −65°C.[12]

Iodine is generally more soluble in the solvents in which brown solutions are obtained. The iodine is diatomic in its solutions. When the mole fraction solubility of iodine in violet solutions is plotted against the reciprocal of the temperature for various solvents, a family of curves is obtained. Deviations from the ideal curves can be related to differences in internal pressure. When the same procedure is followed with solvents favoring brown solutions, the curves do not fall in the same family as for

TABLE 4.2. SOLUBILITY OF IODINE IN 95 PER CENT ETHANOL

$T°C$	Solubility $(g/100 \text{ ml})$	$T°C$	Solubility $(g/100 \text{ ml})$
0	9.45	−12	8.3
−1	9.38	−15	8.1
−2	9.32	−18	7.81
−3	9.25	−20	7.55
−4	9.21	−22	7.31
−5	9.11	−25	7.03
−6	8.99	−30	6.6
−7	8.85	−35	6.31
−8	8.79	−40	5.80
−9	8.62	−45	5.64
−10	8.5	−50	5.41
		−55	5.21
		−60	5.03
		−65	4.84

violet solutions; in fact, there is no general trend for iodine solubility in the "brown solution" solvents. It is definitely shown by spectral data that new molecular species ($I_2 \cdot x$ solvent) are formed in the brown solutions.[13]

The distribution coefficient of iodine between two solvents which form violet solutions or between two solvents which form brown solutions is relatively independent of temperature and concentration. The coefficient in the case of two solvents, one of which forms a brown solution and the other a violet solution, is influenced by temperature and concentration. When the distribution coefficient of iodine between a solvent favoring a

[12] E. S. Skvirskaya and T. S. Reĭzer, *Aptechnoe Delo* 2, No. 1, 13 (1953).

[13] J. Hildebrand, *Solubility of Nonelectrolytes*, 2nd Ed., Reinhold Publishing Corp., New York, 1936, p. 153; J. Kleinberg and A. W. Davidson, *Chem. Revs.* 42, 601 (1949).

TABLE 4.3. SOME THERMAL DATA FOR IODINE DISSOLVED IN ORGANIC SOLVENTS

Solvent	Heat of Solution (kcal/mol)	G I$_2$/l	Heat of Complex Formation (kcal)	Color of Solution
Cyclohexane	−5.8 ± 0.2	0.2*	—	blue
Benzene	−4.25 ± 0.05	6.7	+0.85	blue
Ethanol	−1.65 ± 0.05	7.7	+2.1	brown
Nitrobenzene	−1.70 ± 0.1	6.7	+2.75	brown
Carbon tetrachloride	−5.8 ± 0.2	2.	—	blue
Toluene	−3.85 ± 0.5	7.8	+1.45	blue-brown
Methanol	−1.85 ± 0.1	7.6	+1.7	brown
Pyridine	+3.6 ± 0.1	2.5	+7.95	yellow

* Solubility is 0.2 g I$_2$/2.5 g cyclohexane.

brown solution and one favoring a violet solution is plotted against temperature, the successive differences in value of the coefficient become smaller as the temperature increases. This observation is in accordance with the already mentioned fact that brown solutions change to violet when heated.

The heat of solution and the heat of complex formation for a number of "blue" and "brown" solvents are recorded in Table 4.3.[14]

Considerable information on the nature of brown and violet (or blue) solutions of iodine is derived from spectrochemical data. The location of the maximum of brown solutions shifts toward the region expected for a violet solution as the temperature is raised. Violet solutions absorb strongly in the low-frequency region, and brown solutions absorb strongly in the high-frequency region. There is marked similarity between the spectrum of iodine vapor and that of a violet solution, the former being a line spectrum and the latter a band spectrum. Evidence is definitely in favor of a 1:1 complex being formed for iodine dissolved in "brown" solvents as well as in benzene (an intermediate solvent). Spectral evidence, on the other hand, does not favor any such complexes in "violet" solvents. Three distinct spectroscopic and chemical types of complex derivatives are proposed:[15] (1) simple benzene; (2) ether, alcohol, and water; and (3) ketones. The complexes formed by iodine appear to be analogous to those formed by iodine chloride. The basis for the division mentioned is largely the extent to which the λ5200 absorption region of the iodine molecule is shifted toward the ultraviolet.

Some information is available on the nature of iodine in polar and highly acidic solvents, such as sulfuric acid, hydrogen fluoride, acetic

[14] K. Hartley and H. A. Skinner, *Trans. Faraday Soc.* **46**, 621 (1950).
[15] R. S. Mulliken, *J. Am. Chem. Soc.* **72**, 600 (1950).

acid, and trifluoroacetic acid. The solubility of iodine in varying concentrations of H_2SO_4 shows a minimum at 75 to 80 per cent. The spectra of these solutions shows a λ maximum shift in the visible. This shift may be considered as arising from two related effects: (1) since iodine and sulfuric acid are both Lewis acids, no electron exchange should occur when they are mixed; (2) the water in the iodine-water complex should be displaced by the H_2SO_4 molecule since the latter is the stronger acid. The λ maximum shift is toward the violet as expected in an *inert* solvent. If any I_2-H_2SO_4 complex does exist, it must then be very weak.[16]

Iodine dissolves only slowly in liquid HF. The spectrum shows a broad maximum centered at about 514 mμ. The solution is violet. No second absorption peak is noted as far as 220 mμ. When iodine is dissolved in ether containing 10 parts of HF by weight, the solution is orange-red, and the absorption peak is shifted to 508 mμ. Increasing the HF content to $2:1 = Et_2O:HF$ heightens the orange color of the solution and gives a peak at 500 mμ. At $3:1$ ratio of Et_2O to HF the iodine solution is yellow-brown, and a principal peak is located at 360 mμ with a minor peak at 460 mμ.[17]

In general, the absorption spectra studies on solutions of iodine (as well as ICl and Br_2) in H_2SO_4, and CF_3COOH indicate about the same behavior as in nonpolar solvents. The behavior of iodine in acetic acid is considerably different. Acetic acid complexes the iodine strongly. The equilibrium constants for I_2 and ICl in acetic acid are 3.4 ± 0.3 and 18 ± 0.07, respectively. The value for I_2 and acetic acid is zero (no interaction).[18]

The complex formed between benzene and substituted benzene solvents is suggested as $Ar^+I_2^-$ or Ar^+I^-I. The iodine molecule lies above the plane of the benzene ring with its axis parallel to the latter. Polar forces are aided by a partial C—I bonding. In the ether (ROR')-iodine complexes, the iodine molecule stands against the oxygen atom, with its axis perpendicular to the ROR' plane. A similar form of ketone (RCOR')-iodine complexes is proposed except that the iodine axis is coplanar with the RCOR' skeleton.

[16] J. G. Bower and R. L. Scott, *J. Am. Chem. Soc.* **75**, 3583 (1953).
[17] L. I. Katzin and J. J. Katz, *J. Am. Chem. Soc.* **75**, 6057 (1953).
[18] R. E. Buckles and J. F. Mills, *J. Am. Chem. Soc.* **75**, 552 (1953).

Polar forces in the cases of ROR′ and RCOR′ are aided by partial O^+—I

bonding. Conjugation exists between the $\diagdown C$=O and I—Iπ electrons
to aid polar forces further. A strong absorption peak at 363 mμ has also been reported for the acetone-iodine system attributable to the I_3^- ion formed by the following mechanism:[19]

$$CH_3C\overset{O}{{-}}CH_3 \rightleftharpoons CH_3C\overset{OH}{=}CH_2$$

$$CH_3C\overset{OH}{=}CH_2 + I_2 \rightleftharpoons CH_3C\overset{O}{{-}}CH_2I + H^+ + I^-$$

$$I^- + I_2 \rightleftharpoons I_3^-$$

Very intense absorption exists for aromatic solvent-iodine complexes near λ3000 A. This absorption may be due to an intermediate charge transfer process during light absorption.

Since the visible absorption of the benzene-iodine ($C_6H_6 \cdot I_2$) complex at 5000 A, $\epsilon \sim 1300$, is similar to the visible peak of the free halogen in an inert solvent, 5200 A, $\epsilon \sim 910$, it is assumed that the electronic states of the halogens are only slightly perturbed by complex formation with benzene. Conversely, there should be little perturbation of the electronic states of benzene when complexed with iodine. The same deduction has been made in regard to the $C_6H_6 \cdot Br_2$ complex.[20] The spectra of $C_6H_6 \cdot I_2$ and $C_6H_6 \cdot Br_2$ in the ultraviolet have been reported. A band at 260 mμ is of theoretical interest and is not attributable to a halogenated benzene derivative.

Part of the evidence for the 1:1 complex formed between iodine and benzene is the intense ultraviolet absorption peak with a maximum at λ = 297 mμ. It is assumed that the equilibrium constant for the reaction

$$C_6H_6 + I_2 \rightleftharpoons C_6H_6 \cdot I_2$$

is the same for all concentrations of benzene.[21] The values of K for the 1:1 complex in the noncomplexing solvents carbon tetrachloride and n-heptane are reported as 1.9 and 1.4, respectively. These values were calculated using the 297 mμ peak and a value of 14,000 for ϵ_c, the extinc-

[19] H. A. Benesi and J. H. Hildebrand, *J. Am. Chem. Soc.* **72**, 2273 (1950).
[20] H. S. Ham *et al.*, *J. Chem. Phys.* **19** (10), 1301 (1951).
[21] H. A. Benesi and J. H. Hildebrand, *J. Am. Chem. Soc.* **71**, 2703 (1949).

tion coefficient of the complex. In pure benzene the value of K is reported as 2.3.

Molecular complexes for iodine and naphthalene are comparable to those of iodine and benzene. The spectra of the complexes are shifted spectra of the pure aromatic compound.[22]

The values of ΔH and K for the $C_6H_6 \cdot I_2$ complex in carbon tetrachloride at 25° are given in Table 4.4.[23]

Solutions of iodine in alkyl halides have been studied in terms of the vapor pressure of iodine (p in mm) and the mole per cent (x) concentration of iodine.[24] The following K distribution coefficients at $25 \pm 0.05°$ $(K = p/x)$ are reported: 2.67×10^{-1} for CCl_4; 1.30×10^{-1} for butyl chloride; 5.08×10^{-2} for ethyl and butyl bromides; and 1.52×10^{-2} for ethyl iodide. The thermal stability from spectral data increases for the iodine complexes in the order RCl, RBr, and RI. The degree of interaction, then, between iodine and the organic solvent increases in the order RCl < RBr < RI. The nature of the R (alkyl group) is secondary.

TABLE 4.4. BENZENE $\cdot I_2$ COMPLEX IN CARBON TETRACHLORIDE

x_a (mol fraction of benzene)	$[I_2]$ (mol/liter)	ΔH (calories)	K
1.00	17.35×10^{-5}	-1452 ± 80	2.17
0.620	5.04×10^{-5}	-1416 ± 14	1.87
0.434	141.00×10^{-5}	-1349 ± 34	1.84
0.0217	246.00×10^{-5}	-1317 ± 50	1.91

A study of the ultraviolet absorption bands (not found for either the solute or solvent alone) of iodine in saturated hydrocarbon and alkyl halide solvents leads to an extension of the Mullikin theory of the frequencies of molecular complexes. A relation exists between the frequencies of the absorption bands of the complexes and the ionization potentials of the solvents. It has been shown that

$$h\nu = I_B - D + 2\beta/(I_B - D)$$

where $h\nu$ is the absorption frequency of the iodine complex; I_B is the ionization potential of the base (electron pair donor); D is equal to $E_A + e^2/r - C_{AB}$; E_A is the electron affinity of the acid; e^2/r is the coulomb attraction term; C_{AB} is the sum of all other energy terms; and β is an ap-

[22] M. W. Blake et al., J. Am. Chem. Soc. 73, 4437 (1951).
[23] T. M. Cromwell and R. L. Scott, J. Am. Chem. Soc. 72, 3825 (1950).
[24] S. A. Shchukarev et al., Doklady Akad. Nauk S.S.S.R. 85, 1333 (1952).

proximate constant term arising from the quantum mechanical treatment.[25]

Spectro-chemical data are reported (Table 4.5) for several iodine-olefinic as well as halogen substituted olefinic molecular complexes.[26] The heat of formation for each complex (except I), calculated from the temperature dependence of K_x is below 1 kcal/mol.[27] Double-bond character for each agent (II, IV, V) appears to decrease because of resonance with p_z electrons of chlorine.

Conductance measurements[28] and dipole moment measurements[29] have added to the information on the nature of iodine in brown solutions. The former measurement, made in pyridine, shows an abnormally high

TABLE 4.5. SPECTROCHEMICAL DATA OF SOME IODINE-OLEFINIC COMPLEXES

Complexing Agent	T, °C	λ max, A	ϵ max	K_x (association constant)
I. Diisobutylene	10	3000	16,600	3.7
II. Cyclohexene	25	3020	14,000	3.4
III. *cis*-Dichloro-ethene	14	2620	14,000	0.25
IV. Trichloroethene (in hexane solvent)	14.5	2700	12,500	0.19
V. Tetrachloroethene	14	2770	16,600	0.11

conductance at infinite dilution. It is possible that the initial nonconducting addition compound, $C_5H_5N \cdot I_2$ (PyI$_2$), is converted to a ternary salt:

$$Py + I_2 \rightleftharpoons IPy^+ + I^- \rightleftharpoons Py^{+2} + 2 I^- \qquad (1)$$

$$2[Py \cdot I_2] \rightleftharpoons IPy^+ + I \cdot PyI_2^- \qquad (2)$$

$$2I_2 + Py \rightleftharpoons IPy^+ + I_3^- \qquad (3)$$

The electrical conductivity of iodine in pyridine as a function of concentration and time has been investigated.[30] The total conductance may be split into two portions by extrapolation. One part is ascribed to the reaction of iodine with solvent; and the second part, to an electrolytic dissociation reaction of the iodine-pyridine complex formed in the first step (see equation (1) above). This latter step is time-constant. The

[25] S. H. Hastings *et al.*, *J. Am. Chem. Soc.* **75**, 2900 (1953).
[26] J. A. A. Ketelaar and C. van de Stolpe, *Rec. trav. chim.* **71**, 805 (1952).
[27] See data of Hartley and Skinner, *loc. cit.*, ref. 14.
[28] L. F. Audrieth and E. J. Birr, *J. Am. Chem. Soc.* **55**, 668 (1933).
[29] F. Fairbrother, *Nature* **160**, 87 (1947).
[30] G. Kortum and H. Wilski, *Z. physik. Chem.* **202**, 35 (1953).

TABLE 4.6. EQUILIBRIUM CONSTANTS FOR THE IODINE-PYRIDINE REACTION

$c \times 10^4$	$k_c \times 10^8$
0.312	4.2
0.558	4.8
1.00	4.7
2.15	4.8
3.86	4.8
4.75	4.1

following dissociation constants (k_c) of this step have been calculated at various concentrations (c) at 25°C (Table 4.6). The agreement of the various k_c values over the wide range in concentrations indicates a weakly dissociated complex. Infrared spectroscopy data confirm the existence of the $[PyI^+][I^-]$ complex as well as a similar picoline complex. No spectral changes indicating similar complexes are observed when such donor solvents as CS_2, CCl_4, acetonitrile, benzene, toluene, xylene, or 2,6-methylnaphthalene were used. The pyridine and picoline complexes were studied in the solvents CCl_4 and CS_2.[31]

Evidence is furnished for the system IPy^+ and I_3^- by the immediate exchange between elementary radioiodine and pyridine-coordinated unipositive iodine. The exchange is independent of the organic anion in the complex.[32]

TABLE 4.7. DIPOLE MOMENTS OF I_2 IN VIOLET AND BROWN SOLUTIONS

Solvent	Color	Dipole Moment (Debye)
Benzene	Violet-red	0.60
p-Dimethylbenzene	Red	0.9
1–4 Dioxane	Brown	1.3
Diisobutylene	Red-brown	1.5

Dipole moment measurements are given for four solvents (Table 4.7). From the magnitude of the dipole moment it is concluded that, in brown or red-brown solutions, there is a greater polarization of the iodine molecule than in violet solutions. This condition is indicated by the electromeric equilibrium $I^- \!\!-\!\! I^+ \rightleftharpoons I^+ \!\!-\!\! I^-$. An electron pair donor, such as a "brown solvent," might well stabilize either one or the other of these ionic structures.

The same general conclusion as to the strong polarization of iodine, already in the ground state of the complexes, is reached from the rela-

[31] D. L. Glusker *et al.*, *J. Chem. Phys.* **21**, 1407 (1953).
[32] J. Kleinberg and J. Sattizahn, *J. Am. Chem. Soc.* **73**, 1865 (1951).

tively high dipole-moment values of iodine complexes of dioxane, pyridine, benzene, naphthalene, and biphenyl in the solvent cyclohexane. The dipole-moment value for each of the complexes is 3.0, 4.5, 1.8, 2.6, and 2.9 Debye, respectively.[33]

Chemical Properties and Reactions. The chemical activity of iodine as an oxidizing agent is less than that of the other halogens. There is no appreciable reaction with hydrogen or oxygen at ordinary temperatures. The action of iodine with alkali and alkaline-earth metals is similar to that of the other halogens. The activity of iodine is less, however; and the stability of the resulting iodides is less than for the other halogens. The reactions between iodine and the less active metals are shown by treating thin foils of the metals with solid iodine. Tin forms concentric orange and yellow rings attributable to allotropic forms of SnI_2. Aluminum forms white AlI_3, which hydrolyzes in the atmosphere and turns brown. Silver develops colored rings which turn black as a result of the photochemical reduction of silver iodide. Calcium forms a mixture of calcium periodide and calcium hydroxide, and iodine is later evolved. The addition of HCl to this calcium periodide "spot" results in the formation of free chlorine, while heating the compound leaves a residue of calcium iodide and calcium oxide. Zinc and nickel corrode, supposedly by the formation of the simple iodides. Iron forms FeI_2. Bismuth, lead, and gold do not react.[34]

To facilitate the study of the nature of iodine and iodide ion at low concentrations, radioiodine has been used.[35] Carrier free 8 day ^{131}I was used in the form of a $10^{-7}M$ solution of the iodide. Oxidation of I^- by $Ce(IV)$ and $CrO_4^=$ in sulfuric acid results in the formation of I_2 and three additional unidentified chemical fractions. None of these fractions is readily exchangeable with I^-, I_2, or IO_3^-, however, two of them were extractable from the sulfuric acid solution by organic solvents. One fraction was converted by NaOH to a water-soluble form, exchangeable with I_2. This fraction appears to be quite inert to oxidation and reduction and may be the result of molecular or colloidal impurities. Hot concentrated sulfuric acid solutions of $Ce(IV)$ converts I^- to IO_3^- or at least to a product exchangeable with IO_3^-. The IO_3^- so produced is readily reduced at room temperature by $Fe(II)$ to I^-.

Iodine is a nonprotolytic solvent. At 130–140°C iodine dissolves sulfur, selenium, tellurium, and the iodides of Li, Na, K, Rb, Cs, Al, Fe(II), NH₄, Tl(I), Hg(II), P(III), As(III), Sb(III), and Bi(III).

[33] G. Körtum and H. Walz, Z. Elektrochem. **57**, 73 (1953).
[34] E. Montignie, Bull. soc. chim. France **1947**, 747.
[35] M. Kahn and A. C. Wahl, J. Chem. Phys. **21**, 1185 (1953).

Some examples of type reactions carried out in iodine as a solvent are:[36]

(Neutralization) $KI + IBr \rightarrow KBr + I_2$

(Solvolysis) $NaCN + I_2 \rightarrow NaI + ICN$

(Solvation) $KI + I_2 \rightarrow KI_3$

(Metathesis) $PbCl_2 + 2KI \rightarrow PbI_2 + 2KCl$

Iodine reacts with sodium and lithium borohydrides at 200 and 120°C, respectively, to form BI_3. Tetraiododiborane, B_2I_4, and lower iodides, B_yI_x (x is greater than y), are prepared by the action of an electrodeless discharge at room temperature upon vapors of BI_3 under 1 to 3 mm pressure. Tetraiododiborane is a well-crystallized, pale yellow solid which slowly decomposes at room temperature to BI_3 and a residue of a polymer $(BI)_x$. The lower boron iodides have reducing properties, as is illustrated by their ready reduction of silver ion to the metal.[37]

Iodine oxidizes hydrazine to nitrogen:

$$N_2H_4 + 2I_2 \rightarrow N_2 + 4HI$$

If an excess of hydrazine is used, or if the hydrate of hydrazine is used, hydrazine hydroiodide is produced:

$$5N_2H_4 \cdot H_2O + 2I_2 \rightarrow 4N_2H_4HI + 5H_2O + N_2$$

With sodium azide the reaction represented by

$$2NaN_3 + I_2 \rightarrow 2Na + 3N_2$$

takes place and is catalyzed by traces of inorganic sulfides, thioketones, or mercaptans.

The slight hydrolysis of iodine,

$$H_2O + I_2 \rightarrow HIO + H^+ + I^-$$

is indicated by the magnitude of the K hydrolysis, 4.6×10^{-13}. This value has been calculated from the equilibrium value 1.4×10^{-3} for the system $I_3^- \rightleftharpoons I_2 + I^-$.[38]

Iodine dissolved in a strong solution of KI serves admirably as a standard oxidizing solution in titrimetric analyses (iodimetry). The thiosulfate ion, $S_2O_3^=$, is oxidized quantitatively to the tetrathionate ion, $S_4O_6^=$, in a bicarbonate buffered solution. In strongly alkaline solution

[36] G. Jander and K. H. Bandlow, *Z. physik. Chem.* **A191**, 321 (1943).

[37] W. C. Schumb *et al., J. Am. Chem. Soc.* **71**, 3225 (1949).

[38] G. Horiguchi and H. Hagesawa, *Bull. Inst. Phys. Chem. Research* (Tokyo) **22**, 661 (1943).

the oxidation of thiosulfate to the sulfate ion is complete.   Arsenic(III) sulfide is oxidized by iodine to arsenate and sulfate in a strongly alkaline medium:[39]

$$40OH^- + 14I_2 + As_2S_3 \rightarrow 28I^- + 2AsO_4^{-3} + 3SO_4^= + 20H_2O$$

Sulfides may be oxidized to sulfur as is the case when hydrogen sulfide is passed into an iodine solution.

Polyhydric compounds, such as starch, amylose, and amylopectin, form highly colored complexes with iodine. The diffraction pattern shows that the starch chain is actually a helix with a diameter of about 8 A and six glucose residues per "turn." Apparently, the iodine molecule occupies the interior of the helix.[40]   The sensitivity of the starch reaction corresponds to an iodine concentration of 1 to 2 $\times$ $10^{-5}M$ at room temperature and is favored by the presence of the iodide ion.   In the absence of the iodide ion, the color sensitivity is less, as is the case with increasing temperature.   Alcohols, if brought to a high concentration, decrease the sensitivity; there is no color in 50 per cent ethanol.   As the hydrolysis of the starch chain progresses (e.g., by enzyme action) the color changes from a deep violet to a reddish color.   The difference in the color of iodine-amylose and iodine-amylopectin is great enough to permit their individual analyses by colorimetry.

Iodine reacts with the azide ion to give nitrogen and the iodide ion:

$$2N_3^- + I_2 \rightarrow 2I^- + 3N_2$$

The reaction is catalyzed by a number of agents.   In the presence of tetrathionates, the rate of reaction is proportional to the concentration of $S_4O_6^=$ and N_3^- ions but independent of iodine concentration.   The rate determining step is

$$N_3^- + S_4O_6^= \rightarrow N_3S_4O_6^{-3}$$

and succeeding steps are

$$2N_3S_4O_6^{-3} + I_2 \rightarrow (N_3S_4O_6)_2^{-4} + 2I^-$$
$$(N_3S_4O_6)_2^{-4} + 2N_3^- \rightarrow 3N_2 + 2N_3S_4O_6^{-3} \quad \text{(activated ion)}$$

and

$$N_3S_4O_6^{-3} \quad \text{(activated ion)} \rightarrow N_3^- + S_4O_6^{-2}$$

The activation energy for the $N_3S_4O_6^{-3}$ ion from observed values of equilibrium constants is 12,740 cal/mole.   Other ions which catalyze

[39] H. F. Frost, *Analyst* **69**, 90 (1944).
[40] R. E. Rundle and F. C. Edwards, *J. Am. Chem Soc.* **65**, 2200 (1943).

the iodine-azide reaction are the pentathionate, $S_5O_6^=$, hexathionate, $S_6O_6^=$, and the azidodithiocarbonate ion, N_3SCS^-.[41] The last ion, N_3SCS^-, reacts as follows:

$$2N_3SCS^- + I_2 \rightarrow (N_3SCS)_2 + 2I^-$$
$$(N_3SCS)_2 + 2N_3^- \rightarrow 2CS_2 + 2N_3^- + 3N_2$$

and

$$CS_2 + N_3^- \rightarrow N_3SCS^-$$

No iodine azide, IN_3, is postulated, and it is noted that carbon disulfide is regenerated. The rate of the reaction is proportional to the N_3^- ion concentration but independent of the iodine and hydrogen ion concentrations.[42]

A complex sequence of reactions has been proposed to account for the catalytic action of the thiocyanate ion on the iodine-hydrazoic acid reaction.[43]

$$I_2 \rightleftarrows I^+ + I^-$$
$$2[HN_3 + 2H_2O \rightarrow N_2H_4 + HNO_2]$$
$$2[2HNO_2 \rightarrow NO + NO_2 + H_2O]$$
$$I^+ + SCN^- \rightarrow I + SCN$$
$$2[SCN + NO \rightarrow SCN^- + NO^+]$$
$$2[NO^+ + OH^- \rightarrow HNO_2]$$
$$2[NO_2 + N_2H_4 \rightarrow 3/2N_2 + 2H_2O]$$
$$2[H_2O \rightarrow H^+ + OH^-]$$

Thiocyanate ion alone decolorizes an iodine solution according to the equation

$$CNS^- + 4I_2 + 4H_2O \rightarrow CNI + SO_4^= + 7I^- + 8H^+$$

Phosphate and acid carbonate ions act as buffers but not as catalysts when added to the system. The reaction is not entirely analogous to the iodine-azide reaction.[44]

Cystine catalyzes the rate of nitrogen formation in the iodine-azide reaction, the rate being proportional to the concentration of each of the species, I_2, N_3^-, and cystine. The oxidation of the cystine by iodine is slower with azide being present than in its absence. The following chain

[41] N. Hofman-Bang, *Acta Chem. Scand.* **3**, 872 (1949); *ibid.* **4**, 456, 856, 1005 (1950).
[42] N. Hofman-Bang and W. Szybolski, *Acta Chem. Scand.* **3**, 1418 (1949).
[43] E. Abel, *Monatsh.* **83**, 440 (1952).
[44] T. Kozlovskii, *J. Gen. Chem. U.S.S.R.* **17**, 1257 (1947).

is proposed to represent the step-wise sequence of reactions which takes place:

$$\text{RSSR (cystine)} + N_3^- \rightleftarrows RSSRN_3^- \xrightarrow{I_2}$$

$$I^- + RSSRN_3I \xrightarrow{N_3^-} I^- + RSSR + 3N_2$$

The last step is thought to be rapid.[45]

Advantage is taken of the catalytic action of the various sulfur containing compounds on the iodine-azide reaction to determine trace amounts of H_2S in water (0.058 mg in 10 ml of H_2O) and for determining traces of sulfides in minerals.[46]

[45] S. Løvtrup, *Compt. rend. trav. lab. Carlsberg, Ser. chim.* **27**, 63 (1949); D. W. Whitman and R. McL. Whitney, *Anal. Chem.* **25**, 1523 (1953).

[46] M. Soukupova and F. Vydra, *Chemie* **7**, 210 (1951).

CHAPTER 5

ASTATINE

The discovery of element 85 in nature was claimed by F. Allison in 1931, who used magneto-optic measurements.[1] The name alabamine was suggested for the new element at that time. The uncertainties of magneto-optic measurements under the conditions used and later information as to the short half-life of all the isotopes of this radioactive element make doubtful any claims that element 85 might exist in nature.

In 1940 the first quite definite demonstration of element 85 was given by Corson, Mackenzie, and Segrè, who are now credited with its discovery. The name astatine is now accepted for the element and is derived from the Greek word meaning unstable. These investigators produced a radioactive isotope $^{211}_{85}$At by the α, $2n$ reaction on ^{209}Bi by making use of helium ions from the 60-inch cyclotron in Berkeley. The half-life of this isotope was originally reported as 7.5 hr and the decay as 40 per cent by alpha emission and 60 per cent by K-electron capture.[2]

Element 85 has been produced by α-disintegration of radium A and thorium A. Radium A gives rise to an α-radiator with a disintegration energy of 6.75 mev. This isotope is very likely $^{218}_{85}$At. If this surmise is correct, the disintegration scheme of radium is:

$$^{218}_{84}\text{RaA} \rightarrow (\alpha) \ ^{214}_{82}\text{RaB} \rightarrow (\beta) \ ^{214}_{83}\text{RaC}$$

$$^{218}_{84}\text{RaA} \rightarrow (\beta) \ ^{218}_{85}\text{At} \ \rightarrow (\alpha) \ ^{214}_{83}\text{RaC}$$

The energy considerations agree with this scheme. If the α-disintegration of the ground state leads to the ground state of RaC, a disintegration into the excited state of RaC with energies of 0.053 mev and 0.257 mev would be expected. In such a case, the α-radiation should be complex. The experimental data show a broad-range maximum in agreement with this complexity[3] which, for radon, appears to be due to the protons formed by the $N(\alpha,p)O$ process. Astatine-218 resulting in the decay on the walls of

[1] F. Allison and E. J. Murphy, *J. Am. Chem. Soc.* **52**, 3796 (1930); F. Allison, E. R. Bishop, and A. Sommer, *ibid.* **54**, 616 (1932).

[2] D. R. Corson, K. R. Mackenzie, and E. Segrè, *Phys. Rev.* **57**, 672 (1940); G. Friedlander and J. W. Kennedy, *Introduction to Radio Chemistry*, John Wiley & Sons, Inc., New York, 1949, p. 271.

[3] S. Flugge and A. Krebs, *Naturwissenschaften* **32**, 71 (1944); B. Karlik and T. Bernert, *Z. Physik* **123**, 51 (1944).

the radon chamber changes the geometrical counting efficiency, which, in turn, results in erroneous branching ratio. The ratio, β RaA/α RaA is 2.2×10^{-4}.[4] The isotope 217 of astatine appears in the neptunium-237 series. A relative abundance of 6.86×10^{-2}g (total earth's mass) has been estimated.[5]

The $4n+1$ series of radioactive elements is represented by the formation of $^{217}_{85}$At by the α-radiation of $^{221}_{87}$Fr:

$4n+1$ Series of Radioactive Elements

$$^{233}_{91}\text{Pa} \xrightarrow{\beta^-} {}^{233}_{92}\text{U} \xrightarrow[\substack{1.63 \times 10^5 \\ \text{yr}}]{\alpha} {}^{229}_{90}\text{Th} \xrightarrow[7000 \text{ yr}]{\alpha} {}^{225}_{88}\text{Ra} \xrightarrow[14 \text{ d}]{\beta^-} {}^{225}_{89}\text{Ac} \xrightarrow[10 \text{ d}]{\alpha} {}^{221}_{87}\text{Fr}$$

$$\alpha \quad 5 \text{ min}$$

$$^{209}_{81}\text{Tl} \xleftarrow[46 \text{ min}]{\alpha} {}^{213}_{83}\text{Bi} \xleftarrow[0.021 \text{ sec}]{\alpha} {}^{217}_{85}\text{At}$$

$$\swarrow \beta^- \qquad \swarrow \beta^-\ 98\%$$

$$^{209}_{83}\text{Bi} \xrightarrow[3.3 \text{ hr}]{\beta^-} {}^{209}_{82}\text{Pb} \xrightarrow[\substack{3.2 \times 10^{-6} \\ \text{sec}}]{\alpha} {}^{213}_{84}\text{Po}$$

A new α-ray, through which a very α-unstable isotope of mass 218 of element 85 originates, has been found as a result of a dual decomposition of RaA. The range of this α-ray with a half-life of 2 seconds is 5.53 cm. The number of β decompositions per α-decomposition for RaA is 3.3×10^{-4}.[6]

Isotopes of weight 215 and 216 have also been reported from new α-rays in the thorium and actinium series.[7]

The 211-isotope[8] of 8.3 hour half-life has been prepared by bismuth bombardment with 38 mev helium ions by the $(\alpha,3n)$ reaction.[9] The decay is more than 99 per cent by electron capture. There are indica-

[4] F. Hiessberger and B. Karlik, *Österr. Akad. Wiss., Math.-naturw. Kl., Sitzber. Abt. IIa*, **161**, 51 (1952).

[5] I. Asimov, *J. Chem. Educ.* **30** (12), 617 (1953).

[6] B. Karlik and T. Bernert, *Sitzber. Akad. Wiss. Wien, Math.-naturw., Klasse, Abt. IIa*, **152**, 103 (1943).

[7] B. Karlik and T. Bernert, *Anz. Akad. Wiss. Wien, Math.-naturw., Klasse* **81**, No. 1, 2–3 (1944).

[8] E. L. Kelly and E. Segrè, *Phys. Rev.* **75**, 999 (1949).

[9] A. H. W. Aten, Jr., *et al.*, *Analyst* **77**, 774 (1952).

tions of an α-branching of 0.17 per cent,[10] and a maximum α-particle energy of 5.519 mev.

It is not likely that any isotope of astatine is β-stable. It can be shown by closed cycle systematics that, by the time a high enough mass number is reached to reduce the α-instability to the point where β-instability rather than α-instability is limiting, the β-disintegration is very high. There is very little, if any, possibility that a long-lived form of astatine will be discovered. The longest lived, natural isotope of astatine ever noted is [219]At with a 0.9 minute half-life for the emission of 6.27 mev α-particles. This isotope has been found in uranium-238 ores in minute amounts.[11] The astatine-219 was separated chemically from a pure fraction of francium which, in turn, had been separated from a 20-millicurie source of actinium-227. The isotopes $_{85}^{210}At$ and $_{85}^{217}At$ (half-life 0.02 sec) have been reported.[12]

The chemical properties of astatine are considered in light of the tracer techniques used to determine the properties. Such tracer scale experiments are difficult to interpret. The most concentrated solution of the element so far produced (1950) is approximately 10^{-8} molar, and most experiments are performed on 10^{-11} to 10^{-15} molar solutions. A molar solution of [211]At, if it could be produced, would emit 1.54×10^{16} α cm^{-3} sec^{-1}.

In the preparation of [211]At from bismuth for chemical studies, care must be exercised to limit the α-particle energy range to 21–29 mev. Particles with energy above 28 mev produce [210]At by the reaction $(\alpha,3n)$, which decays by orbital electron capture to polonium-210.[13] Such a contamination by polonium is detrimental to later chemical tests on [211]At. The bismuth samples for bombardment are prepared by evaporating the metal onto aluminum disks. The beam energy is reduced to less than 28 mev by aluminum absorbers in front of the target.

The greater volatility of astatine in comparison to bismuth permits a concentration of activity. The astatine is distilled in an all-glass system and collected in a tube cooled with liquid nitrogen. The cooled tube is washed with a drop of concentrated nitric acid, allowed to stand, then washed by distilled water into a stock bottle. The final solution is $0.5M$ in nitric acid and contains 10^7 disintegrations/sec of astatine. It is con-

[10] R. W. Hoff and F. Asaro, private communication to E. K. Hyde; E. K. Hyde, *J. Phys. Chem.* **58**, 21 (1954).

[11] E. K. Hyde and A. Ghiorso, *Phys. Rev.* **90**, 267 (1953).

[12] F. Hagemann *et al.*, *Phys. Rev.* **72**, 252 (1947); A. C. English *et al.*, *ibid.* **72**, 253 (1947).

[13] E. L. Kellog and E. Segrè, *Phys. Rev.* **72**, 746 (1947).

sidered to be 2.1×10^{-10} molar with regard to that element. The polonium content is very low. A double separation may be used to remove astatine from bismuth and from polonium. The yield of astatine by this technique is not appreciably reduced, while the polonium impurity is decreased by a factor of a thousand (from 0.001 to 10^{-6}).

In the analytical studies of ^{211}At, either alpha or x-ray radiation can be measured. The former particles are more easily and efficiently counted. Astatine-210 is a γ-ray emitter and thus is more easily followed in tracer studies than is ^{211}At.

The volatility of astatine from glass appears to be unique. It is held very weakly on the surface of this material. The loss of astatine activity by volatilization at room temperature may be more than that by decay. The volatilization loss is much lower from metallic surfaces. No observable loss by volatilization is noted from gold or platinum in a 24-hour period, if the astatine is deposited by evaporation of a nitric acid solution. Certain metals have greater selective absorption for astatine than others have. Aluminum, nickel, copper, and bismuth show poor absorption. There appears to be a significant difference in the volatility behavior of iodine and astatine.

Migration experiments show that astatine migrates as a negative ion under a voltage of 100 volts and a migration current less than 10 milliamperes. When astatine is oxidized with hot persulfate and subjected to electrolysis, there appears to be no consistent deposition of the element at the cathode. Likewise, when astatine is dissolved in sulfuric acid, no deposition is noted at the cathode. With the addition of chromate ion to the electrolyte, deposition does take place. The critical deposition potentials of astatine from various solutions are noted in Table 5.1.

Pioneer workers in the chemistry of astatine claim that solvent-extraction technique provides a highly useful tool. The evidence points to a disproportionation of At° to At^{+x} and At^{-} when an astatine solution in

TABLE 5.1. CRITICAL DEPOSITION POTENTIALS OF ASTATINE SOLUTIONS

Solution	Concentration of Astatine (mol/liter)	Critical Deposition Potential; Normal H_2 Electrode (± 0.0250 v)
0.066M HNO$_3$	2.8×10^{-13}	-1.225
1.0M HNO$_3$	5×10^{-14}	-1.24
0.075M H$_2$SO$_4$, 0.1M Na$_2$Cr$_2$O$_7$	6×10^{-13}	-1.20
0.066M HNO$_3$ 3 mg Au	1×10^{-13}	-1.22
0.066M HNO$_3$ (repeat)	4×10^{-14}	-1.22

an organic solvent such as CCl_4 is extracted with successive quantities of 0.01M HNO_3 followed by extraction of the solvent phase with 0.1M NaOH. The astatine in the NaOH solution is completely precipitated by silver ion (using AgI as a carrier). This behavior indicates that the negatively charged as well as the positively charged astatine forms insoluble salts with the silver ion. Elemental astatine is readily extracted from a water solution by benzene or carbon tetrachloride. It cannot be extracted from an alkaline solution by these solvents, as is the case with iodine.

The element is not reduced by iron(II) ion to At^{-1}; however, it is reduced by SO_2 and by zinc. Silver and thallium(I) astatides are insoluble. The element has a strong affinity for silver, and, if metallic silver is produced in its presence by reduction with zinc, all the astatine is carried with the metallic silver.

Bromine oxidizes astatine in some manner different from that caused by hypochlorous acid or a persulfate. The latter two agents appear to carry the astatine to a state in which it behaves like the iodate. It is carried with silver iodate. Bromine oxidation and, to some extent, iron(III) oxidation give a product in which the astatine possesses a lower oxidation level. From the present knowledge it seems likely that astatine has the two oxidized forms corresponding to the ions AtO^- and AtO_3^-; the reduced form is At^-.

CHAPTER 6

THE HYDROHALIDES

GENERAL CONSIDERATIONS

The stability of the hydrohalides is in an inverse relation to the molecular weight of HX.   This fact is shown in Table I.1 in which the individual heats of formation of the hydrohalides are compared.   The close approach of the hydrogen and fluorine atoms in HF accounts for its high degree of stability.   With increasing molecular weight, the hydrohalides show increasing reducing properties.   This factor influences the method of preparation of HBr and HI.   The usual displacement of the halide from a salt as the hydrohalide cannot be accomplished in these cases except by the use of an acid, itself very resistant to reduction.

The bond moments for the molecules HF, HCl, HBr, and HI may be calculated, and are in agreement with the experimental, from the equation $\mu = C_i{}^2 \cdot er_{AB}$, in which e is the electronic charge; r_{AB} is the bond distance; and $C_i{}^2$, in its reciprocal form, is defined by $1\text{-}(H_{ii} - E)/(H_{cc} - E)$.   The two terms H_{cc} and H_{ii} are the energies of the ideal covalent and ideal ionic bonds, respectively.[1]

The ionic volumes of the halide ions Cl⁻, Br⁻, and I⁻ in solution are smaller than those in crystals.   This fact is not surprising when the discontinuous nature of water is considered and the nature of the charge of each ion in solution is compared to the charge in the crystalline state.

All the hydrohalides are colorless gases when pure and under normal conditions.   The ease of decomposition of hydrogen iodide, and to a lesser extent of hydrogen bromide, makes difficult the preparation of pure colorless solutions of these acids.   With the exception of hydrogen fluoride, aqueous solutions of all the hydrohalides are good conductors of current.   Hydrogen fluoride in $0.1N$ solution is about 15 per cent ionized.   In the pure liquid state the hydrohalides are nonconductors.   As the molecular weight of the halogen atom increases, there is less polarization.   The polarization tendency is so strong in the case of liquid hydrogen fluoride that an electrostatic bond is favored between two molecules to form a dimer.   The ion FHF⁻, derived from the salt KFHF, has been interpreted according to the transverse Raman effect (illumination parallel to the tetragonal axis).   The lines ($\Delta\gamma$) at 595 and 604 cm⁻¹ are at-

---

[1] T. Ri and N. Murayama, *Proc. Imp. Acad. Tokyo* **20**, 93 (1944).

tributed to a totally symmetrical vibration of the FHF$^-$ ion. Doubling is observed and may be due either to resonance between two configurations of the ion or to coupling between the oscillations of the ions in the unit cell.[2] In the vapor state, under normal conditions of temperature and pressure, the polymer of hydrogen fluoride, H_6F_6, is favored.[3] Electron diffraction data indicate chain rather than ring configurations for the polymers in HF vapor.[4] None of the other hydrohalides have such a polymerizing tendency. The vapor pressure-molecular weight curve illustrates this tendency. Thus, the position of hydrogen fluoride is anomalous with respect to that of the other hydrohalides.

The coordination tendency of all the halide ions and the hydrohalides is illustrated in the formation of the complexes $HX + MX_3 \rightleftharpoons HMX_4$. The stability of the fluoride complexes is greater than that of any other halide complex because of the small size of the fluoride ion. Thus, the complex HBF_4 is stable, whereas HBI_4 does not exist. The hexafluoaluminate ion, $[AlF_6]^{-3}$ is extremely stable as compared to the lesser stability and questionable existence of the other aluminohalates.

The hydrohalides form the hydrates $HCl \cdot H_2O$, $HCl \cdot 2H_2O$, $HCl \cdot 3H_2O$, $HBr \cdot 2H_2O$, $HBr \cdot 3H_2O$, $HBr \cdot 4H_2O$, $HI \cdot 3H_2O$, and $HI \cdot 4H_2O$. The constant-boiling mixtures which are typical of hydrohalide solutions do not depend on any stoichiometric combination of water and the HX molecule, since the compositions vary continuously with changes in the total pressure.

HYDROGEN FLUORIDE

General Considerations. Hydrogen fluoride is the poorest reducing agent of any of the hydrohalides. It resembles water more in many respects than it does hydrogen chloride. In the system

$$HF + (HF)_n \rightleftharpoons (HF)_{n+1}$$

the molecule $(HF)_2$ predominates at low pressures. At higher pressures, n becomes greater than 2. The heat of this reaction is 28 kcal. For large molecules the heat of reaction is 7.3 to 2.7 kcal. The heat of association of HF appears to decrease as the size of the supermolecules increases.[5] The structure of the polymer is still uncertain in spite of the x-ray, electron diffraction, and Raman investigations. From a practical standpoint, the H_2F_2 molecule is of no more importance than molecules of higher states of polymerization. Measurement of the dielectric constant at 26°C up

[2] L. Coutre and J. P. Mathieu, *Compt. rend.* **228**, 555 (1949).
[3] J. H. Simons and J. H. Hildebrand, *J. Am. Chem. Soc.* **46**, 2183 (1924).
[4] S. H. Bauer *et al.*, *J. Am. Chem. Soc.* **61**, 19 (1939).
[5] G. Briegleb, *Naturwissenschaften* **29**, 420 (1941).

to a pressure of 551 mm, and at 38°C up to 707 mm, and the calculation of the polarization show that a ring structure cannot predominate. The indications are for the existence of more or less extended chains.[6]

The Raman spectrum for crystalline plates of $KF \cdot HF$ gives some clue as to the nature of the FHF^- ion.[7] The energy of the H_2F_2 molecule is calculated from two models, one a twin of the form $F—H \cdots \cdot F$, and the other a quadrupole $F—H$. The first form does not account for the

$$F—H \cdots \cdot F \overset{\displaystyle H}{\diagup}$$

$$F—H \underset{\displaystyle H\dot{F}}{\overset{\displaystyle |}{}}$$

stability of the H_2F_2 molecule unless the polarity of the hydrogen atoms is taken into account. This accounting is done by multiplying each exchange integral by a suitable coefficient. A negligible ΔE value is found with $F—F$ distances of 2.55 A and an angle of $\theta = 60°$. It is assumed that the twins associate further. An increase in the molecular polarization should result and is in agreement with experimental fact. Three H_2F_2 twins associate to give the hexamer. Either a ring or a chain may result. The first has an energy of 34 kcal and the latter 32 kcal. Both models are in agreement with the high dielectric constant. The chain association accounts for the high value (0.612) of the ratio of heats of fusion and evaporation. The dissociation energy of hydrogen fluoride is reported as $E = 6.68$ ev or 153.97 kcal. The H—F distance is 0.92 A. The dipole moment is 1.91 D.[8]

Vapor pressures measured in a dynamic system over a temperature range of 0 to 105°C have been fitted to two equations: (1) $\log p = 8.38036 - 1952.55/335.53 + t$ and (2) $\log p = 1.91173 - 918.24/T + 3.21542 \log T$. The normal boiling point calculated from the first equation is $19.51 \pm 0.05°C$, a value agreeing fairly well with the values reported by others: 19.6°C;[9] 19.9°C;[10] 19.4°C;[11] and 19.56°C.[12]

Some physical data on hydrogen fluoride including the association factors for several temperatures are given in Table 6.1.

The values of $Z^v{}_{sat}$ and T are equated in the expression $\log \left(1 - \dfrac{1}{Z_{sat}}\right)$

$= -0.56577 + 126.28/T$ (1) over the temperature 24 to 105°C.

[6] H. A. Benesi and C. P. Smyth, *J. Chem. Phys.* **15**, 337 (1947).

[7] L. Coutre and J. P. Mathieu, *Compt. rend.* **228**, 555 (1949).

[8] G. F. Tsitsishvil, *Izvest. Akad. Nauk, S.S.S.R., Otdel. Khim. Nauk* 1950, 162–168

[9] J. Simons, *J. Am. Chem. Soc.* **46**, 2179 (1925).

[10] W. H. Claussen and J. H. Hildebrand, *ibid.* **54**, 129 (1932).

[11] J. Simons and W. K. Bouknight, *ibid.* **54**, 129 (1932).

[12] K. Fredenhagen, *Z. anorg. u. allgem. Chem.* **210**, 210 (1933).

TABLE 6.1. VAPOR PRESSURE, VAPOR DENSITY, ASSOCIATION FACTOR AND
HEAT OF VAPORIZATION FOR HYDROGEN FLUORIDE

$T°K$	Vapor Pressure (using Eq. (1))	Vapor Density, g/l	Association Factor, Z^v_{sat}	H^* cal/20 g
273.16	363.8	2.015	4.717	1257
293.16	773.2	3.170	3.743	1616
313.16	1516	4.976	3.315	1925
333.16	2778	7.645	2.934	2194
353.16	4801	11.44	2.677	2427
373.16	7891	16.64	2.453	2631

$^* H = (H^v - H^l) = T(V^v - V^l)(dP/dT).$

The function $\left(1 - \dfrac{1}{Z^v_{sat}}\right)$ of equation (1) has a definite significance if the saturated vapor is composed only of linear chains. If n_1^v, n_2^v, etc., be the numbers of moles of (HF), $(HF)_2$, etc., in one formula weight of vapor, then the number of polymer bonds, n_H^v (hydrogen bridges), per formula weight of vapor is expressed by

$$\sum_{i=1}^{\infty} (i - 1)n_i^v = 1 - \frac{1}{Z^v_{sat}} = n_H^v/N \qquad (2)$$

in which N is Avogadro's number. If, as has been suggested by dipole moment measurements,[13] the HF polymer molecules exist partially (or chiefly) as cyclic groups, then equation (2) would not give the number of hydrogen bridges per formula weight.[14]

The vapor pressures at various temperatures of hydrogen fluoride are expressed as empirical equations which show the relationship between the partial pressures to the weight per cent (w) of hydrogen fluoride in solution:

At 25°C $\log (pHF + 0.172) = -0.72956 + 0.031541\ w$

$\log (34.14 - pH_2O) = 1.00817 + 0.010473\ w$

At 40°C $\log (pHF + 0.455) = -0.31390 + 0.03489\ w$

$\log (70.95 - pH_2O) = 1.20161 + 0.013532\ w$

At 60°C $\log (pHF + 1.465) = 0.18759 + 0.033478\ w$

$\log (212.1 - pH_2O) = 1.7957 + 0.01029\ w$

At 75°C $\log (pHF + 3.012) = 0.50190 + 0.033194\ w$

$\log (368.3 - pH_2O) = 1.9076 + 0.013475\ w$

[13] R. W. Long et al., J. Am. Chem. Soc. **65**, 182 (1943); A. A. Oriani and C. P. Smyth, ibid. **70**, 125 (1948).
[14] R. L. Jarry and W. Davis, Jr., J. Phys. Chem. **57**, 600 (1953).

The constant-boiling mixture of aqueous HF contains 36 per cent of the acid at 120°C.

The heat and entropy of ionization of aqueous hydrofluoric acid have been calculated from the heat of solution (ΔH) of NaF (213 ± 10 cal/mol) and the temperature coefficients of the equilibrium constants for the dissociation of aqueous hydrogen fluoride.[15] The value for the heat of ionization of aqueous HF is −3180 ± 15 cal/mol, while the corresponding entropy is −25.2 eu. The partial molal entropy of HF_2^- is 26 eu.

A calculated value of 0.267 for the ionic character of hydrogen fluoride is lower than the observed value of 0.43. The latter value is, in turn,

TABLE 6.2. HALOGEN BOND ENERGIES[a]

Molecule or Group	Bond Energy, kcal	Molecule or Group	Bond Energy, kcal
H—H	103.4	Br—I	42.8[d]
H—F	147.5 (130.8)[d]	O—F	58.5[d]
H—Cl	102.7 (87.6)[d]	O—Cl	49.5[d]
H—Br	87.3	N—F	78.1[d]
H—I	71.4 (71.2)[b]	N—Cl	46.2[d]
F—F	63.5 (70)[b]	N—Br	43[c]
Cl—Cl	57.8 (56.9)[b]	N—I	36[c]
Br—Br	46.1 (45.2)[b]	P—F	93[c]
I—I	36.2	As—F	85[c]
Cl—F	86.5[d]	Si—F	147.4[d]
Cl—Br	53.0[d]	Si—Cl	90.3[d]
Cl—I	50.5[d]	P—Cl	75.5[d]
		P—Br	61.7[d]
		P—I	42.4[d]

[a] Except where otherwise indicated, the values given are those of Pauling (*op. cit.*).
[b] S. K. K. Jathar and S. B. Kulkarni, *Current Sci.* 18, 131 (1949).
[c] C. Postner, *Helv. Chim. Acta* 32, 1438 (1949).
[d] H. A. Skinner, *Trans. Faraday Soc.* 41, 645 (1945).

lower than the estimated value of about 0.6.[16] In Table 6.2, the energies for the various halogen-hydrogen bonds are noted along with certain other halogen bond energies for purposes of comparison.

Hydrogen Fluoride as a Solvent. The dielectric constant of hydrogen fluoride is sufficiently high to make it an ionizing solvent (see Table 6.3). Although hydrogen fluoride is a weak acid with regard to its proton availability in water, the latter is a strong electrolyte in hydrogen fluoride. The explanation for this fact is not immediately evident. In spite of the

[15] L. G. Hepler *et al.*, *J. Am. Chem. Soc.* **75**, 2809 (1953).
[16] L. Pauling, *Nature of the Chemical Bond*, Cornell Univ. Press, Ithaca, N. Y., 1940, p. 49.

TABLE 6.3. PHYSICAL PROPERTIES OF HF AND RELATED COMPOUNDS

	Freezing Point, °C	Boiling Point, °C	Molar Heat of Fusion, Calories	Molar Heat of Vaporization, Calories	Dielectric Constant
HF	−83	19.5	1,090	6,020	83.5 (0°)*
HCl	−114	−85.8	500	3,600	4.60 (27°)
HI	−53.6	−36	720	4,400	2.9 (22°)
H₂O	0	100	1,340	9,720	80 (20°)
H₂S	−85.5	−61.8			5.75 (10°)
NH₃	−77	−38.5	1,840		14.9 (24.5°)
PH₃	−132.5	−86.4			2.71 (−25°)
HCN	− 13.8	26.5			95 (21°)

*The specific conductivity of hydrogen fluoride is less than 1.4×10^{-5}. The dielectric constant is 174.8 at $-73°C$ and 134.2 at $-42°C$.

apparent weakness of hydrogen fluoride as an acid in water, it must be considered a powerful acid on the basis of the mechanism of its acid catalysis of alkylations and related organic reactions. The molar heat of neutralization of hydrofluoric acid is 16.3 kcal instead of the expected 13.7 kcal. Since the total heat evolved is the algebraic sum of the heat of dissociation of the acid and the heat of formation of the water from its ions, there must be an abnormally large amount of heat evolved in the reaction, $HF + H_2O \rightleftharpoons H_3O^+ + F^-$.

Anhydrous HF to be used as a solvent may be prepared by the industrial method or by the reaction commonly used in the laboratory:

(1) $\quad KHF_2 \text{ (damp)} \longrightarrow KHF_2 \text{ (dry)}$

(2) $\quad KHF_2 \text{ (dry)} \xrightarrow{500°C} KF + HF$

or

$$CaF_2 + H_2SO_4 \xrightarrow{700°C} 2HF + CaSO_4$$

The drying reaction (1) is accomplished by electrolysis. Use as a solvent requires the removal of all water from the acid.

Electron diffraction data show that HF exists as supermolecules in the liquid state. Polarization and coulombic attraction are the underlying causes of the association rather than resonance or dipole attraction.[17]

Substances which contain the fluoride ion exhibit the same order of solubility in hydrogen fluoride as do the corresponding hydroxides in

[17] G. Brieglieb, *Z. physik. Chem.* **B51**, 9, 38 (1941).

TABLE 6.4. SOLUBILITY OF INORGANIC SUBSTANCES IN ANHYDROUS
HYDROGEN FLUORIDE

Soluble	Slightly Soluble	Insoluble	Soluble with Reaction
H_2O	MgF_2	AlF_3	Alkali halides
NH_4F	CaF_2	ZnF_2	Alkaline-earth halides
TiF_4	SrF_2	FeF_3	KCN
NaF	BaF_2	PbF_2	NaN_3
KF	$CaSO_4$	CuF_2	K_2SiF_6
RbF	$KClO_4$	HgF_2	$KClO_3$
CsF	H_2S	HCl	$Ba(ClO_3)_2$
TlF	CO	HI	Hydroxides
$Hg(CN)_2$	CO_2	HBr	
HNO_3		HN_3	
$NaNO_3$		SiF_4	
$AgNO_3$		$Cu(NO_3)_2$	
K_2SO_4		$Bi(NO_3)_3$	
Na_2SO_4		$Pb(NO_3)_2$	
Organic molecules containing O, S, N, or $C{=}C$		$Co(NO_3)_2$	
		$ZnSO_4$	
		$CdSO_4$	
		$CuSO_4$	
		Ag_2SO_4	

Reacts with Formation of Insoluble Product	Insoluble Unreactive
$AlCl_3$	$ZnCl_2$
$FeCl_2$	$SnCl_2$
$MnCl_2$	$NiCl_2$
$CeCl_3$	$CdCl_2$
MgO	$CuCl_2$
CaO	HgI_2
SrO	AgCl
BaO	HgO
PbO	PbO_2
BaO_2	MnO_2
Al_2O_3	SnO_2
CuO	Cr_2O_3
	WO_3
	Saturated hydrocarbons

water. Table 6.4 includes a number of compounds classified according to their solubility or their tendency to react with anhydrous hydrogen fluoride.

Some additional data on the solubility of a few metal fluorides in liquid hydrogen fluoride are given in Table 6.5.[18]

[18] A. W. Jacke and G. H. Cady, *J. Phys. Chem.* **56**, 1106 (1952).

TABLE 6.5. TEMPERATURE-SOLUBILITY DATA OF SOME METAL
FLUORIDES IN HYDROGEN FLUORIDE

MF	Solubility, g/100 g HF	$T°C$
TlF	580 ± 45	11.9
	305 ± 15	−25.2
AgF, NaF, SrF₂, LiF, BaF₂	5.6 ± 0.12	12.2
	3.61 ± 0.01	−23.0
PbF₂, Hg₂F₂, CaF₂, HgF₂, SbF₃	0.536 ± 0.005	−11.9
	0.191 ± 0.003	−23.8

Hydrogen fluoride is analogous to water and ammonia in its auto-ionization:

$$2H_2O \rightarrow H_3O^+ + OH^-$$
$$2NH_3 \rightarrow NH_4^+ + NH_2^-$$
$$2HF \rightarrow FH_2^+ + F^-$$

According to the theory of solvent systems, any substance capable of increasing the concentration of the cation of a self-ionizing solvent acts as an acid with respect to that solvent. Conversely, any substance increasing the concentration of the anion of the solvent acts as a base. The ions derived from the solvent itself represent the strongest acids and bases for that particular solvent. The strongest possible base in hydrogen fluoride is the fluoride ion, and the strongest acid is the H_2F^+ or fluoronium ion. Contrary to the situation common in the water and ammonia systems, there are few if any compounds capable of donating protons readily to hydrogen fluoride. The behavior of a number of acids which are strong in aqueous solutions behave as follows in hydrogen fluoride:

(1) Nitric acid is a base
$$HONO_2 + HF \rightarrow (OH)_2NO^+ + F^-$$
(2) Perchloric acid is amphiprotic
$$HClO_4 + HF \rightarrow H_2ClO_4^+ + F^- \quad (HClO_4 \text{ acts as a base})$$
$$HClO_4 + HF \rightarrow H_2F^+ + ClO_4^- \quad (HClO_4 \text{ acts as a weak acid})$$
(3) $HMnO_4$ is a base
$$HMnO_4 + 2HF \rightarrow MnO_3F + H_3O^+ + F^-$$
(4) H_2SO_4 is a base
$$H_2SO_4 + 2HF \rightarrow HOSO_2F + H_3O^+ + F^-$$

Several comparisons may be made in the organic system. Trichloracetic acid, Cl_3CCOOH, is very slightly ionized in hydrogen fluoride inasmuch as it has only a very weak tendency to take a proton from HF.　In water it is a stronger acid than is acetic acid.　Phenol is also a poor conductor in hydrogen fluoride.　Alcohols act as binary electrolytes in hydrogen fluoride.　Either a fluoride ion and water are formed:

$$ROH + HF \rightarrow H_2O + RF$$

or a proton is added to the alcohol and the fluoride ion is formed:

$$ROH + HF \rightarrow ROH_2^+ + F^-$$

In this latter case the alcohol is acting as a weak base.

The only compounds which seem to have the potentialities for competing with the proton for the fluoride ion are electron pair acceptors, such as boron trifluoride and antimony(V) fluoride:

$$BF_3 + 2HF \rightarrow BF_4^- + H_2F^+$$
$$SbF_5 + 2HF \rightarrow H_2F^+ + SbF_6^-$$

Although a number of atoms of high oxidation level form fluorides analogous to BF_3 and SbF_5, they do not act effectively as acids in HF due to the formation of high fluocomplexes at the expense of the H_2F^- ion.　Certain of the atoms do not have a sufficiently great number of bonding orbitals available to form their salts (fluorides) which are acids in the hydrogen fluoride system.　This lack of available orbitals is particularly true of the elements in the second period of the long periodic table (atomic numbers 3 through 10).　The ideal fluoacid-forming element is one which is large enough to hold a relatively large number of fluorine atoms and thus form an anion of low charge; SbF_5 and SeF_4 form such anions.　If a compound is polymeric and has a high boiling point, its acid strength is greater than an analogous compound which is not associated and has a lower boiling point.　This relationship is well illustrated by the two fluorides, AsF_5 (bp $-53°C$) and SbF_5 (bp $151°C$).　The latter is the stronger acid in the hydrogen fluoride system.

Amphoterism in systems in which hydrogen fluoride is the solvent is illustrated by its dissolution of cryolite, Na_3AlF_6, and the precipitation of aluminum fluoride when the solution is treated with the acid, boron trifluoride:

$$Na_3AlF_6 + 3BF_4^- \rightleftharpoons AlF_3 \downarrow + 3NaBF_4 + 3F^-$$

This reaction is analogous to the following one in the water system:

$$NaAlO_2 + H_3O^+ \rightarrow Al(OH)_3 \downarrow + Na^+$$

Potassium hexafluorochromate(III), K_3CrF_6, dissolves in hydrogen fluoride but undergoes solvolysis, precipitating chromium(III) fluoride:

$$K_3CrF_6 \xrightarrow{\text{(HF)}} CrF_3 \downarrow + 3KF$$

An analogous reaction in the water system is

$$K_3Cr(OH)_6 \xrightarrow{\text{(H}_2\text{O)}} Cr(OH)_3 \downarrow + 3KOH$$

The precipitated CrF_3 is soluble in sodium fluoride and is reprecipitated from this solution by the addition of boron trifluoride:

$$CrF_3 + 3NaF \rightarrow Na_3CrF_6$$
$$Na_3CrF_6 + 3BF_3 \rightarrow 3NaBF_4 + CrF_3 \downarrow$$

Oxidation-reduction reactions between acid in hydrogen fluoride and metals are not greatly different from those between nitric acid and metals in the aqueous system. The following equations are illustrative of this similarity:

$$3HAsF_6 + 2Ag \rightarrow 2AgAsF_6 + AsF_3 \text{ (liq.)} + 3HF$$
$$7HIF_6 + 6Ag \rightarrow 6AgIF_6 + HI \text{ (gas)} + 6HF$$
$$4HNO_3 + 3Ag \rightarrow 3AgNO_3 + NO + 2H_2O$$

Preparation of Hydrogen Fluoride. Although hydrogen fluoride results from the combination of its constituent elements, the reaction is not used for either the industrial or the laboratory preparation of the compound. Two preparations for anhydrous hydrogen fluoride for solvent purposes have previously been mentioned. Hydrogen fluoride which is prepared from fluor spar and sulfuric acid usually contains silicon tetrafluoride and sulfur dioxide. If the HF is absorbed in fluosulfonic acid, SO_3HF, silicon tetrafluoride is left behind in the tail gas. Pure HF is obtained by stripping the acid solvent at 160°C. Ordinary steel equipment is satisfactory for this purpose.

Hydrogen fluoride is evolved during the catalytic alkylation of paraffin hydrocarbons. Fluosulfonic acid, as well as perfluoromethylcyclohexane, is a suitable solvent of the HF so produced. If sulfur dioxide is present to the extent of even less than 1 per cent, it is detrimental in catalytic conversions of petroleum hydrocarbons. It may be removed from the HF by passing the mixture of gases through an olefin. The sulfur compounds formed remain in the nonaqueous layer on water extraction.

Hydrogen fluoride is evolved when fluor spar and the oxides or hydroxides of iron or aluminum are heated to incandescence in the presence of superheated steam.

Anhydrous hydrofluoric acid is handled safely in carbon steel containers. The boiling point of 66.9°F is often exceeded during transportation; consequently the acid must be shipped in pressure-tested containers. Acid of 65 per cent strength is safely handled in a container of neoprene-butyl carcass stock to which a butyl compound has been vulcanized. Acid of 70 per cent strength can be shipped in steel drums. High concentration acid (65–85 per cent) undergoes gradual decomposition in steel, forming hydrogen gas unless inhibited with sulfuric acid or hydrofluosilicic acid. There is a slow decrease in the rate even in uninhibited acid as the concentration rises above 63 per cent. In the storage of HF, a layer of a heavy alkalate may be added to the storage tank to reduce diffusion of HF. The heavy alkalate must be immiscible with liquid HF, should boil between 350 and 500°F, and should have a density less than that of liquid HF.

Reactions of Hydrogen Fluoride. Anhydrous hydrogen fluoride is relatively inert. No reaction is noted at ordinary temperatures with metals other than those of the alkali group. Potassium reacts explosively even at ordinary temperatures. Industrial hydrogen fluoride usually contains some sulfur or sulfur compounds, whose presence contributes to rapid corrosion of metals.[19] In the presence of small amounts of moisture, hydrogen fluoride reacts in the same manner as the other hydrohalides. The noble metals are not attacked. The vigorous action with glass makes possible the wide use of HF, either in solution or in the gaseous state, as an etching agent:

$$CaSiO_3 + 6HF \rightarrow CaF_2 + SiF_4 + 3H_2O$$
$$SiF_4 + 2HF \rightarrow H_2SiF_6$$

Anhydrous HF reacts with phosgene at about 80°C and 280 psi to form carbonyl chlorofluoride, $COClF$ (mp $-138°C$; bp at 760 mm $-42°C$).[20] Hydrogen fluoride liberates chlorine dioxide from chlorates, hydrogen cyanide from cyanides, hydrazoic acid from azides, and silicon tetrafluoride from fluosilicates. It is an excellent dehydrating agent.

Anhydrous hydrogen fluoride is widely used in the petroleum industry as a catalyst in the alkylation of paraffins.[21] It is one of the starting materials used in the production of the various Freons.

[19] W. R. Meyers and W. B. DeLong, U.S.A.E.C., MDDC—1465 (Declassified Nov. 13, 1947); M. H. Brown, U.S.A.E.C., MDDC—144 (Declassified June 26, 1946).
[20] J. H. Simons, D. F. Herman, and W. H. Pearlson, *J. Am. Chem. Soc.* 68, 1672 (1946).
[21] J. H. Simons, *Petroleum Refiner* 22, 189–193 (1943); *Ind. Eng. Chem. (Analytical Ed.)* 17, 7 (Adv.) (1945); C. B. Linn and A. V. Grosse, *Ind. Eng. Chem.* 37, 924–929 (1945).

Aqueous hydrogen fluoride is the parent acid of most of the fluorides produced commercially; approximately 90 per cent of the production of aqueous HF goes into this use. Smaller amounts are used for such purposes as the pickling of special stainless steels and the removal of sand from metal castings. The metal fluorides are formed by direct treatment of metal oxides and hydroxides with hydrogen fluoride. There are marked differences in the solubilities of fluorides and chlorides of metals. The small size of the fluoride ion contributes to its tendency to react with metal ions to form soluble and stable complex salts. Some typical examples are K_3ThF_7, $KThF_5$, $KF \cdot 3ThF_4$, $RbYF_5$, Cs_3LaF_6, H_2SiF_6, KBF_4, HBF_4, and Na_3AlF_6. Potassium fluoride and magnesium fluoride form the compounds, $KMgF_3$ and K_2MgF_4. Rubidium fluoride and magnesium fluoride yield two similar compounds: $RbMgF_3$ (mp 912°C) and Rb_2MgF_4 (mp 792°C).[22] The double salt $MgF_2 \cdot ZnF_2$ is prepared by covering a 1:1 mole ratio of $MgCO_3$ and ZnO with excess liquid hydrogen fluoride. The salt $SrF_2 \cdot ZnF_2$ is made by treating a mixture of ZnO and $SrCO_3$ with excess HF. Other double salts prepared by similar methods are $BaF_2 \cdot ZnF_2$ and $MnF_2 \cdot ZnF_2$.[23]

The direct treatment of phosphorus(V) oxide with aqueous HF results in the formation of three fluophosphates, H_2PO_3F, HPO_2F_2, and HPF_6. The silver salt of monofluophosphoric is prepared according to the reaction:

$$2AgNO_3 + H_2PO_3F \rightarrow Ag_2PO_3F + 2HNO_3$$

The corresponding alkali metal salts are prepared from the silver salt and the desired alkali metal halide:

$$2NaCl + Ag_2PO_3F \rightarrow Na_2PO_3F + 2AgCl$$

The alkyl derivatives $(CH_3)_2PO_3F$ and $(C_2H_5)_2PO_3F$ are prepared from the alkyl iodides:

$$2CH_3I + Ag_2PO_3F \xrightarrow{50°C} (CH_3)_2PO_3F + 2AgI$$

$$2C_2H_5I + Ag_2PO_3F \xrightarrow{100°C} (C_2H_5)_2PO_3F + 2AgI$$

If a long contact period is permitted between HF and P_2O_5 the formation of the difluo- and hexafluophosphates are favored and are isolated by the addition of nitron.[24] Metal difluophosphates are obtained by adding the appropriate metal nitrate to nitron difluophosphate. Nitron nitrate pre-

[22] E. P. Dergunov and A. G. Bergman, *J. Phys. Chem.* **22**, 625 (1949).
[23] E. Ingerson and G. W. Morey, *Am. Minerologist* **36**, 788 (1951).
[24] W. Lange and E. Müller, *Ber.* **63B**, 1058 (1930).

cipitates from the solution. The difluophosphates are stable but are hydrolyzed at high temperatures. In practice almost any compound of quinquevalent phosphorus (H_3PO_4, P_2O_5, HPO_3, $H_4P_2O_7$, H_2PO_3F, HPO_2F_2, POF_3, PF_5) can be fluorinated by direct treatment with hydrofluoric acid to form crystals of $HPF_6 \cdot 6H_2O$ (mp 31.5°C). The reaction is carried out at a low temperature and under pressure to prevent the escape of gaseous compounds:

$$P_2O_5 + 12HF \rightarrow 2HPF_6 + 5H_2O$$

Hexafluophosphoric acid is useful as a condensing, polymerizing, and esterifying catalyst. Its salts are applicable in electroplating and in electrodeposition of metals.[25] The hexafluophosphate ion, PF_6^-, may also be prepared by heating SbF_5 with PCl_5. Antimony pentafluoride may, in turn, be prepared by treating $SbCl_5$ with anhydrous HF in an aluminum vessel. On distillation, crude SbF_5 is obtained. Hexafluophosphates are in general extremely stable, being decomposed only by molten alkalies and boiling strong acids.

Freshly distilled hydrofluoric acid (37–40 per cent strength) is used to prepare antimony(III) fluoride suitable for catalytic use. The HF is added to Sb_2O_3 in a platinum container. After 10 min reaction time, the excess HF is evaporated to give a theoretical yield of crude SbF_3. The crude product is mixed with methanol, filtered, and the residual methanol evaporated. After a final washing with ether, a pure active form of SbF_3 is obtained in 78 per cent yield. Silver fluoride for catalytic use is prepared by reacting an excess of 40 per cent hydrogen fluoride with Ag_2CO_3. Purification is carried out by the same general process as that described for SbF_3. Silver fluoride is highly hygroscopic, sensitive to sunlight, and attacks glass slowly. A relatively stable solution of AgF may be prepared by dissolving 14–15 g of AgF in a liter of anhydrous methanol.[26]

The reaction of hydrogen fluoride with the transition metal oxide CrO_3 results in the formation of CrO_2F_2. A tenfold excess of HF is added to the CrO_3 in an aluminum phosphate glass reactor. The chromyl fluoride is slightly soluble in HF at −78°C and separates as violet-red crystals. The crystals melt at 31.6°C forming a red-orange liquid. An 85 per cent yield is reported.[27] Tin(II) oxide wetted with water under a nitrogen atmosphere and heated to 60°C with HF yields SnF_2.[28]

[25] W. Lange and R. Livingstone, U. S. 2,488,298, Nov. 15, 1949.
[26] F. A. Andersen et al., Acta Chem. Scand. 7, 236 (1953).
[27] A. Engelbrecht and A. V. Grosse, J. Am. Chem. Soc. 74, 5262 (1952).
[28] W. H. Nebergall, J. Am. Chem. Soc. 74, 1604 (1952).

Fluoboric acid, HBF_4, as well as HF may be used in the preparation of metal fluorides. The synthetic production of double salts of aluminum fluoride as an intermediate in aluminum metal production has become important. The salt $NH_4F \cdot AlF_3$ is prepared as follows:

$$HBF_4 + Al(OH)_3 + NH_4OH \rightarrow NH_4F \cdot AlF_3 + H_3BO_3 + H_2O$$

or

$$2HBF_4 + 2Al(OH)_3 + (NH_4)_2CO_3 \rightarrow$$
$$2NH_4F \cdot AlF_3 + 2H_3BO_3 + H_2O + CO_2$$

The fluoboric acid is prepared in solution from fluor spar, sulfuric acid, boric acid, and ammonium sulfate. Excess sulfuric acid is removed by treatment with calcium carbonate. The filtered solution is treated with aluminum hydroxide and ammonia to form the desired ammonium aluminum fluoride, $NH_4F \cdot AlF_3$.[29]

HYDROGEN CHLORIDE

Preparation. The first two steps of the Le Blanc process,

$$NaCl + H_2SO_4 \rightarrow NaHSO_4 + HCl$$

and

$$NaHSO_4 + NaCl \rightarrow Na_2SO_4 + HCl$$

are still being utilized for the production of hydrogen chloride. This procedure also serves as a satisfactory laboratory method for its preparation. Any alkali or alkaline-earth metal chloride may be similarly used. Heavy-metal chlorides are not so used for the preparation of HCl. Chlorides of elements with a high positive charge (e.g., $SiCl_4$, $AlCl_3$, $SnCl_4$, PCl_5, BCl_3) in general are hydrolyzed with the formation of HCl:

$$BCl_3 + 3H_2O \rightarrow B(OH)_3 + 3HCl$$

Hydrogen chloride is evolved as a by-product in the chlorination of hydrocarbons: $C_nH_{(2n+2)} + Cl_2 \rightarrow C_nH_{(2n+1)}Cl + HCl$. The impurities found in the effluent gaseous mixture are largely chlorinated hydrocarbons and the hydrocarbon itself. Scrubbing with water serves to absorb the hydrogen chloride. Hydrogen chloride is also formed when gaseous hydrocarbons and chlorine, heated separately at temperatures from 1200–2000°F, are brought together.[30] The heat of the reaction may be used to preheat the reactants.

Passage of a mixture of chlorine and water vapor over glowing charcoal results in the reduction of chlorine to hydrogen chloride:

$$C + H_2O + 2Cl_2 \rightarrow 2HCl + CO$$

[29] Swiss 245,666 Cl 36m, Aug. 16, 1947; 245,667 Cl 36m, July 16, 1947.
[30] U. S. 2,403,735, July 9, 1946.

The hydrides of most metals and the hydrogen compounds of P, N, As, and S react with chlorine at ordinary temperatures to produce HCl and the corresponding chlorides.

Technically, hydrogen chloride is produced by the direct combination of the elements. Gaseous hydrogen and chlorine are brought together and caused to react in an open-mouthed combustion chamber submerged in a body of hydrochloric acid. This body of acid is in direct heat transfer with the burning gases and the walls of the reaction vessel. The combustion flame is caused to impinge directly on the surrounding body of acid. The temperature of the acid is maintained at about 10°C below the boiling point of the acid.[31] Improvements in the production of HCl by direct combination are related largely to more efficient heat exchange and to the lowering of the temperature within the reaction vessel. Although HCl is very soluble in water, a large amount of heat is generated when absorption takes place. If no cooling system is provided a maximum concentration of about 14.5 per cent HCl is possible. A more effective way of producing HCl has been suggested in which the combustion is caused to take place in an atmosphere of dry HCl. The problem of cooling the chamber walls is reduced since the reaction temperature is not as great. The chance of flashback from the combusion to the mixing chamber is likewise reduced.[32] The high heat-exchange capacity of tantalum makes this metal very satisfactory for the construction of the absorption chamber.

Commercial 31.45 per cent hydrogen chloride may be made anhydrous by passing it into a vertical rectification column at an intermediate point which is preheated to 215°F. A stream of 98 per cent sulfuric acid is passed down the column. The sulfuric acid becomes diluted, and substantially anhydrous HCl passes out of the top.[33]

Hydrogen chloride is freed from the oxides of nitrogen by passing the gaseous mixture into either sulfuric acid or a sulfamate solution. If hydrogen fluoride constitutes an appreciable impurity, the gaseous mixture is brought into contact with an inert aqueous solution containing some HCl in an absorption tower. The resulting solution is heated to 35–45°C. The gaseous HCl, which is evolved, is practically free from HF.[34] The addition of borates or boric acid to a hydrogen chloride solution containing soluble fluorides also permits the volatilization of HCl, since the fluorides are retained by the boric acid solution.

[31] A. H. Maude, **U. S. 2,330,440**, Sept. 28, 1944.
[32] E. S. Hill, **U. S. 2,444,256**, June 29, 1948.
[33] R. C. Cole, **U. S. 2,376,328**, May 22, 1945.
[34] A. F. Benning *et al.*, **U. S. 2,345,696**, April 4, 1944.

Impure waste hydrogen chloride gas is converted to chlorosulfonic acid, HSO_3Cl, by sulfur trioxide at about 90°C. As desired, the HCl may be liberated from the HSO_3Cl by thermal decomposition of the latter.

Physical Properties of Hydrochloric Acid. Hydrogen chloride is a colorless gas with a strong, irritating odor. At 10°C and under pressure of 40 atmospheres, it condenses to a liquid. The critical temperature and pressure are 51.45°C and 81.6 atm, respectively. The gas fumes strongly in moist air forming droplets of hydrated HCl. The boiling point is −83.7°C, and the melting point is −112°C. The relative density (air = 1) is 1.126, and the liter density 1.6394 g. At STP one volume of water dissolves 503 volumes of hydrogen chloride gas. The high degree of ionic hydration accounts for the abnormal solubility. As the temperature increases, the solubility decreases. A saturated solution at 15°C has a density of 1.231 and contains 43.4 per cent of hydrogen chloride. Aqueous solutions of hydrogen chloride form a continuous series of constant boiling mixtures. At pressures of 50, 700, 760, and 800 mm, the compositions of the solutions with regard to HCl are 23.2, 20.4, 20.24 and 20.2 per cent, respectively. These percentages do not represent actual stoichiometric hydrates, although the hydration value at 760 mm is very close to 10. The density of the constant-boiling mixture at 760 mm is 1.1012 g/ml. The entropy of HCl calculated from spectroscopic data is 44.645 cal/deg/mol.[35]

The strength of the H—Cl bond is relatively large as shown by the low percentage of thermal decomposition. At 1700°C there is less than 0.4 per cent dissociation into hydrogen and chlorine. This bond is largely covalent, as indicated by the lack of conduction of liquid hydrogen chloride. In contrast to hydrogen fluoride, there is no evidence for the association of hydrogen chloride molecules in the gaseous state.

Chemical Properties of Hydrogen Chloride. Perfectly dry hydrogen chloride is relatively inert. No reaction is found with such metals as zinc, magnesium, and iron. Oxides which readily react with the damp gas do not react with anhydrous gas. More active metals, such as those of the alkali or alkaline earth groups, burn in HCl. Sodium burns with a bright yellow flame, $2Na + 2HCl \rightarrow 2NaCl + H_2$. Hydrogen chloride and carbon monoxide react in an electrical discharge with a contraction of volume. A suggested reaction is $CO + HCl \rightarrow HCOCl$. However, no formic acid results when the reaction product is moistened. If the gases are carefully dried, no reaction occurs even under the influence of pressure and in the presence of catalysts.[36]

[35] R. H. Sherman and W. F. Giauque, *J. Am. Chem. Soc.* **75**, 2007 (1953).
[36] N. Felice, *Compt. rend. trav. faculte sci., Marseille* **1**, 49 (1941).

Aqueous solutions of hydrogen chloride have all the properties of a strong acid. The tendency of the proton, which dissociates itself from the chloride ion, to accept an electron pair, results in the formation of the hydrated hydrogen ion, or the hydronium ion, H_3O^+. The equivalent conductance of a $0.001N$ solution is 377 and is 300.5 for a $1.0N$ solution (at 18°C). This variation represents a change in apparent ionization from 99 to about 79 per cent.

Hydrochloric acid reacts with active metals to form hydrogen and the metal ion. The rate at which hydrogen is formed depends not only on the concentration and temperature but also on the solubility of the metal chloride. Thus, the reaction between lead and hydrochloric acid does not proceed beyond the formation of a thin surface layer of $PbCl_2$. Mercury is not attacked at all and platinum is only slowly attacked if some oxygen is present. The metal chlorides are, in general, highly soluble. Exceptions are found when the mass, size, and charge of the metal ion favor highly covalent-polar bonds as in Hg_2Cl_2 and $AgCl$, or when hydrolysis results in the formation of an oxychloride, such as $SbOCl$ or $BiOCl$. Oxides and hydroxides of metals react readily, as might be expected in any neutralization.

Hydrochloric acid attacks aluminum[37] with a speed that is proportional to the acid concentration and reaches a maximum at $9M$. The attack rate is related to the speed with which the protecting film of $Al(OH)_3$ dissolves. The following factors are of importance:

1. The speed of attack is slow initially but rises after an induction period to a constant higher value.

2. The duration of the induction period depends upon the pretreatment of the aluminum surface and the concentration of the acid.

3. The attack is strongly affected by traces of impurities in the metal, especially iron and silicon. Heat increases the rate as would be expected.

4. The rate increases with the concentration of the acid, as previously stated, up to a $9M$ concentration.

5. Stirring the acid in contact with the aluminum has little affect.

Gaseous hydrogen chloride converts barium sulfate to $BaCl_2$ at a temperature of 600°C according to the reaction represented by

$$BaSO_4 + 2HCl \rightarrow BaCl_2 + H_2O + SO_2 + \tfrac{1}{2}O_2$$

The yield increases with an increase of temperature. At 1100°C with 3 to 4 g of HCl per g of $BaSO_4$, the yield is reported to be 100 per cent. Either pure or naturally occurring $BaSO_4$ has the same rate of reaction

[37] T. G. Owe Berg, *Z. anorg. u. allgem. Chem.* **273**, 96 (1953).

with HCl at 1000°C; however, at lower temperatures the pure compound reacts faster.[38]

The behavior of HCl solutions under the influence of an electric current depends upon the concentration of the solution. A $3N$ solution at a potential of 1.4 to 1.5 volts gives chlorine at the anode. As the solution becomes more dilute, the anode product may be $HClO$, $HClO_3$, or $HClO_4$.

The reducing nature of aqueous HCl has been mentioned in its reaction with concentrated nitric acid. Chlorine and nitrosyl chloride are the products. After long heating, concentrated HCl and amorphous phosphorus yield PH_3.

The chloride ion shows a strong coordinating tendency. The nature of the complex appears to depend upon the concentration of the chloride ion. For a divalent metal whose normal coordination number is four, a series of complexes from $[MCl]^+$ to $[MCl_4]^{-2}$ may be expected in an aqueous solution. For the zinc(II) ion, the chlorocomplexes, such as $[ZnCl]^+$, are more stable than those of the iodocomplexes, such as $[ZnI]^+$.[39]

Hydrogen chloride adds directly to a number of metal chlorides to form complex salts. The alkali chlorides absorb HCl in the cold with the evolution of a small quantity of heat, as 0.03 kcal for KCl and HCl. Among the other complex salts reported are $CuCl_2 \cdot HCl$, $CuCl_2 \cdot 3HCl$, $CuCl_2 \cdot 2HCl \cdot 5H_2O$, $SnCl_2 \cdot HCl \cdot 3H_2O$, $HgCl_2 \cdot HCl$, $HgCl_2 \cdot 2HCl$, $AuCl_3 \cdot HCl \cdot 4H_2O$, $PtCl_4 \cdot 2HCl \cdot 6H_2O$. Most of these complexes become familiar when their formulas are written so as to indicate their complex values, as $H_2[PtCl_6] \cdot 6H_2O$. Calcium oxalate reacts with HCl to form a double salt of the composition $CaC_2O_4 \cdot CaCl_2 \cdot 2H_2O$, as well as a heptahydrate.

The chloride ion catalyzes the decomposition of hydrogen peroxide to oxygen according to the mechanism:

$$H_2O_2 + 2H^+ + 2Cl^- \rightarrow 2H_2O + Cl_2$$
$$H_2O_2 + Cl_2 \rightarrow 2H^+ + 2Cl^- + O_2$$

The iodide ion is more effective than the chloride in this catalysis. The decomposition of peroxide in the presence of chloride ion is accelerated at a high pH.[40] Chloride ion is also said to catalyze the reaction

$$H_3AsO_3 + 2HNO_2 \rightarrow H_3AsO_4 + 2NO + H_2O$$

Hydrogen chloride acts as a promoter for the reaction and the chloride ion may play a principal part in the oxidation.[41]

[38] Ya. G. Buchukuri, *Soobshcheniya Akad. Nauk Gruzinskoĭ S.S.R.* **10**, 329 (1949).
[39] L. G. Sillen and B. Liljeqvist, *Svensk Kem Tid.* **56**, 85 (1944).
[40] B. A. Skopinstev, *Doklady Akad. Nauk, U.S.S.R.* **68**, 869 (1949).
[41] Y. Oishi, *J. Chem. Soc. Japan* **54**, 313 (1951).

HYDROGEN BROMIDE

Preparation. Hydrogen and bromine combine directly only at ele-vated temperatures. In the cold there appears to be no reaction even in the presence of sunlight. At 190–200°C the catalytic effect of sunlight becomes appreciable. This behavior is in contrast to that of hydrogen with chlorine. When a gaseous mixture of bromine and hydrogen is passed over heated charcoal, combination takes place at an easily con-trolled rate. Finely divided platinum metals catalyze the formation of hydrogen bromide in a hot tube reaction. An equilibrium is established since platinum also catalyzes the decomposition of hydrogen bromide. The difference in combining tendency for hydrogen with bromine and hydrogen with chlorine is shown in the respective heats of formation of the hydrohalides. The greater thermal instability and ease of oxidation of HBr is apparent also from a comparison of their heats of formation. The thermal dissociation of HBr into its elements takes place to the extent of 1.15 per cent at 1220°C. This amount is less than that noted for HCl.

Hydrogen bromide may be prepared by the hydrolysis of phosphorus-(III) bromide in a continuous process. Red phosphorus and water are treated with liquid bromine:

$$2P + 6H_2O + 3Br_2 \rightarrow 6HBr + 2H_3PO_3$$

The hydrogen bromide formed is passed through a train containing red phosphorus, which traps any bromine vapor passing along with the HBr. The presence of orthophosphoric acid in the reaction residue shows that some of the phosphorus may have been converted to its pentabromide.

In the presence of water a number of reducing agents convert bromine to hydrogen bromide. Among these agents are hypophosphites, hydro-gen sulfide, hydrogen iodide, sulfur dioxide, and sodium thiosulfate:

$$H_2PO_2^- + 2Br_2 + 2H_2O \rightarrow 4Br^- + PO_4^{-3} + 6H^+$$

$$2HI + Br_2 \rightarrow 2HBr + I_2$$

$$Br_2 + H_2S \rightarrow 2H^+ + 2Br^- + S$$

$$Br_2 + SO_2 + 2H_2O \rightarrow 4H^+ + 2Br^- + SO_4^=$$

$$Na_2S_2O_3 + 2H^+ \rightarrow S + SO_2 + 2Na^+ + H_2O$$

followed by

$$SO_2 + Br_2 + 2H_2O \rightarrow 4H^+ + 2Br^- + SO_4^=$$

The side reaction $2S + Br_2 \rightarrow S_2Br_2$ must be considered whenever ele-mental sulfur is produced in the presence of bromine.

A mixture of concentrated sulfuric acid and a bromide first yields hydrogen bromide. However, an equilibrium mixture of bromine and hydrogen bromide is soon formed as the result of the reducing properties of the latter.   Dilute sulfuric acid reacts with barium bromide to yield a solution of hydrogen bromide.

Hydrogen bromide is produced when organic compounds are brominated.   Paraffin reacts with bromine vapor at 185°C to give hydrogen bromide.   Likewise, benzene, toluene, and their derivatives yield hydrogen bromide on bromination.   Anhydrous hydrogen bromide of high purity may be prepared by the reduction of heavy metal bromides by either hydrogen or a hydrocarbon at elevated temperatures.

Physical and Chemical Properties of Hydrogen Bromide.   Hydrogen bromide is a colorless gas with a penetrating odor.   Its liter density is 3.6445 at standard conditions.   The boiling point of the pure liquid is $-6.7°C$ and the melting point is $-88.5°C$.   The pure liquid is a nonconductor as is also the pure gas.   At 0°C and under a pressure of one atmosphere, 100 g of water dissolves 221 g of the gas to form a solution whose density is 1.78 g/ml.   A solution of HBr and water gives a constant boiling mixture of 47.8 per cent HBr at 126°C.   At 325°C the dissociation of HBr into its elements takes place to the extent of 3.5×10^{-3} per cent, which is some 1000 times greater than the value for HCl at the same temperature.   The liquid conductivity of HBr is 3×10^{-9} mho/cm.[42]

Three regular phases are recognized for solid HBr.   Phase I is stable from its melting point of 186.7 to 117.1°K.   Phase II exists over the temperature range 109.5 to 89.1°K, and phase III from 85.7 to 70.0°K. An intermediate phase (between I and II) exists from 116.6 to 112.5°K. The phase II shows a dielectric constant peak of 200 at 89°K.   The maximum falls to 32 at 70°K in phase III.   Two dispersions have been reported.   A principal dispersion is noted below 89°K, following a circular arc locus with $\alpha = 0.3$, and a rate expression with activation energy of 2.7 kcal/mol.   A second dispersion is observed at high frequencies with energy 1.59 kcal/mol.   The two dispersions very likely are due to crystal anisotropy.[43]

Hydrogen bromide in aqueous solution is a strong acid.   Three hydrates of HBr have been identified: $HBr \cdot 2H_2O$ (mp $-11.2°C$), $HBr \cdot 3H_2O$ (mp $-47.5°C$) and $HBr \cdot 4H_2O$ (mp $-55.8°C$).

With the exception of the bromides of silver, mercury (I), and lead (II), bromides are soluble in water.   Metal bromides are formed by the reaction of hydrobromic acid on metals, metal oxides, hydroxides, and carbonates; the decomposition of metal bromates; and the reduction of

[42] C. P. Smyth and C. S. Hitchcock, *J. Am. Chem. Soc.* **55**, 1830 (1933).
[43] N. L. Brown and R. H. Cole, *J. Chem. Phys.* **21**, 1920 (1953); W. F. Giauque and R. Wiebe, *J. Am. Chem. Soc.* **50**, 2193 (1928).

bromates with carbon ($KBrO_3 + 3C \rightarrow KBr + 3CO$); by the decomposition of a heavy metal nitrate in the presence of HBr; and by the action of bromine on an iodide. Ammonium bromide is formed by the direct treatment of ammonia with bromine:

$$3Br_2 + 8NH_3 \rightarrow 6NH_4Br + N_2$$

Oxides of metals are not all easily converted to bromides by many brominating agents. This fact is illustrated by the action of a number of these agents on magnesium oxide. Table 6.6 gives the results in terms of per cent transformation of the oxide to the bromide. The amount of transformation is independent of the calculated heat of reaction.[44]

The bromide ion has a strong tendency to form complex and double salts with the transition elements as well as with the representative elements. A few of the common complexes are $M[CuBr_3]$, $M_2[CuBr_4]$, $M[MgBr_3]$, $M_2[ZnBr_4]$, $M_2[CdBr_4]$, $M[HgBr_3]$, $M_2[HgBr_4]$, $M_2[Sn$-

TABLE 6.6. BROMINATION OF MAGNESIUM OXIDE

Reagent	Per Cent Transformation
S_2Br_2	90
$C + Br_2$	$\frac{1}{2}$
$CO + Br_2$	1
CBr_4	40
C_2Br_4	55
$CS_2 + Br_2$	65
$P + Br_2$	53
PBr_5	62

$Br_4]$, $M_2[MnBr_4]$, $M_2[PdBr_4]$, and $M_2[SbBr_7]$ or $2MBr \cdot SbBr_5$ (M represents a univalent metal ion). The composition of the complexes varies with the concentration of the simple salts.

The reducing action of hydrogen bromide is used to advantage in the production of UF_4 from UF_6. The temperature for the conversion of uranium(VI) fluoride to uranium(IV) fluoride using HBr is 100°C. A similar reduction using HCl requires a temperature of 300°C.[45]

HYDROGEN IODIDE

Preparation. The strong reducing properties of hydrogen iodide preclude its preparation by the methods usually applicable to the preparation of HCl and HF. Very little HI, for instance, escapes oxidation by hot sulfuric acid when the latter is treated with KI:

$$KI + H_2SO_4 \rightarrow HI + KHSO_4$$
$$8HI + H_2SO_4 \rightarrow H_2S + 4H_2O + 4I_2$$

[44] R. Rohmer and J. Pregent, *Bull. soc. chim. France*, **1949**, 655.
[45] A. D. Tevebaugh and F. Vaslow, U. S. 2,638,406, May 12, 1953.

The direct combination of hydrogen and iodine is very slow, and, at temperatures which sufficiently activate the molecules, the equilibrium favors the decomposition of HI. At 444.6°C, the boiling point of sulfur, 79 per cent of the elements combine. The heat of formation of hydrogen iodide from solid iodine and hydrogen is −12 kcal. This value is somewhat misleading, since the heat of sublimation of iodine is about 15 kcal. The heat of formation of HI from gaseous H_2 and I_2 is therefore about 3.1 kcal. As the Le Châtelier principle predicts, the decomposition of HI is favored by high temperatures.

When hydrogen sulfide is passed into a water suspension of iodine, aqueous hydrogen iodide is produced:

$$H_2S + I_2 \rightarrow 2H^+ + 2I^- + S$$

The reaction is favored by the heat of solution of hydrogen iodide and continues until an acid of 50 per cent strength is formed. Sulfites are also oxidized by iodine to form hydroiodic acid and the sulfate ion:

$$H_2SO_3 + I_2 + H_2O \rightarrow 2I^- + SO_4^= + 4H^+$$

Hydrogen iodide is most conveniently produced, without the interference of other ions or colloidal sulfur, by the same method as was used in the preparation of HBr. Red phosphorus and iodine combine directly to from PI_3, which is then hydrolyzed to form HI. A minimum of water is used in the hydrolysis to prevent the loss of HI:

$$PI_3 + 3H_2O \rightarrow 3HI + H_3PO_3$$

or

$$2P + 5I_2 + 8H_2O \rightarrow 10HI + 2H_3PO_4$$

Dry hydrogen iodide is liberated when a hydrocarbon such as tetralin (tetrahydronaphthalene) is iodinated. The reaction is best carried out at the boiling point of tetralin (207.2°C). At this temperature the decomposition of hydrogen iodide is about 16 per cent.

Physical and Chemical Properties of Hydrogen Iodide. Hydrogen iodide is extremely soluble in water and, on cooling, forms hydrates of the composition $HI \cdot 2H_2O$ (mp −43°C), $HI \cdot 3H_2O$ (mp −48°C), and $HI \cdot 4H_2O$ (mp −36.5°C). A maximum boiling mixture of aqueous HI contains 53 per cent HI at one atmosphere and 127°C. The vapor of HI is colorless and has a penetrating odor. When liquefied, it boils at −35.38°C and the solid melts at −50.8°C. It is a nonconductor of electricity.

The thermal decomposition of HI as compared to DI has been studied spectrophotometrically by the rate of formation of iodine vapor. The velocity constants for $2HI \rightarrow H_2 + I_2$ and $2DI \rightarrow D_2 + I_2$ are given by $\log K_{HI} = -10,030/T + 0.5 \log T + 13.001$ and $\log K_{DI} = -10,150/T$

+ 0.5 log T + 12.914, respectively.   The activation energies for HI and DI are 45.9 kcal and 46.4 kcal per mole, respectively.[46]   Aqueous hydriodic acid is readily oxidized by atmospheric oxygen.   The iodine formed is best removed by distilling the impure acid over red phosphorus just prior to its being used.

Hydrogen iodide is a strong monoprotic acid, but not as strong as HBr or HCl.   It reacts normally with active metals, oxides, hydroxides, and carbonates to form iodides.   The iodides of silver, mercury(I), lead(II) are colored and less soluble than the corresponding chlorides or bromides.

Hydrogen iodide is an active reducing agent.   It reduces vanadic acid by a bimolecular reaction.   The speed of reduction is proportional to the concentration of acids, neutral salts, complex ions, or iodine.   All strong acids have about the same effect on the speed; chlorides have a greater effect than nitrates, but all neutral salts increase the speed markedly; multivalent cations have no specific action; complex ions such as $[Fe(CN)_6]^{-3}$, $[Fe(CN)_6]^{-4}$, and $[CuCl_4]^{-2}$ increase the speed of reduction even though only present to the extent of 10^{-4} to $10^{-5} M$.   Vanadium(V) oxide oxidizes HI to iodine in a CO_2 atmosphere and is itself reduced to vanadium(IV) oxide.   It may be that the vanadate ion catalyzes the oxygen oxidation of HI.

The strong reducing action of HI is illustrated by its reaction with nitrogen compounds.   Nitrogen(I) oxide is reduced to the ammonium ion:

$$N_2O + 10HI \rightarrow 2NH_4^+ + 2I^- + H_2O + 4I_2$$

Nitrites are reduced to NO with the formation of iodine:

$$HNO_2 + HI \rightarrow NO + \tfrac{1}{2}I_2 + H_2O$$

Nitric acid is reduced by hydrogen iodide:

$$HNO_3 + 2HI \rightarrow HNO_2 + I_2 + H_2O$$

The mechanism[47] for this reaction is suggested as

$$HNO_3 + HNO_2 \rightarrow N_2O_4 + H_2O$$
(rate determining step, k = 1.6–0.8 (l/mol min^{-1})^2)
$$N_2O_4 \rightleftarrows 2NO_2$$
$$2(NO_2 + I^- \rightarrow NO_2^- + I)$$
$$2I \rightleftarrows I_2$$
$$2(NO_2^- + H^+ \rightleftarrows HNO_2)$$

[46] N. F. Bright and R. P. Hagerty, *Trans. Faraday Soc.* **43**, 697 (1947).
[47] E. Abel, *Monatsh.* **81**, 339 (1950).

Aqueous HI acts as a solvent for such sulfides as PbS, CdS, Bi_2S_3, HgS, and Ag_2S. The last three sulfides do not dissolve in acidified chloride solutions.[48]

When an aqueous dilute solution of HI is treated with any of the sulfur-chlorine compounds—S_2Cl_2, SCl_2, $SOCl_2$ and SO_2Cl_2—iodine is liberated. The intermediate in every case is found by spectrophotometric observations to be the iodine analog of the chlorine compound, as S_2I_2, SI_2, etc. The over-all reactions are represented by

$$S_2Cl_2 + 6HI \rightarrow 2H_2S + 6I + 2HCl$$
$$SCl_2 + 4HI \rightarrow H_2S + 4I + 2HCl$$
$$SOCl_2 + 6HI \rightarrow H_2S + 6I + H_2O + 2HCl$$
$$SO_2Cl_2 + 8HI \rightarrow H_2S + 8I + 2H_2O + 2HCl$$

Hydriodic acid reacts with N_4S_4, S_6NH_2 and $H_4S_4N_4$ according to the following equations:

$$N_4S_4 + 24HI \rightarrow 4H_2S + 4NH_4I + 20I$$
$$S_6NH_2 + 14HI \rightarrow 6H_2S + NH_4I + 13I$$
$$H_4S_4N_4 + 20HI \rightarrow 4H_2S + 4NH_4I + 16I$$

Certain thioamines react with HI according to the following equations:

$$S_2(NEt_2)_2 + 8HI \rightarrow 2H_2S + 2NHEt_2 \cdot HI + 6I$$
$$S(NEt_2)_2 + 6HI \rightarrow H_2S + 2NHEt_2 \cdot HI + 4I$$
$$C_6H_5NSO + 7HI \rightarrow H_2S + C_6H_5NH_2 \cdot HI + H_2O + 6I$$

The reduction of H_2S_2 and H_2S_3 with HI in dry CCl_4 proceeds according to the equations

$$H_2S_2 + 2HI \rightarrow 2H_2S + 2I$$

and

$$H_2S_3 + 4HI \rightarrow 3H_2S + 4I$$

In the former reaction, the ratio of iodine to H_2S is 1.0, and in the latter, 1.33.[49]

[48] I. M. Korenman, *J. Gen. Chem., U.S.S.R.* 16, 165 (1946).
[49] A. R. Vasudeva Murthy, *Proc. Indian Acad. Sci.* **36A**, 23 (1952).

CHAPTER 7

OXYCOMPOUNDS OF THE HALOGENS

Oxycompounds of Fluorine

The first indication as to the existence of oxides of fluorine dates to 1909. A mixture of fluorine, oxygen, nitrogen, and chlorine was subjected to an electric arc in a platinum vessel. After condensing the products, as well as the unreacted gases, there was evidence for, but no proof of, the formation of an oxide of fluorine.[1] At about the same time a mixture of ozonized oxygen and fluorine was found to undergo a violent reaction. The cause of this explosive reaction was attributed to the formation and subsequent decomposition of some unstable oxide of fluorine.[2] It was not until nearly two decades later that the existence of oxygen difluoride was proved and a definite and controllable method of preparation was suggested.[3] It was noted that the presence of a small amount of moisture in the KHF_2 electrolyte used for the preparation of fluorine favored the formation of a gaseous impurity which did not etch glass, was only slightly soluble in water, and whose analysis indicated the compound OF_2. This oxide is the most stable of the known oxides of fluorine. Those which have been reported in addition to the difluoride are OF, O_2F_2, and O_3F_2. In view of the greater electronegativity of the fluorine atom, these compounds are more correctly described as fluorides of oxygen. The last three oxycompounds are of little more than theoretical importance. In contrast, the chemistry of OF_2 has been made the subject of intensive study. It has potentialities as a lightweight, moderately stable, oxidizing agent for rocket fuels. The physical properties of OF_2 and O_2F_2 are noted in Table 7.1. These values may be modified as more work is done on the compounds. Unfortunately, much of the latest work on OF_2 is in the classified literature and has not been released for general information (1954).

The evidence for both OF and O_3F_2 is not sufficiently conclusive to permit their acceptance as well-defined oxycompounds of fluorine. The method reported for the preparation of OF is by the decomposition of O_2F_2. This decomposition could lead to a mixture of oxygen and fluorine

[1] O. Ruff and J. Zedner, *Ber.* **42**, 1037 (1909).
[2] G. Gallo, *Chem. Zentr.* **81**, I, 1952 (1910).
[3] P. Lebau and A. Damiens, *Compt. rend.* **185**, 652 (1927).

TABLE 7.1. PHYSICAL PROPERTIES OF OF_2 AND O_2F_2*

Property	OF_2	O_2F_2
Melting point, °C	−223.8	−163.5
Boiling point, °C	−144.8	−57
Density at bp, g/ml	1.53	1.45
Latent heat of vaporization, kcal/mol	2.650	4.57
Trouton constant	20.65	21.2

* O. Ruff and W. Menzel, *Z. anorg. u. allgem. Chem.* **198**, 39 (1931); O. Ruff, *Angew. Chem.* **46**, 739 (1933); O. Ruff and W. Menzel, *Z. anorg. u. allgem. Chem.* **217**, 85 (1934).

whose density would correspond to that proposed for OF.[4] Although liquid fluorine and liquid oxygen are reported as reacting under the influence of ultraviolet light to give a compound corresponding to the formula O_3F_2, the existence of this compound as well as OF must be regarded with skepticism.[5]

Dioxygen Difluoride, O_2F_2. This fluoride is prepared by feeding an equimolecular mixture of oxygen and fluorine at 20 mm pressure through a liquid-air-cooled quartz reaction vessel, equipped with two electrodes 12 cm apart. Under the stress of a silent electric discharge, a yellow to red-orange solid is deposited on the walls of the vessel. The vapor density of the product indicates the formula O_2F_2, but the vapor contains some ozone as an impurity. This fact probably accounts for the discrepancies in the melting point reported by various investigators; the values vary from 160 to 163.5°C. A second but less effective preparation of O_2F_2 makes use of the action of liquid oxygen on liquid oxygen difluoride under the influence of ultraviolet light:[6]

$$2OF_2 + O_2 \rightarrow 2O_2F_2$$

The compound O_3F_2 is also reported as being formed in small quantities in this same preparation. Gaseous O_2F_2 is pale brown, becoming colorless at higher temperatures. It may be vaporized and fractionated with very little decomposition below −100°C. Above this temperature, oxygen and fluorine are formed. The compound, OF, as a decomposition product is doubtful.

The vapor pressure curve of O_2F_2 below −100°C is represented by log $p = 7.515 − 1000/T$. At −86°C the vapor pressure is 162 mm, and at −132°C the vapor pressure is 3 mm.[7] The structure is best repre-

[4] P. Frisch and H. J. Schumacher, *Z. anorg. u. allgem. Chem.* **229**, 423 (1936); *Z. Chem.* **B34**, 322 (1936); O. Ruff, *Ber.* **69A**, 191 (1936).
[5] S. Aoyama and S. Sakabura, *J. Chem. Soc. Japan* **59**, 1321 (1938); **62**, 208 (1941).
[6] Aoyama and Sakabura, *loc. cit.*
[7] O. Ruff and W. Menzel, *Z. anorg. u. allgem. Chem.* **217**, 85 (1934).

sented by the formula $O{=}O{=}F_2$. The molecular diameter is 7 A.[8] The rate of decomposition of O_2F_2 between -25 and $-60°C$, and between pressures of 25 and 400 mm is given by the following equation:

$$-d[O_2F_2]/dt = 10^{12.4} \times 10^{-17,000/4.57T} \times [O_2F_2]$$

The reaction is homogeneous and unimolecular. The heat of activation is 17.3 kcal.[9]

Oxygen Difluoride, OF₂. Oxygen difluoride is prepared in a continuous process by bubbling fluorine into a 2 per cent solution of sodium hydroxide:[10]

$$2F_2 + 2OH^- \rightarrow 2F^- + OF_2 + H_2O$$

The contact time between the caustic and fluorine must be short to avoid the decomposition of OF_2 according to the equation:

$$OF_2 + 2OH^- \rightarrow O_2 + 2F^- + H_2O$$

The oxide is freed from fluorine by bubbling the mixture through water. The water vapor, in turn, is removed by passage through an acetone-CO_2 cold trap. The final OF_2-oxygen mixture is condensed at liquid air temperature. An 85 mole per cent OF_2-O_2 mixture is obtained by distillation in glass apparatus. A final fractional distillation is carried out, and activated charcoal is used to adsorb the OF_2 vapor as it is evolved. It is essential that the adsorption take place slowly to avoid explosion. Every precaution should be taken against the highly poisonous effects of the oxide. All outlets in the distillation apparatus should be provided with traps containing alkaline potassium iodide. The intensely yellow pure liquid OF_2 has a density of 1.65 at $-190°C$.

The reaction between oxygen difluoride and sodium hydroxide is first order.[11] First-order rate equations express the results:

$$K = 0.34 \text{ min}^{-1} \text{ for } 10\% \text{ NaOH at } 29°C$$
$$K = 0.10 \text{ min}^{-1} \text{ for } 1\% \text{ NaOH at } 59°C$$
$$K = 0.045 \text{ min}^{-1} \text{ for } 1\% \text{ at } 21°C$$

The rate increases sharply with agitation of the caustic.

The heat of formation for OF_2 has not been definitely established. Values of -11.5 ± 2, -8.0 ± 2 and -14.8 ± 1.7 kcal/mol, respectively,

[8] P. Frisch and H. J. Schumacher, *Z. physik. Chem.* **B37**, 1 (1937).

[9] P. Frisch and H. J. Schumacher, *ibid.* **B34**, 322 (1936).

[10] H. S. Booth *et al.*, *Inorganic Syntheses*, McGraw-Hill Book Co., Inc., New York, 1939, pp. 109–111.

[11] E. Simons *et al.*, *Natl. Nuclear Energy Ser., Div. II*, **16**, *Eng. Developments in the Gaseous Diffusion Process*, 122 (1949).

ιave been reported based on the following three independent reactions :[12]

$$2KOH + OF_2 \rightarrow 2KF + H_2O + O_2$$
$$6KI + OF_2 + 2HF \rightarrow 4KF + 2KI_3 + H_2O$$
$$4HBr + OF_2 \rightarrow 2HF + H_2O + 2Br_2$$

)ther values which have been found for the heat of formation are -9.2 ± 2 kcal[13] and -7 ± 2 kcal. All the values are in such obvious disagreement that it is doubtful that any one of them may be accepted as correct.

The vapor pressure curve of OF_2 is expressed by the equation log) = $7.3892 - 578.64/T$. The values for the vapor pressure at various temperatures are noted in Table 7.2.[14] The density of liquid OF_2 up to he critical temperature $(-81°C)$ is represented by the linear curve whose equation is $d = 2.1315 - 0.004695\ T$.[15] The density at the boiling point s 1.52 g/ml and 1.90 g/ml at the melting point. The packing density

TABLE 7.2. VAPOR PRESSURE OF OF_2

Temperature, °C	Vapor Pressure, mm
-192.2	1.6
-181.9	10.9
-171.3	50.4
-160.4	180.4
-151.2	439.5
-146.1	680.9
-145.2	733.1
-144.8	760.0

(ratio of the calculated molecular volume to the measured volume) determines the size of the molecule. This value is subject to changes in molecular structure and to dissociation and association. The packing density increases with decreasing temperature. It is 52.3 per cent at the boiling point of OF_2 and 74 per cent at 0°K.

More recent studies (1952) have in some instances reported values for certain physical properties of oxygen difluoride not in agreement with earlier ones.[16] The purity of the gas used in the later measurements was checked not only by iodometric titration, constancy of vapor pressure for successive fractions, but also by infrared spectrum. The vapor pressure curve over a temperature range from -195.4 to $-145.3°C$ indicates a linear relationship between log P_{mm} and $1/T$ for pressures greater than

[12] H. von Wartenberg and G. Klinkott, *Z. anorg. u. allgem. Chem.* **193**, 409 (1930).
[13] O. Ruff and W. Menzel, *ibid.* **198**, 375 (1931).
[14] O. Ruff and W. Menzel, *ibid.* **190**, 257 (1930).
[15] O. Ruff and W. Menzel, *ibid.* **198**, 39 (1931).
[16] Ruff and Menzel, *loc. cit.*

15 mm. Calculations of the contants by the method of least squares gives the relation

$$\log P_{mm} = 7.2242 - 555.42/T$$

From this equation the calculated boiling point is $-145.3°C$. The viscosity of liquid OF_2 at its boiling point is 0.2826 centipoise. A plot of viscosity against $1/T \times 10^3$ gives a straight line defined by the equation

$$\log \eta = 131.5/T - 1.5768$$

The critical temperature, volume, and pressure are reported as $-58.0 \pm 0.1°C$, 97.6 cc/mol, and 48.9 atm, respectively.[17]

Electron diffraction studies on the OF_2 molecule indicate an O—F distance[18] of 1.4 ± 0.1 A as compared to a calculated distance of 1.30 A. More recent electron diffraction measurements give a value of 1.413 ± 0.019 A. This value agrees with the value of 1.418 A using spectroscopic rotational constants.[19] The bond is estimated to be approximately 6 per cent ionic. The F—O—F angle is about 100°. The values recorded for this angle are $100.6°$,[20] $100 \pm 3°$,[21] $101.5 \pm 1.5°$ from infrared spectrum,[22] $103.8 \pm 1.5°$ from electron diffraction measurements, $103.2°$ from spectroscopic rotational constant calculations,[23] and $105 \pm 5°$ from electron diffraction.[24] A bond angle slightly greater than that for H—O—H would be expected since the groups attached to the oxygen are heavier in the case of OF_2. A value of 15° for the total deformation of the F—O—F angle has been calculated from the following data:

Observed bond distance, F—O	1.4 A
Valence angle	$105° \pm 5°$
Distance of F—F, calcd. for 90°	1.98 A
Distance of F—F, observed	2.22 A
2 × radius (minimum)	3.1 A
Difference (2 × radius − calculated F—F distance)	1.1 A
Total deformation	15°

The repulsive forces of the fluorine atoms are sufficient, then, to deform the valence angle, but not strong enough to distort appreciably the

---

[17] R. Anderson *et al.*, *J. Phys. Chem.* **56**, 473 (1952); J. G. Schnizlein *et al.*, *ibid.* **56**, 233 (1952).

[18] L. E. Sutton and L. O. Brockway, *J. Am. Chem. Soc.* **57**, 473 (1935).

[19] J. H. Ibers and V. Schomaker, *J. Phys. Chem.* **57**, 699 (1953).

[20] G. Hettner, R. Pohlman, and H. J. Schumacher, *Naturwiss.* **23**, 114 (1935).

[21] H. Boersch, *Monatsh.* **65**, 311 (1935).

[22] H. S. Bernstein and J. Powling, *J. Chem. Phys.* **18**, 685 (1950).

[23] Ibers and Schomaker, *loc. cit.*

[24] Sutton and Brockway, *loc. cit.*

electron shell of the molecule.[25]   Similar calculations for the Cl_2O molecule show a total deformation of 21° based on a valence angle of 111 ± 2°.

Oxygen difluoride is slightly soluble (with decomposition) in water, acids, and alkali hydroxide solutions.   The solubility in water at 20°C is represented by the equation $C_L = 0.04297 \, C_G$, in which C_L is the volume of OF_2 in 100 ml of solution at standard conditions and C_G is the volume per cent of OF_2 in the gaseous phase.[26]   The solubility of OF_2 in water obeys Henry's law.   About 6.8 cc of OF_2 are absorbed in 100 ml of cold water.   The velocity of the reaction between OF_2 and water in the temperature range 20–35°C depends upon the chemical reaction in the liquid phase and is represented by $-dC_G/dt = kC_L = k'C_G$, in which k and k' are constants of the system.[27]   The temperature coefficient of the velocity constant $(k_t + 10/k_t)$ is approximately 3 over the range 20–35°C; the temperature coefficient for OF_2 in dilute sodium hydroxide solution is about 1.5 over the range 0–30°C.

Oxygen difluoride decomposes into its elements at elevated temperatures.   On sparking OF_2 in a moist atmosphere the reaction

$$OF_2 + H_2O \rightarrow O_2 + 2HF + 74.5 \text{ kcal}$$

occurs explosively.   Apparently pure OF_2 does not have an explosive autodecomposition.

The absorption spectrum of OF_2 is continuous, with maxima at 4210, 3580, and 2940 A, and at some value below 2100 A.   The first three maxima are attributed to a dissociation of OF_2 into O_2 and F_2 or to [F] and [OF].   The maximum below 2100 may be due to atomic fluorine and atomic oxygen.   A photochemical decomposition in quartz yields fluorine, oxygen, and some silicon tetrafluoride; the latter product arises through the action on the apparatus.[28]   The thermal decomposition is homogeneous and unimolecular; however, it follows a second-order reaction rate:

$$-d[OF_2]/dt = 2dp/dt = k_1[OF_2]^2 + k_2[OF_2][O_2]$$
$$+ k_3[OF_2][SiF_4] \cdots k_x[OF_2][X].$$

The O_2 and SiF_4 concentrations must be included because of the inevitable attack on the glass or quartz vessels by the OF_2.   The term [X] accounts

[25] H. A. Stuart, *Z. physik. Chem.* **B36**, 155 (1937).

[26] F. Ishikawa *et al., Bull. Inst. Phys.-Chem. Research (Tokyo),* **12**, 742 (1933).

[27] Ishikawa *et al., loc. cit.;* F. Ishikawa *et al., Science Reports, Tokyo Imp. Univ.* **23**, 431 (1934), first series.

[28] A. Glissman and H. J. Schumacher, *Z. physik. Chem.* **B24**, 328 (1934); W. Koblitz and H. J. Schumacher, *ibid.* **B25**, 283 (1934).

for the pressure of inert gases and nitrogen. The heat of activation of the OF_2 decomposition is 40.6 ± 3 kcal per mol and the lifetime of an activated molecule of OF_2 is 10^{-12} sec. The stability of OF_2 is sufficiently great to permit storage if no moisture is present.[29]

Oxygen difluoride is not as active as elemental fluorine, but its usual reaction is one of fluorination. A marked difference between Cl_2O and OF_2 is noted in their respective reactions with water. The former gives HOCl on reaction with water, but the hydrogen-fluorine bond is too strong to allow anything but hydrogen fluoride to form when OF_2 reacts with water. The strong oxidizing action of OF_2 in aqueous or moist systems may be attributed to the formation of atomic oxygen: $OF_2 + H_2O \rightarrow 2HF + 2[O]$.

Sodium, lithium, and potassium react with OF_2 at about 400°C with the evolution of light, with the complete absorption of OF_2, and with the formation of the metal fluoride. Magnesium, calcium, strontium, and barium react at high temperatures with the evolution of light. Copper acquires a surface covering of a red-brown to black substance. Silver yields silver fluoride on its surface. Gold gives a brown surface deposit which, when put into water, is changed by tin(II) chloride to a reddish violet colored substance. Zinc, boron, aluminum, chromium, silicon, and cadmium powders react vigorously to form their respective fluorides. On warming, mercury reacts to form a brown surface deposit. The platinum metals, when powdered, react to form fluorides such as PtF_4, IrF_6, OsF_6, and PdF_3. Carbon absorbs OF_2 with the evolution of heat. Red phosphorus, heated in OF_2, yields vapors of POF_3 and PF_5. Arsenic and antimony yield the pentafluorides. Chlorine and OF_2 explode mildly on heating to give a mixture of products, probably ClF, $ClOF$, and Cl_2O. An explosion occurs when OF_2 is heated with the other halogens. Dry hydrogen apparently does not react under ordinary conditions, but sparking results in a violent explosion.

Sodium chloride and carbonate react with OF_2 to yield sodium fluoride, chlorine, and oxygen; CO_2 forms in the case of the carbonate. Metal nitrates and nitrites yield nitrogen and metal fluorides. Ammonium chloride gives ammonia. Calcium oxide is converted to the fluoride. Phosphorus(V), arsenic(III), and chromium(VI) oxides react vigorously. Lead(II) oxide yields lead(IV) oxide and lead(II) fluoride.

Sulfur dioxide and OF_2 react with a continuous drop in the total pressure until, after several hours, a layer of $(SO_3)_2$ is deposited on the walls of the reaction vessel. Hydrogen sulfide and methane explode

[29] Koblitz and Schumacher, *loc. cit.*

iolently. Ammonia reacts slowly to form ammonium fluoride. Without activation, NO reacts slowly to form a brown product, probably NO_3F and NOF. On sparking, the NO—OF_2 mixture explodes.

In aqueous solution, silver nitrate reacts with OF_2 to give a black precipitate of AgO. Manganese(II) sulfate is oxidized to hydrated MnO_2. Cobalt(II) and nickel(II) hydroxides are oxidized to their peroxides. The chromium(III) ion is oxidized in solution to the chromate ion. Thiocyanates are oxidized first to sulfur and, with continued passage of OF_2, sulfur dioxide and hydrogen cyanide are formed.[30]

This compound, OF_2, promises to meet certain of the requirements of a jet fuel oxidizer. In performance, fluorine and oxygen surpass OF_2. Fluorine gives a better performance, and oxygen permits lower reaction temperatures. Oxygen difluoride is theoretically the best liquid oxidizer known at the present time (1954) in rocket fuels, although fuming nitric acid is more practical. Hydrogen, lithium, beryllium, and boron appear to be the best performing fuel elements. The boron hydrides, followed by molten lithium and hydrazine, are the best performing fuels of reasonable density. A fuel using a mixture of beryllium and hydrazine or boron hydride as fuel elements with OF_2 as the oxidizer provides extremely high jet velocities. The low-cost production of OF_2 is likely because of the developments in large-scale fluorine production.[31]

THE OXIDES OF CHLORINE

Four oxides of chlorine are known. They are in the order of their oxidation levels Cl_2O, ClO_2, Cl_2O_6, and Cl_2O_7. The physical properties of these oxides are noted in Table 7.3. Other oxides of chlorine about which little is known are ClO and ClO_4.

Chlorine(I) Oxide, Cl_2O. This oxide is prepared by passing a stream of chlorine slowly over a mixture of dry mercury(II) oxide and sand at 0–10°C. The mercury(II) oxide should be formed by precipitation and dried just before it is used.[32] The chlorine(I) oxide is condensed to a liquid when passed into a U-tube immersed in a freezing mixture. The reaction is represented by the equation

$$2HgO + 2Cl_2 \rightarrow HgO \cdot HgCl_2 + Cl_2O$$

At normal temperatures the compound is a gas, but it is easily converted to a liquid boiling at 2°C. It dissolves freely in water (200 volumes in 1

[30] F. Ishikawa and H. Sato, *Bull. Inst. Phys. Chem. Research (Tokyo)* **13**, 1053, 1058 (1934).
[31] A. S. Leonard, *J. Am. Rocket. Soc.* **68**, 12 (1946); **70**, 20 (1947); **72**, 10 (1947).
[32] C. H. Secoy and G. H. Cady, *J. Am. Chem. Soc.* **62**, 1036 (1940).

TABLE 7.3. PROPERTIES OF THE OXIDES OF CHLORINE*

	Cl_2O	ClO_2	Cl_2O_6	Cl_2O_7
Molecular weight	87	67.5	167	183
Melting point, °C	−116	−59	3.5	−91.5
Boiling point, °C	2	11.0	203 (calc)	80
Latent heat of vaporization	6.20	6.52	9.5	8.29
Vapor pressure, mm at 0°C	699	490	0.31	23.7
Density	—	1.64 (at 0°C)	2.02 (at 3.5°C)	1.86 (at 0°C)

* J. Farquarson *et al.*, *Trans. Faraday Soc.* **32**, 790 (1936); E. B. Maxted, *Modern Advances in Inorganic Chemistry*, The Clarendon Press, Oxford, 1947, p. 134.

volume of water at 0°C) to give a yellow solution containing some hypochlorous acid. The monoxide is an active oxidizing agent either in the gaseous or liquid state. On thermal treatment the products are chlorine and oxygen. Below −20°C chlorine(I) oxide is as stable as hypochlorous acid. Photodecomposition of Cl_2O produces chlorine and oxygen according to the following mechanism:

$$Cl_2O + h\nu \rightarrow ClO + Cl$$
$$Cl + Cl_2O \rightarrow Cl_2 + ClO$$
$$ClO + ClO \rightarrow Cl_2 + O_2$$

The heat of formation of Cl_2O is −18.64 kcal/mol, and the heat of solution is 8.74 kcal/mol.[33] The experimental Cl—O distance is reported as 1.71 ± 0.02 A by the correlation method as compared to the calculated distance of 1.65 A. The bond angle of Cl—O—Cl is 111 ± 2°.[34] Data derived from electron diffraction measurements indicate the Cl to O and Cl to Cl distances to be 1.701 ± 0.20 A and 2.791 ± 0.020 A, respectively. The bond angle,[35] Cl—O—Cl, is 110.8 ± 1°.

Chlorine(I) oxide and water form a partially miscible system. The solubilities of water in chlorine(I) oxide at 270 and 194.6°K are 3.4 and 1.8 mol per cent, respectively. The solid phase formed from solutions of concentration greater than 11.7 mol per cent Cl_2O is $HOCl \cdot 2H_2O$.[36]

Since Cl_2O is used in a small concentration with air in the preparation of hypochlorites, it is of interest to know the minimum explosive con-

[33] W. A. Roth, *Z. physik. Chem.* **A191**, 248 (1942).
[34] L. E. Sutton and L. O. Brockway, *J. Am. Chem. Soc.* **57**, 473 (1935).
[35] J. D. Dunitz and K. Hedberg, *J. Am. Chem. Soc.* **72**, 3108 (1950).
[36] Secoy and Cady, *loc. cit.*

centration of Cl_2O with oxygen. At 1 atmosphere and 23°C, the value is 23.5 per cent Cl_2O by volume. In from 25 to 30 per cent Cl_2O, weak explosions are noted, but they must be initiated by sparking.[37]

Chlorine (II) Oxide, ClO. This oxide is not a well-characterized compound of chlorine. The electron affinity of ClO to form ClO⁻ is reported as 51–71 kcal.[38] As was noted in the chemistry of Cl_2O, chlorine (II) oxide is assumed to be an intermediate in the photodecomposition of Cl_2O. The spectrum of Cl_2O from the ultraviolet to near infrared gives three ranges of absorption. These maxima are accounted for by assuming the existence of ClO in the following decompositions:

$$Cl_2O \rightarrow Cl_2 + O$$
$$Cl_2O \rightarrow ClO + Cl$$
$$Cl_2O \rightarrow 2Cl + O$$

The chlorine (II) oxide "radical," ClO, is closely related to the dimer of chlorine (VI) oxide, Cl_2O_6, as indicated by the equilibria

$$ClO + O_2 \rightleftharpoons ClO_3 \ (\sim 0 \ \text{kcal}) \rightleftharpoons \tfrac{1}{2}Cl_2O_6 \ (+ \ 850 \ \text{cal})$$

Chlorine (II) oxide is produced in the reaction of Cl_2O with chlorine atoms[39]

$$Cl + Cl_2O \rightarrow ClO + Cl_2 + 14 \ \text{kcal}$$

as well as by ClO_2 and oxygen atoms:

$$O + ClO_2 \rightarrow ClO + O_2 + 48 \ \text{kcal}$$

Photochemical dissociation of Cl_2O also yields ClO. The spectrum shows a maximum at 6250 A corresponding to an energy of 45.5 kcal/mol. In the decomposition of ClO_2, a chain reaction is established represented by the following:

$$ClO_2 \rightleftharpoons ClO + O - 70 \ \text{kcal}$$
$$2ClO \rightleftharpoons Cl_2 + O_2 + 74 \ \text{kcal}$$
$$2ClO \rightleftharpoons 2Cl + O_2 + 17 \ \text{kcal}$$

When chlorine atoms are produced photochemically and reacted at room temperature with oxygen, there is evidence from flash spectroscopy for ClO radicals. Analysis of the spectra gives values of D (for ClO) of

[37] G. H. Cady and R. E. Brown, *J. Am. Chem. Soc.* **67**, 1614 (1945).
[38] H. A. Skinner, *Nature* **160**, 716 (1947).
[39] W. Finkelnburg *et al.*, *Z. physik. Chem.* **15B**, 127 (1932).

63.26 or 60.74 kcal/mol, depending upon the excited state of the chlorine. It has been postulated that ClOO is an intermediate in the formation of ClO. The reaction of chlorine atoms with oxygen is 46 times more rapid than that of the reaction of chlorine with nitrogen. The decomposition of ClO is suggested from spectroscopic evidence as being a bimolecular process independent of oxygen, chlorine, or total pressure with zero activation energy.[40]   The heat of formation of ClO as calculated spectroscopically is 39.8 ± 6.5 kcal.[41]   The electron affinity of ClO gas is 4.5 ev. $ClO(gas) + e^- \rightarrow ClO^- + 4.5$ ev; and the affinity in aqueous solution is represented by the expression $ClO + e^- + H_2O \rightarrow ClO(H_2O)^- + 16$ ± 5 kcal.[42]

Chlorine(IV) Oxide, ClO_2. This oxide is by far the most important and most extensively studied oxide of chlorine. This attention is in a large part due to its important industrial application as a bleaching agent. Chlorine dioxide is a greenish-yellow to reddish-yellow gas at ordinary temperature. The oxide is strongly irritating, and the odor is similar to that of chlorine, or ozone, or mixtures of the two. The odor is evident at 14–17 ppm, and at 45 ppm the gas may produce adverse physiological symptoms. In concentrations under 6 per cent, its toxic hazards are comparable to chlorine. Over 10 per cent of ClO_2 in air at atmospheric pressure is potentially an explosive mixture; decomposition may be initiated by sunlight, heat, or a spark.

Certain of the general physical properties of ClO_2 in addition to those found in Table 7.1 are discussed. The dielectric constant is 7.0, the specific heat 7.5, and the heat of solution 6600 ± 200 cal/mol. The heat of decomposition is 23,500 cal/mol. The molal susceptibility is 1310 × 10^{-6}. The parachor is 98.7 units, and the structural parachor 4.4 units. The surface tension is 33.1 dynes/sq cm at 0°.[43]   The equilibrium potential of the reversible reaction $ClO_2 + e^- \rightleftharpoons ClO_2^-$ is 0.950 volt.[44] In aqueous solution the heat of formation from the half reaction $ClO + H_2O + e^- \rightarrow ClO_2(H_2O)^-$ is +120 ± 5 kcal.[45]

The chlorine dioxide molecule is paramagnetic as would be expected from a molecule with an odd electron. A three electron bond has been

[40] G. Porter and F. J. Wright, *Z. Elektrochem.* **56**, 782 (1952).
[41] C. F. Goodeve and J. I. Wallace, *Trans. Faraday Soc.* **26**, 255 (1930).
[42] J. Weiss, *ibid.* **43**, 173 (1947).
[43] E. F. King and J. R. Partington, *J. Chem. Soc.* **1926**, 925; G. H. Cheesman, *ibid.* **1930**, 35; H. Mayer, *Z. physik. Chem.* **113**, 220 (1924); H. Booth and E. J. Bowers, *J. Chem. Soc.* **127**, 342 (1925).
[44] G. Holst, *Svensk Papperstidn* **48**, 23 (1945).
[45] J. Weiss, *Trans. Faraday Soc.* **43**, 173 (1947).

suggested, based on electron diffraction studies in the gaseous state:

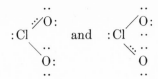

The Cl to O distance is 1.58 ± 0.03 A, which agrees with a predicted value of 1.57 A in a three-electron bond.[46]   A slightly lower value for the Cl to O distance has been reported, also based on the assumption of a three electron bond, as 1.53 A.[47]   The bond angle (O—Cl—O) is $137 \pm 15°$. Electron diffraction data give rather divergent values for the Cl to O distance, $1.49_1 \pm 0.1_4$ A, and the O—Cl—O angle, $116.5 \pm 2.5°$, compared to those noted above.[48]   In many respects, chlorine dioxide behaves more like a diatomic than a triatomic molecule.

The infrared spectrum of chlorine dioxide has a band at 290 cm^{-1} interpreted as being due to polymerization.   The shape of the band varies with the pressure of the ClO_2.   Moments of inertia calculated for a Cl—O distance of 1.49 A and an O—Cl—O angle of 118.5° are as follows: $I_A = 16.09 \times 10^{-40}$ g cm^2; $I_B = 86.34 \times 10^{-40}$ g cm^2; and $I_C = 102.43 \times 10^{-40}$ g cm^2.[49]

Chlorine dioxide is unstable at elevated temperatures and in the presence of light.   Dry ClO_2 in the presence of carbon dioxide is stable up to 85°C.[50]   At the temperature of boiling water it decomposes into chlorine and oxygen.   A chain mechanism is suggested in the thermal decomposition, the first step of which is $ClO_2 \rightarrow ClO + O$.   The rate of decomposition between 35 and 55°C is proportional to the partial pressure of ClO_2 and to the total pressure.   Increasing the pressure with gaseous oxygen, chlorine, or carbon dioxide increases the rate of decomposition, but the presence of chlorine(I) oxide and carbon monoxide retards the decomposition.   The presence of organic material favors a rapid to violent reaction.[51]

The products of the photodecomposition of moist ClO_2 have been identified as chlorine hexoxide and hypochlorous, chlorous, chloric, and perchloric acids. The following mechanism explains the formation of each

[46] L. O. Brockway, *Proc. Nat. Acad. Sci.* **19**, 303 (1933).
[47] A. F. Wells, *Structural Inorganic Chemistry*, Oxford, Clarendon Press, 1945, p. 265.
[48] J. D. Dunitz and K. Hedberg, *J. Am. Chem. Soc.* **72**, 3108 (1950).
[49] A. H. Nielsen and P. J. H. Walz, *J. Chem. Phys.* **20**, 1878 (1952).
[50] H. Booth and E. J. Bowers, *J. Chem. Soc.* **127**, 342 (1925).
[51] H. J. Schumacher and G. Stieger, *Z. physik. Chem.* **B7**, 363 (1930).

of these products:[52]

$$ClO_2 + h\nu \rightarrow (ClO) + O$$
$$ClO + H_2O \rightarrow H_2ClO_2$$
$$H_2ClO_2 + ClO \rightarrow HClO_3 + HCl$$
$$ClO_2 + O \rightarrow ClO_3$$
$$2ClO_3 \rightarrow Cl_2O_6$$
$$Cl_2O_6 + H_2O \rightarrow HClO_3 + HClO_4$$
$$(ClO) + ClO_2 \rightarrow (Cl_2O_3)$$
$$(Cl_2O_3) + H_2O \rightarrow 2HClO_2 \rightarrow HClO + HClO_3$$

Photodecomposition of the dry gas gives mostly chlorine and oxygen together with some chlorine hexoxide, Cl_2O_6, as indicated by the formation of a red liquid on the walls of the decomposition vessel.

Due to its extreme activity, chlorine dioxide is never shipped as such. Rather it is generated at the point of use. The reaction between sulfuric acid and chlorates results in ClO_2 production; however, the reaction is difficult to control:

$$H_2SO_4 + KClO_3 \rightarrow HClO_3 + KHSO_4$$
$$4HClO_3 \rightarrow 4ClO_2 + 2H_2O + O_2$$

If the pH of the chlorate solution is about 1 and the temperature is not over 70°C, chlorine dioxide is formed on the addition of hydrogen peroxide. Potassium chlorate may be reduced with oxalic acid at 70°C.[53] Chlorine dioxide and carbon dioxide are formed:

$$2H^+ + 2ClO_3^- + H_2C_2O_4 \rightarrow 2CO_2 + 2ClO_2 + 2H_2O$$

A variety of reducing agents have been suggested, other than oxalic acid.[54] Primary reducing agents having a normal redox potential of 1.0 to 1.6 volts at a temperature above 70°C are most favorable. Such conditions minimize chlorine formation when a chlorate is treated. A secondary reducing agent may then be added having a redox potential less than 1.0 volt at a temperature below 40°C. The first reducing agent is brought back to its original oxidation level and is then ready for recyclization.[55] The following are suggested as reactions likely to take place in the reduc-

[52] E. J. Bowen and W. M. Cheung, *J. Chem. Soc.* **1932**, 1200.
[53] R. W. Brown, *Tappi* **35**, 75 (1952).
[54] H. G. Henk, *Reyon, Synthetica, Zellwolle* **29**, 318 (1951).
[55] S. H. Persson, **Brit. 581,931**, Oct. 30, 1946.

ion of a chlorate:

$$ClO_3^- + 2H^+ + e^- \rightarrow ClO_2 + H_2O$$

$$\left.\begin{array}{c} ClO_2 + 4H^+ + 5e^- \rightarrow Cl^- + 2H_2O \\ Cl^- \rightarrow \tfrac{1}{2}Cl_2 + e^- \end{array}\right\} \text{side reactions}$$

Sulfur dioxide reduces the chlorate ion in an acid solution according o the reaction:[56]

$$H_2SO_3 + HClO_3 \rightarrow HClO_2 + H_2SO_4$$

nd

$$HClO_2 + HClO_3 \rightarrow 2ClO_2 + H_2O$$

A 90 per cent yield of ClO_2 is possible. The addition of water inhibits the ormation of ClO_2, and too high an acid concentration causes a spontane-ous and uncontrollable decomposition of the $HClO_3$.[57] The chlorine content of the evolved ClO_2 varies from 0 to 5 per cent.

When a 33 per cent solution of $NaClO_3$ is treated with a $HCl—H_2O—$ H_2SO_4 mixture, a reaction takes place in which the HCl reduces the $HClO_3$ with the formation of ClO_2:

$$2HClO_3 + 2HCl \rightarrow 2ClO_2 + Cl_2 + 2H_2O$$

The mixture of chlorine and ClO_2 is carried off by a stream of inert gas. A gaseous mixture containing the desired concentration of HCl is obtained by passing air through azeotropic aqueous hydrogen chloride.[58] The yields reported for this $HCl—HClO_3$ reaction are as high as 90 per cent. The permissible temperature range for optimum yields is 10 to 40°C.[59] Sodium chloride may be added to the $HCl—H_2SO_4$ mixture. The result-ng reaction product containing chlorine as well as ClO_2 is passed into a water-sulfur mixture. The chlorine reacts with sulfur to produce HCl and H_2SO_4. These acids may be brought into contact with fresh sodium chlorate, forming more chlorine dioxide with a lower chlorine content. Eventually, the chlorine dioxide is recovered substantially free from chlorine.[60] The same principle is adhered to in the treatment of a solid chlorate or a chlorate-chloride mixture with gaseous HCl in the presence of moisture. Sulfur dioxide is also added, primarily as a water binding agent, but it also serves in the role of a reducing agent of any chlorine

[56] **Brit. 639,085**, June 21, 1950; **649,562**, Jan. 31, 1951; **672,440**, May 21, 1952.
[57] G. Holst, *Svensk Kem. Tid.* **56**, 369 (1944).
[58] W. S. Hutchinson, **U. S. 2,409,862**, Oct. 22, 1946.
[59] **Swed. 137,571**, Oct. 14, 1952.
[60] G. L. Cunningham, **U. S. 2,317,443**, April 27, 1943.

generated.[61]   In a continuous process, sulfur dioxide without the presence of hydrogen chloride may also be used.   Burner gas (15–18 per cent SO_2) and a solution of sodium chlorate are passed continuously through a packed tower, jacketed for cooling so as to prevent the interaction of SO_2 and ClO_2.   Some chlorine is produced, but the amount is minimized by careful control of the SO_2 influx and the rate of ClO_2 formation.[6] Chlorine dioxide which is practically free from chlorine is produced by passing a stream of nitrogen and air, or nitrogen containing sulfur dioxide through a rather highly acidified and concentrated sodium chlorite solution.   The rate of sulfur dioxide absorption determines the speed of the reaction resulting in chlorine dioxide formation.[63]

Nitrogen oxides are oxidizing agents in the conversion of chlorites to chlorine dioxide.[64]   Nitrogen(IV) oxide, produced in an Alsop electrical apparatus, is passed with air through a column of solid sodium chlorite or calcium chlorite at 20–50°C.   In addition to chlorine dioxide, sodium nitrite is formed:[65]

$$NaClO_2 + NO_2 \rightarrow NaNO_2 + ClO_2$$

Potassium chlorate acidified with HNO_3 may also be used with electrolytically produced NO_2 to form ClO_2 according to the following:[66]

$$ClO_3^- + NO_2 \rightarrow NO_3^- + ClO_2$$

Chlorine dioxide is produced by passing a solution of sodium chlorate downward and nitrogen dioxide upward in a tower packed with alundum. A 40–50 per cent conversion to ClO_2 is claimed for this method.[67]   The sodium chlorate solution may also be acidified with dilute nitric acid and the upward stream of nitrogen dioxide mixed with a small percentage of air.

Nitrogen trichloride, NCl_3, reacts with chlorites to produce ClO_2 according to one or the other of two mechanisms:

(1) $NCl_3 + 3H_2O + 6NaClO_2 \rightarrow 6ClO_2 + 3NaCl + 3NaOH + NH_3$

(2) $2NCl_3 + 6NaClO_2 \rightarrow 6ClO_2 + 6NaCl + N_2$

[61] J. W. Sevon and F. V. Sundman, **Swed. 122,766,** Sept. 21, 1948.

[62] W. H. Rapson and M. Wayman, **U. S. 2,481,240,** Sept. 6, 1949.

[63] G. Holst, *Svensk Papperstidn* **47,** 537 (1944).

[64] **Brit. 663,218,** Dec. 19, 1951.

[65] W. S. Hutchinson, **Brit. 595,813,** Dec. 17, 1947; W. S. Hutchinson and R. I. Derby *Cereal Chem.* **24,** 372 (1947).

[66] J. F. Haller, **U. S. 2,451,826,** Oct. 19, 1948.

[67] **Brit. 673,769,** June 11, 1952; **Brit. 675,541,** July 9, 1952.

The preferred reaction is represented by equation (1). Nitrogen trichloride is the oxidizing agent and sodium chlorite the reducing agent:

$$NCl_3 + 3H^+ + 6e^- \rightarrow NH_3 + 3Cl^-$$
$$NaClO_2 \rightarrow ClO_2 + Na^+ + 1e^-$$

Chlorine dioxide for pulp-mill use is made by the electrolysis of hydrochloric acid. The carrier for the oxygen is a solution of sodium chlorate, which continuously circulates between the dioxide reactor and an electrolytic cell for fortification. The process is continuous and well suited for automatic control. Chlorine dioxide for the milling and tallow industries is most conveniently prepared by the action of chlorine on sodium chlorite:

$$2NaClO_2 + Cl_2 \rightarrow 2NaCl + 2ClO_2$$

Two general methods have been adopted in carrying out this reaction— a "dry" type and a wet type,[68] employing a solid-and-gas system. The former is a high capacity process and has found greater use in the fat rendering industry, whereas the latter method provides a relatively low gas capacity and is almost solely used in the flour milling industry. The "wet" process is patented under the name of "Dyox."

The "dry" process is the more dangerous one. It is carried out in a vertical tower containing 90 to 100 lb of dry, technical-grade sodium chlorite, a pipe line into the bottom of the tower delivering a 2 per cent chlorine-in-air mixture, and an outlet line emerging from the top of the tower carrying a 4 per cent chlorine dioxide-in-air mixture to the bleaching chamber. The danger lies in allowing the chlorine content to build up to a level beyond 2 per cent. The pressure control must permit rupture at 25 to 30 lb/sq in.

A considerably less dangerous variation of the preceding dry-type process is one in which an air—HCl—H_2O mixture, obtained by passing air through azeotropic aqueous HCl at room temperatures, is conducted upward through a column of solid chlorate or chlorite.[69] Safe concentrations (below 30 mm) of ClO_2 are obtained.

The "wet" generator operates on the principle of the accurate metering and proportioning of a 3 per cent chlorine-in-air mixture into a reaction tower which contains sodium chlorite solution (13.5 lb of $NaClO_2$ in 5.92 gal of water). The safety feature of this process is found in the fact that should there be an interruption of the air supply, which would cause an

[68] E. R. Woodward, *Chem. & Eng. News* **22**, 1092 (1944).
[69] U. S. 2,409,862, Oct. 22, 1946.

explosion in the "dry" process, the reaction stops without an explosion. Increases in the yield are possible if the chlorine and an inert gas are introduced into the tower via separate entry tubes. In this way no coalescence is observed between the bubbles of inert gas and the chlorine, and the chances of the reaction going to completion are greater.[70] Organic anhydrides added to the chlorite also increase the yield of ClO_2. Acetic anhydride increases the yield some thirtyfold.[71] A continuous and stable generator of chlorine dioxide is prepared from a solid mixture of alkali or alkaline earth chlorite, an organic anhydride, a desiccant, and a diluent, as Na_2O, $NaOH$, or $CaCl_2$. The addition of water initiates the production of ClO_2.

Chlorites treated with weak acids such as formic, acetic, or boric in the presence of a salt of the weak acid and formaldehyde decompose to chlorine dioxide.[72] This reaction is suggested as being an autooxidation-reduction of the chlorite induced by the organic reducing agent. It may also be a coupling reaction in which the aldehyde actually reacts but is reformed.[73] Aqueous solutions of furfuraldehyde and dextrose are capable of initiating the reaction at a pH of 9 and within a 20–80°C range in temperature.[74]

Since acidified chlorite solutions are used in bleaching operations, it is advantageous under certain conditions to inhibit the evolution of chlorine dioxide. This loss of ClO_2 is repressed by the addition of hydrogen peroxide. In practice an aqueous solution of a chlorite is not as vigorous an oxidizing agent as an aqueous solution of chlorine dioxide. The action of the latter is also much more rapid.[75]

Mixtures of fluorine and chlorine dioxide react explosively at 25°C to form chlorine, chlorine dioxyfluoride (ClO_2F), and oxygen. A smooth reaction takes place between F_2 and ClO_2 in air, when the partial pressures of these gases are, respectively, 54.0 mm, 25.6 mm, and 540.7 mm, to form ClO_2F (mp −115°C, bp −6°C). The vapor pressure of the compound is 8.8 mm at −78°C and 740 mm at −6.3°C. The molecular heat of formation is 6.2 kcal; Trouton's constant is 23.2. The compound fumes in moist air.[76]

Chlorine dioxide in carbon tetrachloride coordinates with pyridine or its homologues at low temperatures. So-called sodium amidochlorate,

[70] U. S. 2,388,202, Oct. 30, 1945.
[71] U. S. 2,436,134, Feb. 17, 1948.
[72] Can. 414,114, July 27, 1943.
[73] Brit. 561,229, May 10, 1944.
[74] U. S. 2,323,593, July 6, 1944.
[75] J. D. MacMahon, U. S. 2,358,866, Sept. 26, 1944.
[76] H. Schmitz and H. J. Schumacher, *Z. anorg. u. allgem. Chem.* 249, 238 (1942).

Na(NH$_2$ClO$_2$), is prepared by the action of chlorine dioxide on sodium amide. This compound is considered to be more of a Werner type coordination compound than a valence type compound.[77]

Metal chlorites are produced by treating the desired metal hydroxide with aqueous chlorine dioxide. The reaction is easily controlled. The presence of ammonia in the solution of the metal hydroxide prevents the formation of chlorates. The chlorites of cadmium, zinc, magnesium, and aluminum result in 66, 57, 64, and 34 per cent yields, respectively, when the metal dusts are treated with chlorine dioxide. Liquid (anhydrous) ClO$_2$ does not react with either zinc or magnesium metal. Nickel filings and chlorine-free ClO$_2$ give a 100 per cent yield of Ni(ClO$_2$)$_2$ at 16–25°C. On elevating the temperature to 45°C, this chlorite is converted to the chloride and chlorate.[78]

The action of chlorine dioxide on sulfur to produce S$_2$Cl$_2$ and SO$_2$ may proceed with explosive violence. If the reaction takes place in a large amount of water, sulfuric acid is formed at a controllable rate. Carbon dioxide and air are suitable inert diluents for ClO$_2$.[79]

The oxidizing capacity of chlorine dioxide is made use of to a limited extent in organic syntheses and identifications. Alkyl groups are readily oxidized, whereas carboxyl groups are not attacked. The phenolic OH group reacts readily with chlorine dioxide. In fact, this reaction has been used as a test for the presence of the phenolic OH group.[80] Lignin reacts with ClO$_2$ to form oxalic acid, carbon dioxide, and maleic acid. Phenolic groups protected by methylation, acetylation, or halogenation are less readily attacked by ClO$_2$.

As has been mentioned, much of the interest in ClO$_2$ is related to its use in bleaching and in water purification. Chlorine dioxide is about 30 times more effective on a weight basis in flour bleaching than is chlorine; 1.5 g of ClO$_2$ is used per barrel as compared to 43 g of chlorine.[81]

Chlorine dioxide has been officially approved as a replacement for NCl$_3$, known as *agene*, in the bleaching and maturing of flour. The chemical nature of the change produced in proteins by treatment with NCl$_3$ is not known, but it has been shown that a convulsant agent, which injures animals after oral administration to them, is present. On the other hand, it has been found impossible to detect any injury to human health attendant upon the intake of agenized flour. Furthermore, ani-

[77] G. Beck. *Z. anorg. u. allgem. Chem.* **233**, 155 (1937).

[78] M. Bigorgne, *Compt. rend.* **225**, 527 (1947); **226**, 1197 (1948).

[79] F. Taradoire, *Bull. soc. chim. France* [5] **8**, 860 (1941); *Chem. Zentr.* **1942**, II, 1325.

[80] P. B. Sarkar, *J. Indian Chem. Soc.* **12**, 470 (1935); E. Schmidt and K. Braunsdorf, *Ber.* **55B**, 1529 (1922).

[81] W. S. Hutchinson and R. I. Derby, *Ind. Eng. Chem.* **37**, 813 (1945).

mals showed no evidence of injury at intake levels comparable to those normal for humans.[82]

The unpleasant taste of water containing algae and/or industrial wastes is intensified by treatment with chlorine because the latter converts the contaminants into chlorinated products whose tastes and odors are generally more disagreeable than those of the original compounds.[83] However, the chlorine demand of a water should be met by prechlorination, which is then followed by a ClO_2 treatment to oxidize both the chlorinated and unchlorinated contaminants to tasteless substances.[84] Chlorine dioxide is added after the filtration which commonly follows the treatment with chlorine.

Chlorine Hexoxide, Cl_2O_6.   Illumination of chlorine dioxide at 8–9°C decomposes it with the formation of red droplets of Cl_2O_6.   The freezing point of 3.50 ± 0.05°C can be sharply altered by the presence of impurities as well as by its own decomposition products.   At the decomposition temperature there is also condensation of any chlorine dioxide present, but the difference in volatility of the two compounds permits their separation by fractional distillation.   Molecular weight determinations on the red liquid prove it to be $(ClO_3)_2$.   Another method of preparation uses the reaction between ozone and chlorine dioxide, with or without the addition of carbon dioxide[85] as a diluent for the ClO_2.   The reaction vessel must be cooled to about 0°C.   The hexoxide is separated from ClO_2 and the heptoxide, also formed in the reaction, by fractional distillation.

Another reaction product isolated in the preparation of Cl_2O_6 from chlorine dioxide and ozone is nitronium (or nitroxyl) perchlorate, $NClO_6$. It exists as white, needle-shaped crystals with low vapor pressure, is soluble in $POCl_3$, but insoluble in CCl_4.   It decomposes rapidly, but not explosively, at 120°C.   It reacts with most organic compounds, in some cases explosively.   With iodine, it gives I_2O_5 and probably ICl.   In solution, positive tests are obtained for the nitrate and perchlorate ions, but there is no positive evidence for chloride, chlorate, or nitrite ions. The mechanism appears to be the initial formation of N_2O_5 from air and ozone, followed by dissociation of N_2O_5 into NO_2 and NO_3 and the formation of ClO_3 from ClO_2 and ozone, and finally the combination of NO_3 and

[82] *Chem. & Eng. News* **27**, 21 (1949).

[83] G. P. Vincent, *The Frontier* **9**, No. 1, 12 (1946); *C. A.* **40**, 5857 (1946); G. P. Vincent, J. D. MacMahon, and J. F. Synan, *Am. J. Pub. Health* **36**, 1035–1037 (1946).

[84] W. D. MacLean, *Water and Sewage* **84**, No. 5, 21, 55 (1946).

[85] C. F. Goodeve and F. D. Richardson, *J. Chem. Soc.* **1937**, 294; E. B. Maxted, *op. cit.*, p. 132 (see ref. to Table 7.3).

ClO_3 to form NO_2ClO_4.[86] X-ray examination of the compound indicates that the crystals of nitronium perchlorate consist of NO_2^+ and ClO_4^- ions in a monoclinic cell.   The NO_2^+ ion is linear, with an N—O distance of approximately 1.1 A.   The ClO_4^- ion is tetrahedral with a Cl—O distance of about 1.5 A.   In view of the chemical behavior, a tautomeric equilibrium is suggested:[87]

$$NO_3^+ClO_3^- \rightleftharpoons NO_2^+ClO_4^-$$

Chlorine hexoxide has the highest melting point, density, and latent heat of evaporation, but the lowest vapor pressure of any of the oxides of chlorine (Table 7.3).   These properties are understandable if its structure is assumed to be that of two trigonal pyramids joined at the apices:

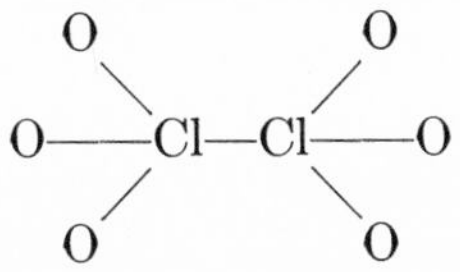

These symmetrical molecules form close-packed crystals.   On the contrary, the oxygen atom linking the chlorines in the heptoxide, Cl_2O_7,

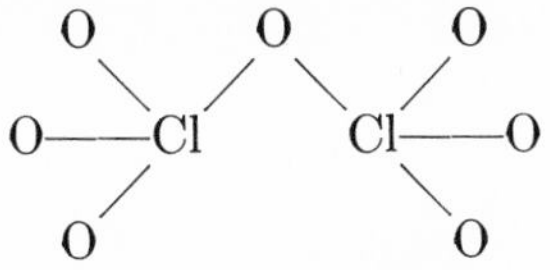

prevents the close-packed arrangement found for Cl_2O_6.   The Longuet-Higgins structure of N_2O_4, which is planar with two resonance states

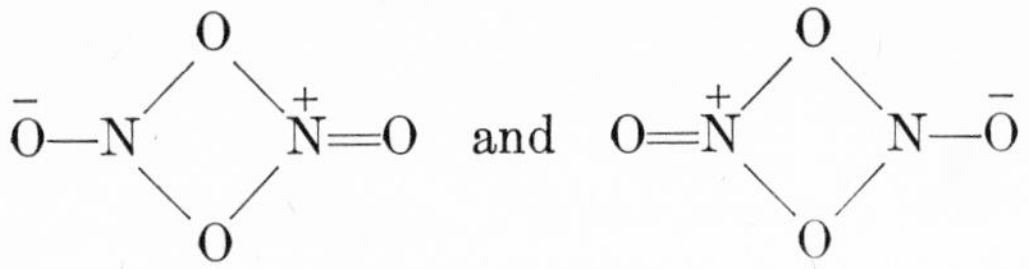

suggests the following structure for Cl_2O_6:

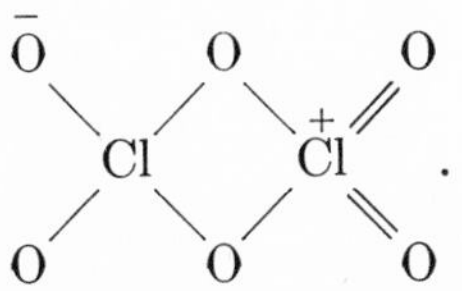

[86] W. E. Gordon and J. W. T. Spinks, *Can. J. Res.* **18B**, 358 (1940).
[87] E. G. Cox, G. A. Jeffrey, and M. R. Truter, *Nature* **162**, 259 (1948).

The chlorine atoms are probably tetrahedral, in which case the hexoxide is geometrically analogous to the dimeric aluminum chloride, Al_2Cl_6.[88] Exact values for the vapor pressure and melting point of Cl_2O_6 are difficult to determine since the compound decomposes into chlorine and oxygen at its melting point. The observed melting point becomes lower as the sample stands. The vapor pressure of the solid and liquid is given by the equations:[89]

$$\log p(\text{solid}) = -2690/T + 9.3$$

and

$$\log p(\text{liquid}) = -2070/T + 7.1$$

The liquid oxide is predominantly dimeric; however, the presence of the monomer, ClO_3, is demonstrated by magnetic measurements. The monomer contains an unpaired electron and is therefore paramagnetic. The diamagnetic susceptibility of the dimer is less than calculated because of the presence of some monomer. The mole per cent of ClO_3 increases from 1.46 at $-40°C$ to 1.99 at $10°C$. The change in the equilibrium constants calculated from these percentages for the system $Cl_2O_6 \rightleftharpoons 2ClO_3$ is from 2.55×10^{-3} to 4.91×10^{-3}.[90]

In the formation of Cl_2O_6, mechanisms have been proposed[91] which involve the dimerization of ClO_3. The evidence appears, however, to be overwhelmingly against ClO_3, and for ClO as an intermediate.[92]

Liquid Cl_2O_6 has strong absorption throughout the region from about 6000 to 2000 A. The absorption of the gaseous Cl_2O_6 is continuous with two maxima, one at 2780 A and one beginning at 2170 A. A molecule with such a continuous spectra would be expected to dissociate. The heat of dissociation is low as expected, about 1.5 kcal. The dissociation equilibria are indicated. The first is

$$Cl_2O_6 \rightleftharpoons 2 \; ClO_3$$

A second dissociation

$$ClO_3 \rightleftharpoons ClO + O_2$$

[88] H. C. Longuet-Higgins, *Nature* **153**, 408 (1944).

[89] Goodeve and Richardson, *loc. cit.*

[90] J. Farquarson *et al.*, *Trans. Faraday Soc.* **32**, 790 (1936); C. F. Goodeve and F. A. Todd, *Nature* **132**, 514 (1933).

[91] M. Bodenstein *et al.*, *Z. physik. Chem.* **5B**, 209 (1929); *Z. anorg. u. allgem. Chem.* **147**, 233 (1925); *Z. physik. Chem.* **5B**, 233 (1929); A. J. Allmand and J. W. T. Spinks, *J. Chem. Soc.* **1932**, 599; G. K. Byrns and A. C. Rollefson, *J. Am. Chem. Soc.* **56**, 364, 2245 (1934).

[92] R. G. W. Norrish and G. H. J. Neville, *J. Chem. Soc.* **1934**, 1864.

is nearly thermoneutral as seen from the equations:[93]

$$2 \text{ ClO} \rightleftharpoons \text{Cl}_2 + \text{O}_2 + 74 \text{ kcal}$$
$$2 \text{ ClO}_3 \rightleftharpoons \text{Cl}_2 + 3\text{O}_2 + 74 \pm \text{kcal}$$

Little is known of the reactions of Cl_2O_6. It doubtless reacts with ozone, which reaction is inhibited by foreign gases capable of deactivating the energetic molecules capable of propagating the chain. The activation energy for the decomposition of Cl_2O_6 is about 22 kcal, a value which includes the heat of evaporation, 9.5 kcal.[94]

Chlorine Heptoxide, Cl_2O_7. This oxide is obtained by heating perchloric acid with phosphorus(V) oxide:

$$2\text{HClO}_4 + \text{P}_2\text{O}_5 \rightarrow \text{Cl}_2\text{O}_7 + 2\text{HPO}_3$$

It is, therefore, the normal anhydride of perchloric acid. Although it is the most stable oxide of chlorine, it may be exploded by heat or shock. The physical properties are noted in Table 7.3. The structure was described under the discussion of the hexoxide. No polymeric forms of Cl_2O_7 are known.

Chlorine Tetroxide, ClO_4. The identity of this oxide is uncertain. If it exists at all, it is probably a free radical. Its possible preparation is carried out by the following reaction:

$$2\text{AgClO}_4 + \text{I}_2 \rightarrow 2\text{AgI} \downarrow + 2\text{ClO}_4$$

Some perchloric acid is also formed in the reaction, and most of the evidence for the tetroxide may be explained by the presence of perchloric acid in the solution. Ether solutions of the oxide have been reported, but attempts to isolate the free compound have been unsuccessful. Ebullioscopic measurements indicate a dimer, $(\text{ClO}_4)_2$. Free radical studies involving the triaryl methyl group, $\text{R}_3\text{C}—$, indicate that it forms an addition compound with the oxide, $\text{R}_3\text{C}—\text{ClO}_4$.[95]

THE OXIDES OF BROMINE

Three oxides of bromine and possibly a fourth are known.

Bromine(I) Oxide, Br_2O. Bromine(I) oxide is a dark brown solid, melting at $-17.5 \pm 0.5°C$.[96] It is susceptible to photodecomposition and is stable only in the dark at low temperatures, as $-40°C$. No vapor

---

[93] C. F. Goodeve and A. E. L. Marsh, *Trans. Faraday Soc.* **32**, 8790 (1936).

[94] C. F. Goodeve and F. D. Richardson, *J. Chem. Soc.* 284 (1937).

[95] M. Gomberg, *J. Am. Chem. Soc.* **45**, 398 (1923); M. Gomberg and H. R. Gomrath, *Trans. Faraday Soc.* **30**, 24 (1934); R. Schwarz and H. Wiele, *J. prakt. Chem.* **152**, 157 (1939).

[96] R. Schwarz and H. Wiele, *Naturwiss.* **26**, 742 (1938).

pressure or boiling point data are available because of the ready decomposition of the oxide.

The method used for the preparation of chlorine (I) oxide is adaptable to that of Br_2O, provided a lower temperature is used for the precipitation and drying of the mercury (II) oxide. A temperature of from 50–60°C for the drying operation yields HgO which gives the desired reaction with bromine:[97]

$$2Br_2 + 2HgO \rightarrow Hg_2OBr_2 + Br_2O$$

With carbon tetrachloride as a reaction medium, concentrations of Br_2O up to 50 per cent are possible. The oxide content is determined by iodometric titration. Pure bromine monoxide is obtained when the dioxide, BrO_2, is thermally decomposed in a vacuum. Fractional sublimation removes elemental bromine.

In carbon tetrachloride solution Br_2O reacts normally with an alkali metal hydroxide at 0°C to form a hypobromite. Undiluted bromine monoxide mixed with a cold solution of an alkali forms bromates as well as bromites. A quantitative oxidation to iodine takes place with iodide.

Tribromine Octoxide, Br_3O_8. Pure Br_3O_8 is deposited as a white flocculent solid on the walls of a reaction vessel when pure ozone reacts with bromine at −5 to 10°C and under a pressure of 2–15 mm. The system must be free of any organic material such as an organic stop cock grease. The oxide is stable only at very low temperatures (−85°C) or when in the presence of ozone at the temperature at which the formation of the oxide was carried out.

Two allotropic forms differing in crystal form and stability are known for Br_3O_8. The more stable form is obtained as fine white needles on cooling the oxide for several hours at −40°C. At −35 ± 3°C a transition to the less stable form takes place.[98] The oxide dissolves in water to give a colorless solution; no oxygen or bromine is evolved.

Bromine (IV) Oxide, BrO_2. Bromine (IV) oxide is prepared by passing a mixture of oxygen and bromine at low pressure through a cooled discharge tube (100 milliamps at 6,000 volts).[99]

This oxide is a yellowish solid, stable only below −40°C. As the temperature rises, decomposition takes place to give bromine and oxygen. Decomposition at low pressures favors the formation of bromine (I) oxide.

The heat of formation of bromine dioxide has been determined from the reaction $BrO_2(solid) \rightleftarrows \frac{1}{2}Br_2 + O_2$ as −12.5 ± 0.7 kcal/mol. This

[97] E. Zintl and G. Reinacker, *Ber.* **63**, 1098 (1930).
[98] Maxted, *op. cit.*, p. 139.
[99] R. Schwarz and H. Wiele, *J. prakt. Chem.* **152**, 157 (1939).

value is less negative than that for the heat of formation of ClO_2. The reason for the greater instability of BrO_2 is certainly not obvious from its heat of formation.[100]

A white solid analyzing as $BrO_2 \cdot 3NO_2$ is prepared by passing a mixture of oxygen, nitrogen, and bromine through a glow discharge at liquid air temperature and low pressure. The compound is said to be stable up to $-50°C$. At $-40°C$ the compound slowly decomposes to BrO_2 and NO_2. The compound reacts with water, bases, benzene, and ether. Solutions in $CHCl_3$ and acetone are stable to $-30°C$. The same compound is formed by direct addition of NO_2 to BrO_2 at $-40°$. Using similar techniques, no compounds are formed with BrO_2 and CO, SO_2, NH_3, or SeO_2. In each case, the bromine dioxide oxidizes the potential additive. When the bromine is replaced by chlorine in the O_2—N_2—Br_2 system under glow discharge conditions, the compound $NOCl_4$ results. Iodine used in place of bromine yields I_2O_5.[101]

Bromine(VII) Oxide, Br_2O_7. The only evidence for the existence of the heptoxide is a white deposit formed, along with the brown Br_2O, on the low-pressure decomposition of bromine(IV) oxide.

THE OXIDES OF IODINE

The only true oxide of iodine appears to be I_2O_5, the anhydride of iodic acid. Although a number of other oxycompounds have been prepared and studied, none is an oxide in the sense of a single definable oxidation level for the iodine atom. The oxides in which the oxidation level of the iodine atoms would be $+1$ and $+3$ (I_2O and I_2O_3) are unknown in the free state. Only derivatives, such as the sulfates, have been prepared. Evidence for a monoxide, IO, is indicated by the results of spectral studies.[102]

Iodine Pentoxide, I_2O_5. When iodic acid is heated to about $170°C$ the pentoxide is formed by a normal dehydration process:

$$2HIO_3 \rightarrow I_2O_5 + H_2O$$

The pentoxide is a white crystalline material which decomposes at about $300°C$ into iodine and oxygen. A mixture of iodine pentoxide, silicon dioxide, and concentrated sulfuric acid serves as an excellent quantitative oxidizing agent for carbon monoxide even at room temperature. As the oxidant is discharged through use, iodine is liberated.

[100] A. Pflugmacher, R. Schwarz, and H. J. Rabben, *Z. anorg. u. allgem. Chem.* **264**, 204 (1951).

[101] A. Pflugmacher, *Z. anorg. u. allgem. Chem.* **273**, 41 (1953).

[102] E. H. Coleman *et al.*, *Nature* **162**, 108 (1948).

Iodine pentoxide does not oxidize methane at room temperature but does oxidize ethylene and hydrogen sulfide. Nitrogen(II) oxide is oxidized by iodine pentoxide if the latter is activated by trivalent iodine in the form of the sulfate, $I_2(SO_4)_3$.[103]

Diiodine Tetroxide, I_2O_4 (or I_4O_8). The oxide I_2O_4 is a yellow, non-hygroscopic crystalline solid. It is only slightly soluble in water. The thermal decomposition of I_2O_4 is rapid at 135°C:[104]

$$5I_2O_4 \rightarrow 4I_2O_5 + I_2$$

There is no evidence that the iodine atom is in the $+4$ oxidation state in the compound I_2O_4. On the contrary, the evidence is much better for the existence of the $+3$ and $+5$ states. In order for the iodine atom to exist in the trivalent state, it must be stabilized by association with an acid group as is the case in the compounds $I(ClO_4)_3 \cdot 2H_2O$, $I(CH_3COO)_3$, and $(IO)_2SO_4$. When the IO group is combined with the iodate radical, a compound of the molecular formula I_2O_4 is formed. Actually, the latter compound is better described as iodyl iodate, $IO(IO_3)$, than as an oxide, I_2O_4. The most suitable preparation of I_2O_4 is by the action of concentrated sulfuric acid on solid iodic acid. As soon as iodine vapors are noted, the mixture is allowed to cool and is then desiccated for a long period of time. Washing with cold water and alcohol leaves a product analyzing as $(I_2O_4)_n$.[105]

Magnetic susceptibility measurements on the solid by the Gouy technique give a molal value of -76.0×10^{-6} for I_2O_4. The diamagnetic value shows that the monomeric IO_2 unit must not exist in the solid state. The solid must be $(IO_2)_n$, where n is an even number. Assuming the existence of the iodyl iodate, $(IO^+)(IO_3^-)$ model, the molal susceptibility for the iodyl ion is -24.88×10^{-6}.[106]

The compound, I_2O_4, is decomposed by hot water to form iodic acid and iodine. With absolute alcohol the principal decomposition product is I_2O_5. In alkaline and in acid solution, respectively, the following reactions occur:

$$3I_2O_4 + 6OH^- \rightarrow 5IO_3^- + I^- + 3H_2O$$

and

$$I_2O_4 + 8H^+ + 8Cl^- \rightarrow 3Cl_2 + 2ICl + 4H_2O$$

Tetraiodine Enneaoxide, I_4O_9 [or $I(IO_3)_3$]. This substance is probably analogous to I_2O_4 in being a compound of trivalent (I^{+3}) iodine. It

[103] M. Schutze, *Ber.* **77B**, 484 (1949).
[104] R. K. Bahl and J. R. Partington, *J. Chem. Soc.* **1935**, 1258.
[105] M. M. P. Muir, *J. Chem. Soc.* **95**, 656 (1909).
[106] W. K. Wilmarth and S. S. Dharmatti, *J. Am. Chem. Soc.* **72**, 5789 (1950).

is a light-colored powder, and, unlike I_2O_4, it is hygroscopic. It decomposes at 75°C:

$$4I_4O_9 \rightarrow 6I_2O_5 + 2I_2 + 3O_2$$

One method for the preparation of I_4O_9 is similar to one used for making I_2O_4. Concentrated phosphoric acid is added to iodic acid, and, after the appearance of iodine vapors is noted, the product is washed with sulfuric acid and dried. Also, a vapor phase reaction between iodine and ozonized oxygen may be utilized.[107] Lastly, iodine in a suitable solvent is treated with ozonized oxygen. This reaction, however, is still considered to be a vapor phase oxidation of iodine.

The products of the partial hydrolysis of I_4O_9 are strong evidence for the formula $I(IO_3)_3$:

$$3I(IO_3)_3 + 9H_2O \rightarrow 3I(OH)_3 + 9HIO_3$$

Subsequent stages of the reaction with water result in the formation of iodic acid, hydrogen iodide, and iodine:

$$3I(OH)_3 \rightarrow 2HIO_3 + HI + 3H_2O$$
$$5HI + HIO_3 \rightarrow 3H_2O + 3I_2$$

Direct treatment of I_4O_9 with hydrochloric acid results in the formation of iodine monochloride:

$$I_4O_9 + 18HCl \rightarrow 4ICl + 9H_2O + 7Cl_2$$

Diiodinetrioxide, I_2O_3. The sesquioxide, I_2O_3, has never been prepared in the free state. The thermal decomposition of I_2O_5 in the presence of sulfuric acid might be expected to lead to the formation of an acid stabilized oxide I_2O_3 and oxygen: $I_2O_5 \rightarrow I_2O_3 + O_2$; however, the free oxide cannot be isolated.[108] When I_2O_4 is prepared by the action of sulfuric acid on iodic acid, an acid stabilized oxide $I_2O_3 \cdot SO_3$ is formed in small amounts. If the amount of SO_3 in the sulfuric acid is increased to 20 per cent, $I_2O_3 \cdot SO_3$ or $(IO)_2SO_4$ formation is favored. The high SO_3 content is necessary to prevent the further decomposition of I_2O_3. Another crystalline compound, $I_2(SO_4)_3 \cdot H_2SO_4$, has been reported when oleum is used with iodic acid. This substance would be a normal iodine-(III) salt. Good evidence for the formation of I_2O_3 is suggested in the thermal decomposition of I_2O_5 in the presence of fuming sulfuric acid. One mole of oxygen is evolved per mole of I_2O_5, but the formation of iodine is not observed.

---

[107] F. Fichter and H. Kappeler, *Z. anorg. Chem.* **91**, 143 (1915).
[108] I. Masson and C. Argument, *J. Chem. Soc.* **1938**, 1702.

THE OXYACIDS OF THE HALOGENS AND THEIR SALTS

General Considerations.   No oxygen-containing acid of fluorine has ever been definitely established.   The known oxyacids of the other halogens are listed in Table 7.4.

TABLE 7.4.   OXYACIDS OF THE HALOGENS

Oxidation State of the Halogen Atom	Acids of Chlorine	Acids of Bromine	Acids of Iodine
1	HClO	HBrO	HIO
3	HClO$_2$	(HBrO$_2$)	—
5	HClO$_3$	HBrO$_3$	HIO$_3$
7	HClO$_4$	—	HIO$_4$, H$_5$IO$_6$, and H$_4$I$_2$O$_9$

The electronic structures of the chlorine series of acids are given to show the valence orbital electron distribution:

$$H\!:\!\overset{\cdot\cdot}{\underset{\cdot\cdot}{O}}\!:\!\overset{\cdot\cdot}{\underset{\cdot\cdot}{Cl}}\!: \qquad H\!:\!\overset{\cdot\cdot}{\underset{\cdot\cdot}{O}}\!:\!\overset{\cdot\cdot}{\underset{\cdot\cdot}{Cl}}\!:\!\overset{\cdot\cdot}{\underset{\cdot\cdot}{O}}\!: \qquad H\!:\!\overset{\cdot\cdot}{\underset{\cdot\cdot}{O}}\!:\!\overset{\overset{\cdot\cdot}{:O:}}{\underset{\cdot\cdot}{Cl}}\!:\!\overset{\cdot\cdot}{\underset{\cdot\cdot}{O}}\!: \qquad H\!:\!\overset{\cdot\cdot}{\underset{\cdot\cdot}{O}}\!:\!\overset{\overset{\cdot\cdot}{:O:}}{\underset{\underset{\cdot\cdot}{:O:}}{Cl}}\!:\!\overset{\cdot\cdot}{\underset{\cdot\cdot}{O}}\!:$$

Hypochlorous acid	Chlorous acid	Chloric acid	Perchloric acid

Little is known of the actual structures of the unstable classes of acids HXO and HXO$_2$.   The stability of the HXO series decreases in the order HClO, HBrO, and HIO.   The greater stability of the higher oxyacids can be attributed to the formation of multiple bonds, common for chlorine, bromine, and iodine, but nonexistent for fluorine.   It is felt that coordinate bonds are less common for the halogens than was previously thought.[109]   The acids HClO$_2$, HBrO$_3$, and HIO$_3$ show an irregular sequence of stabilities.   The heats of formation are, respectively, 24, 12.5, and 56 kcal.   Iodic acid is thus the most stable, whereas bromic acid is the least stable.   Iodic acid solutions can be concentrated to a point where crystals precipitate.   The maximum concentration attainable for chloric and bromic acids is about 50 mol per cent.   The ions ClO$_3^-$ and BrO$_3^-$ form low pyramids with the halogen atoms at the apex, and an unshared pair of electrons in the fourth tetrahedral position.   The size of the iodine atom contributes to its tendency to coordinate with six

[109] G. M. Phillips, *J. Chem. Soc.* **1945**, 146.

oxygen atoms. The structure of the IO_3^- ion is different from that of either the ClO_3^- or BrO_3^- ion. In fact, the structure of the iodate ion varies, depending on the metal ion with which it is associated. There are 6, 10, and 12 oxygens, respectively, surrounding the iodine atom in the salts $LiIO_3$, $NaIO_3$, and $CsIO_3$. In α-HIO_3 there are discrete IO_3 groups bonded by hydrogen atoms. The oxygens form a distorted octahedron around the iodine atom.

The relative exchange capacity of the halogenates has been determined, using the strongly basic exchange resin Dowex-2, in terms of the equilibrium exchange coefficients. The latter values decrease in the order $ClO_3^- > BrO_3^- > IO_3^-$—that is, in the order of increasing weight

TABLE 7.5. MOLECULAR SUSCEPTIBILITIES OF METAL HALATES*

Cation	Chlorates		Bromates		Iodates	
	Solid	Solution	Solid	Solution	Solid	Solution
NH_4	42.1	42.1	—	—	—	62.3
Li	—	28.8	39.0	38.7	—	46.7
Na	34.7 (33.27)	34.6	44.2	43.3	(51.77)	53.0
K	42.8 (36.81)	—	52.6	—	(64.43)	61.0
Cs	65.0	—	75.1	—	—	83.1
Ca	—	65.0	84.9	84.5	—	101.4
Ca (hydrated)	—	—	97.3	—	—	113.0
Sr	—	73.0	93.5	—	—	108.0
Sr (hydrated)	—	—	—	—	—	122.4
Ba	87.5 (87.74)	85.5	105.8	—	—	122.5
Ba (hydrated)	99.2	—	117.5	—	—	135.0

* Values in parentheses ( ) are those of M. Pascal and D. M. Desai, *Proc. Natl. Inst. Sci., India* 15, 145 (1949).

of the halogenate. The chlorate ion attaches itself more readily than the hydroxide ion, while the BrO_3^- and IO_3^- ions attach themselves to the resin less readily than the hydroxide ion.[110]

The molar susceptibilities of a number of metal chlorates, bromates, and iodates have been determined.[111] The values in Table 7.5 are reported to be accurate to better than 1 per cent for the solids and to better than $\frac{1}{2}$ per cent for the solutions.

There is no stable perbromate, and the perchlorate ion differs markedly from the periodate ion. The instability (in fact nonexistence) of the perbromate ion in constrast to the stability of the IO_4^- and IO_6^{-5} (para-

[110] M. Kikindai, *Compt. rend.* **237**, 250 (1953).
[111] P. Pascal *et al.*, *Bull. soc. chim. France* **1948**, 324.

periodate) ions is in part accounted for by the contribution of $4f$ atomic orbitals in the periodates. The formation of the octahedral[112] IO_6^{-5} ion involves hybridization of d^2sp^3 and/or d^2sf^3 orbitals. The orbitals f^2sp^3 could not be involved. Energy considerations are such that the f contribution of bromine is not likely in forming a BrO_4^- ion.[113]

All perchlorates contain a tetrahedral ClO_4^- ion. Periodates may be derived from the IO_4^- ion or from the IO_6^{-5} ion. The former ion is like the ClO_4^- ion in being tetrahedral, while the IO_6^{-5} ion is octahedral. In the compound $(NH_4)_2H_3IO_6$, the nearly octahedral paraperiodate ions, IO_6^{-5}, are joined by hydrogen bonds. The ratio of oxygen to hydrogen atoms in the ammonium salt is $2:1$. There are sufficient hydrogen atoms to provide a hydrogen bond between every oxygen atom and one other IO_6^{-5} ion. In this respect there is an analogy between $(NH_4)_2H_3PO_6$ and KH_2PO_4.[114]

The Oxyacids of Chlorine and Their Salts. All four oxyacids of chlorine and their salts are considered.

1. *Hypochlorous acid and its salts.* Hypochlorous acid may be formed by the hydrolysis of its anhydride, Cl_2O. The reversibility of the reaction, $H_2O + Cl_2O \rightleftharpoons 2HClO$, is indicated by the strong odor of the oxide above the solution. On heating or on distilling a solution of hypochlorous acid, the oxide is readily liberated. When chlorine is passed into a slurry of yellow mercury(II) oxide, a solution of hypochlorous acid results:

$$2Cl_2 + 2HgO + H_2O \rightarrow HgCl_2 \cdot HgO + 2HClO$$

Some hypochlorous acid is formed when chlorine is bubbled into water:

$$H_2O + Cl_2 \rightleftharpoons HClO + H^+ + Cl^-$$

The reaction may be forced to favor the formation of hypochlorous acid by adding a relatively weak base, such as $CaCO_3$ or $NaHCO_3$, to the solution. The strong acid, HCl, reacts readily with the weak base, but the HClO is too weak to react. The concentration of the solution with regard to HClO is thus favored:

$$2Cl_2 + H_2O + CaCO_3 \rightarrow 2HClO + Ca^{++} + 2Cl^- + CO_2$$

Treatment of a hypochlorite with a weak acid, such as carbonic or boric, produces hypochlorous acid. Bleaching powder serves adequately as a source of the hypochlorite ion. Stronger acids, such as sulfuric and hydrochloric, do not serve in such a capacity since the hydrochloric acid

[112] L. Helmholz, *J. Am. Chem. Soc.* **59**, 2036 (1937).
[113] Z Z. Hugus, *J. Am. Chem. Soc.* **74**, 1076 (1952).
[114] A. F. Wells, *Structural Inorganic Chemistry*, Clarendon Press, Oxford, 1945, p. 272.

formed in, or added to, the system reacts with hypochlorous acid to favor the formation of chlorine:

$$2ClO^- + 2Cl^- + 4H^+ \rightarrow 2H_2O + 2Cl_2$$

This reaction does not take place to any appreciable extent with nitric acid, so it may be used with hypochlorites in the formation of hypochlorous acid. If an aqueous liquor containing an alkali or an alkaline-earth hypochlorite is passed down a heated scrubber or a tower countercurrently to a stream of chlorine and an inert gas, hypochlorous acid vapor passes out the top of the tower:[115]

$$ClO^- + Cl_2 + H_2O \rightarrow Cl^- + 2HClO$$

A solution of hypochlorous acid has a pale golden-yellow color; a very dilute solution is colorless. The maximum concentration attainable is about 5 per cent. The dissociation constant is 1.04×10^{-6} at 30°C.[116] Values of 5.6×10^{-8} at 25°C and 3.8×10^{-8} at 27°C are reported from kinetic studies of the hypochlorite decomposition.[117] A slightly different value of 3.16×10^{-8} is reported from electrometric titrations.[118] The heat of formation of HClO from hydrogen, chlorine, oxygen, and water is 25.8 ± 0.2 kcal.[119] Decomposition into hydrogen chloride, chloric acid, and oxygen takes place on warming and also on exposure to ultraviolet light:

$$2HClO \rightarrow 2H^+ + 2Cl^- + O_2$$
$$H^+ + Cl^- + HClO \rightarrow H_2O + Cl_2$$
$$HClO + 2[O] \rightarrow H^+ + ClO_3^-$$

The decomposition is accelerated by catalysts such as platinum black, manganese dioxide, as well as by the ions of Co, Ni, Cu, and Fe. Hypochlorite solutions are stable to carbon dioxide and the atmosphere if a very small percentage (0.001 to 1 per cent by weight) of an aryl sulfonamide is added. In this way, any hypochlorous acid formed is taken up, thus preventing the transformation noted in the last three equations.

Kinetic data are available on the decomposition of HClO. The mechanism of the decomposition in the presence of a large excess of NaClO (to

[115] C. Carter and E. R. B. Jackson, **Can. 438,018**, Nov. 18, 1946.
[116] J. Høye, *Kgl. Norske Videnskab. Selskabs, Fork.* 14, 1–4 (1941) (in German); 16, 8 (1943).
[117] A. Skrabal and A. Berger, *Monatsh.* 70, 163 (1937); M. W. Lister, *Can. J. Chem.* 30, 879 (1952).
[118] L. Farkas and M. Lewin, *J. Am. Chem. Soc.* 72, 5766 (1950).
[119] J. Weiss, *Trans. Faraday Soc.* 43, 173 (1947).

keep the concentration of HClO essentially constant) is suggested as

$$2HClO \rightarrow 2H^+ + Cl^- + ClO_2^-$$

and

$$HClO + ClO_2^- \rightarrow Cl^- + HClO_3$$

The latter equation expresses the faster step. As the ratio of $[ClO^-]/$ $[HClO]$ increases, the rate constant also increases slightly. This increase is probably due to the reaction represented by

$$HClO + ClO^- \rightarrow ClO_2^- + H^+ + Cl^-$$

The decomposition of HClO to oxygen is first order and is represented by

$$HClO \rightarrow H^+ + Cl^- + \tfrac{1}{2}O_2$$

The velocity constants for the reaction, $2HClO \rightleftharpoons 2H^+ + Cl^- + ClO_2^-$, at 30°C and 40°C are 0.45 and 0.95, respectively. The activation energy for the same reaction is 15.5 ± 0.5 kcal/mol.[120]

The rate of decomposition of HClO in the presence of HCl has also been studied, over a concentration range of 0.1 to 1.2N HCl at room temperature and in the presence of 0.01N H_2SO_4. Initial reaction velocities determined by extrapolation lead to the conclusion that the reaction is second order. The velocity constant for the initial velocity is 0.046.[121]

Hypochlorous acid, as a 0.05M solution ranging from pH 1 to 7 (adjusted by use of H_2SO_4) and with an initial chloride ion concentration ranging from 0 to 4M, decomposes at 25° in accordance with the expression

$$dx/dt = k[Cl^-][ClO^-]^2$$

Any ClO_2^- formed decomposes immediately after its formation. The k values vary from 0.0351 to 0.0467 $(mol/l)^2$ hr^{-1} as the chloride ion concentration varies from 1 to 4M. It is concluded from this variation of k that there is a salt effect as well as an autocatalytic effect of the chloride ion. The ionization of HClO is not taken into consideration in the calculations of k. The ionic strength, μ, of the HClO solution has been varied and velocity constants measured as μ varies. Interpretation of the ionic strength data leads to the conclusion that the primary step involves the action of ClO^- on HClO and not an interaction of ClO^- on ClO^-.[122]

Hypochlorous acid and hypochlorites are strong oxidizing agents (Table 7.6). The same property is shown by all the hypohalites. Calcium

[120] M. W. Lister, *Can. J. Chem.* **30**, 879 (1952).

[121] J. Ibarz Aznárez and J. V. Vinadé, *Anales real soc. espan. fis. y quím.* **49B**, 341 (1953).

[122] Aznárez and Vinadé, *ibid.* **48B**, 653, 673 (1952).

TABLE 7.6. OXIDATION POTENTIALS OF HYPOHALITES

Partial Equations	Cl	Br	I
Acid Solution $H^+ + HXO + e^- \rightarrow \frac{1}{2}X_2 + H_2O$	+1.63	+1.59	+1.45
Basic Solution $XO^- + H_2O + 2e^- \rightarrow X^- + 2OH^-$	+0.94	+0.76	+0.49

hypochlorite may be made up and standardized for use in quantitative analysis as a powerful oxidizing solution. It is stable if it is kept in a dark bottle for protection against light.

Iodine and bromine are oxidized by HClO in aqueous solution to iodates and bromates, respectively. This oxidation is illustrated by the reaction with iodine:

$$I_2 + 5HClO + H_2O \rightarrow 2IO_3^- + 7H^+ + 5Cl^-$$

A second-order reaction occurs between the hypochlorite ion and the bromide ion in the pH range 10–13. The rate of reaction is proportional to the concentration of each of the reactants:

$$HClO + Br^- \rightarrow HBrO + Cl^-$$

This equation represents the rate determining step. There is no measurable oxidation of bromide ion to bromate or bromite under these conditions.[123]

Hypochlorous acid reacts with hydrogen peroxide to form oxygen and the chloride ion. As an intermediate, a peroxyhypochlorous acid is suggested as being formed from hydrogen peroxide and chlorine:

$$H_2O_2 + Cl_2 \rightarrow H^+ + Cl^- + HOOCl$$
$$HOOCl \rightarrow O_2 + H^+ + Cl^-$$

In an HCl solution above $1M$ concentration, the decomposition of HOOCl is the rate determining step. At lower acidity, the slow step is the reaction between hydrogen peroxide and chlorine.[124]

Bleaching powder is essentially a hypochlorite of calcium. Chlorine reacts with slaked lime to form a product smelling of hypochlorous acid. When the absorption of chlorine is complete, powdered lime is blown into the reaction chamber to neutralize any excess chlorine. Ordinary bleach-

---

[123] L. Farkas *et al.*, *J. Am. Chem. Soc.* **71**, 1988 (1949).
[124] R. E. Connick, *J. Am. Chem. Soc.* **69**, 1509 (1947).

ing powder, containing about 35 per cent chlorine, is made in this way. The constitution of bleaching powder has been investigated by x-ray powder photography. Examination in this way was necessary because the crystals resulting from the chlorination of lime are extremely small. No evidence was found for the existence of the mixed chloride-hypochlorite salt represented by the formula, $CaCl(ClO)$. Two substances have been identified in the product, which varies in composition and consists chiefly of $Ca(ClO)_2$ and the compound $CaCl_2 \cdot Ca(OH)_2 \cdot H_2O$. The latter substance is stable, nondeliquescent, and resists chlorination.[125] The commercial product always contains a certain percentage of free lime, calcium chloride, and calcium chlorite. When bleaching powder is exposed to moist air, the series of reactions taking place may be represented by the following equations:

$$Ca(ClO)_2 + 2H_2O \rightarrow Ca(OH)_2 + 2HClO$$
$$HClO \rightarrow HCl + [O]$$
$$Ca(OH)_2 + 2HCl \rightarrow CaCl_2 + 2H_2O$$
$$CaCl_2 + xH_2O \rightarrow CaCl_2 \cdot xH_2O$$
$$HClO + HCl \rightarrow H_2O + Cl_2$$

Sodium and potassium hypochlorite are utilized as bleaches. They are prepared by the direct addition of chlorine to the desired hydroxide, or by the electrolysis of a cold potassium or sodium chloride solution in an iron cell, which serves as the cathode. The anode and cathode products are allowed to mix at low temperatures. Evaporation of sodium hypochlorite solutions results in the precipitation of deliquescent crystals of $NaClO \cdot 6H_2O$, which melt at about 18°C. Hypochlorite solutions themselves may be electrolytically oxidized to chlorate according to the following mechanism:[126]

$$5ClO^- + 8H_2O - 16e^- \rightarrow 3ClO_3^- + 2Cl^- + 2O_2 + 16H^+$$
$$6ClO^- + 3H_2O - 6e^- \rightarrow 2ClO_3^- + 4Cl^- + 3[O] + 6H^+$$
$$2OH^- - 2e^- \rightarrow [O] + H_2O$$
$$ClO^- + 2[O] \rightarrow ClO_3^-$$

Solutions of commercial sodium hypochlorite sometimes show a red-violet coloration due to the presence of iron in quantities ranging from 1 to 6.5 mg/100 g of $NaClO$. The colored solutions are, however, more stable than the purer uncolored ones.[127]

[125] C. W. Bunn, *Chemical Crystallography*, Clarendon Press, Oxford, 1945, p. 124.
[126] A. Rius and J. M. Mari, *Anals fís. y quím.* **41**, 1395 (1945).
[127] G. Curli, *Chimica* **8**, 181 (1953).

Pure calcium hypochlorite, $Ca(ClO)_2$, is prepared by the action of chlorine on calcium hydroxide. Fairly stable crystals of $Ca(ClO)_2 \cdot 4H_2O$ are precipitated on vacuum evaporation of the chlorinated solution of lime water. A dry stable bleach, sold originally as HTH (High Test Hypochlorite), does not contain calcium chloride, which is largely responsible for the chemical instability of the ordinary lime bleach. Sodium hypochlorite whose formation is shown in the stoichiometric equation

$$2NaOH + Cl_2 \rightarrow NaClO + NaCl + H_2O$$

is reacted with the calcium chloride, produced in the chlorine treatment of milk of lime,

$$2Ca(OH)_2 + 2Cl_2 \rightarrow Ca(ClO)_2 + CaCl_2 + 2H_2O$$

so as to eliminate the $CaCl_2$ and form more calcium hypochlorite:

$$NaClO + CaCl_2 \rightarrow Ca(ClO)_2 + 2NaCl$$

Lithium hypochlorite, $LiClO$, is prepared by treating either the sulfate or carbonate with calcium hypochlorite. The product may be obtained essentially free of lithium chloride. A second method of $LiClO$ preparation is from $NaClO$ and $LiCl$. The $NaCl$ is filtered from the more soluble $LiClO$. If a slurry of $LiOH$ is treated with chlorine, a monohydrate, $LiClO \cdot H_2O$, is formed which can be dehydrated at 20–60°C under a pressure of 0.1 atm.[128] In contrast to $NaClO$, which loses about 30 per cent of its available chlorine in 40 days, $LiClO$ was found to lose only about 2 per cent in 53 days.

2. *Chlorous acid, $HClO_2$, and its salts.* Chlorine dioxide reacts with a solution of an alkali to form a chlorite and a chlorate:

$$2OH^- + 2ClO_2 \rightarrow ClO_2^- + ClO_3^- + H_2O$$

Chlorous acid may be formed by reducing chlorine dioxide with hydrogen peroxide:

$$2ClO_2 + H_2O_2 \rightarrow 2HClO_2 + O_2$$

In a neutral aqueous medium, chlorine dioxide dissolves to form a yellow solution which is stable if it is kept cool and away from light. Chlorous acid has never been isolated and exists only in solution. At slightly elevated temperatures, it decomposes into chlorine, chlorine dioxide, and water. The dissociation constant of $HClO_2$ is reported to be 1.01×10^{-2} at 23°C.[129]

---

[128] U. S. **2,384,629**, Sept. 11, 1945; Brit. **581,944**, Oct. 30, 1946.
[129] M. W. Lister, *Can. J. Chem.* **30**, 879 (1952).

The heat of reaction for the formation of $HClO_2$ (aq) from hydrogen, chlorine dioxide, and water is 88 ± 3 kcal:

$$H_2 + 2ClO_2 + 2H_2O \rightarrow 2HClO_2 \cdot H_2O + 88 \pm 3 \text{ kcal}$$

The electron affinity of ClO_2 in forming the chlorite ion in solution is expressed in the following way:[130]

$$ClO_2 + e^- + H_2O \rightarrow ClO_2(H_2O)^- + 120 \pm 5 \text{ kcal}$$

or

$$ClO_2 + e^- \rightarrow ClO_2^- + 2.8 \text{ ev}$$

The fundamental frequencies of the ClO_2^- ion have been determined both for an aqueous solution and for a monocrystal.[131] For the solution the frequencies 396 ± 5 (medium, polarized), 797 ± 5 (strong polarized) were noted; for the crystal 57 ± 3 (strong), 402 ± 3 (strong), 786 ± 2 (very strong), 844 ± 2 (strong), and 1104 ± 3 (weak) were obtained. The symmetrical vibrations ν_1 and ν_2 are assigned to ~790 and 400, respectively. Assuming an angle for $O\!-\!Cl\!-\!O$ of $110°$, the calculation of ν_3 yields 860 and $k_1 = 4.35 \times 10^5$ dynes cm^{-1}, $k\delta/l^2 = 0.53 \times 10^5$ dynes cm^{-1}. These values suggest an assignment of ~840 to ν_3. The value of 400 for ν_2 is in disagreement with a value of 860 previously reported.[132]

The ultraviolet spectrum of highly purified sodium chlorite has been reported.[133] At 2600 A there is an absorption maximum, a minimum at 2400 A, and an inflection at 2800 A. The Lambert-Beer laws hold for concentrations of 3.03 to $5.02 \times 10^{-3}M$. The spectrum of lead chlorite is essentially identical to that of $NaClO_2$. Since the spectrum of ClO_2 is very different from that of $NaClO_2$, the two substances may be detected and estimated in the presence of one another. The spectrum of ClO_2 is considerably more like that of NO_2.

Sodium chlorite, $NaClO_2$, is the best known and most important industrial salt of chlorous acid. It has been in commercial production by leading alkali manufacturers since 1940. Pure chlorites are made on a large scale by the action of alkali and hydrogen peroxide on chlorine dioxide. A cycle is utilized in which a mixture of chlorine dioxide and chlorine is generated from hydrochloric acid and an alkali or alkaline-earth chlorate. The chlorine dioxide is purified first by physical absorption and desorption to remove the chlorine. Then the oxide is

[130] J. Weiss, *Trans. Faraday Soc.* **43**, 173 (1947).
[131] J. P. Mathieu, *Compt. rend.* **234**, 2272 (1952).
[132] C. Duval *et al.*, *Bull. soc. chim. France* **1951**, 745–746.
[133] N. Konopek *et al.*, *Monatsh.* **84**, 214 (1953).

brought into contact with a calcium hydroxide slurry to remove any remaining chlorine. Lastly, the ClO_2 is absorbed in alkali to form a mixture of chlorate and chlorite. The former salt is available for the production of more chlorine dioxide, and the latter may be sold as such or be
used as a source of chlorine dioxide.[134]

Technical grade sodium chlorite comes on the market in the form of
tan flakes which contain 2 to 5 per cent water. The purified grade contains only traces of moisture. The commercial product for large-scale
use has 130 per cent available chlorine; the analytical grade has 153 per
cent available chlorine. The solid is nonhygroscopic. It is stable in
neutral solutions even when they are heated to 150°C. Alkaline solutions decompose on boiling to give a chlorate and chloride:

$$3ClO_2^- \rightarrow 2ClO_3^- + Cl^-$$

This reaction also describes the behavior of the salt when it is heated
above 175°C. Acid solutions liberate chlorine dioxide according to the
following equation:

$$11HClO_2 \rightarrow 4ClO_2 + 4ClO_3^- + 3Cl^- + 7H^+ + 2H_2O$$

A chlorite is more stable than a hypochlorite but is less stable than a
chlorate. Potassium chlorite reacts violently with sulfur, rubber, and
fabrics. It is essential, therefore, that no solid chlorite be allowed to
come into contact with, or a solution of it be allowed to dry on, any
organic material. There is enough sulfur in ordinary vulcanized rubber
stoppers to make their use dangerous in conjunction with sodium chlorite.

The use of sodium chlorite (with chlorine) as a starting material for
the production of chlorine dioxide in the flour milling and fat industries
has already been mentioned. Sodium chlorite bleaches cellulosic fibers
without attacking and degrading them. It bleaches cotton, rayon, nylon,
and paper pulp as wood, rag, or flax; textiles as cotton, linen, nylon,
viscose and acetate rayon; straw, hemp, and wood; shellacs and varnishes;
edible and inedible oils and beeswax—all with a minimum change of
chemical and physical characteristics. It is also used in the kiering of
cotton, the manufacture of starch, and the production of chlorine dioxide.
Sodium chlorite is a nonhygroscopic, crystalline material, extremely soluble in water, and thermally stable up to 150°C. The need for careful
control of concentration, pH, and time is not as acute with chlorite
bleaching as it is with hypochlorite. It is possible to produce a high
strength white kraft paper, instead of the usual brown, by the use of a

[134] Brit. 605,983, Aug. 4, 1948.

chlorite bleach. The lowest grade cotton fiber can be bleached with a chlorite and processed to a high-grade stationery. Other bleaches necessitate the use of the best grade cellulose or expensive cotton clippings and rags. In an alkaline solution, chlorite is a very weak bleach and must be activated by a small amount of hypochlorite. Under these conditions, the solution has the properties of a chlorite and not a hypochlorite.[135] Sodium peroxydisulfate, $Na_2S_2O_8$, is also used as an activator for sodium chlorite in the bleaching of fatty oils, soaps, and waxes.[136]

Lead chlorite, $Pb(ClO_2)_2$, precipitates upon the addition of a solution of lead nitrate to a weakly acidified solution of sodium chlorite. The silver and mercury salts are insoluble and are similarly prepared. Mercury(II) chlorite, $Hg(ClO_2)_2$, dissolves in acids, and these solutions decompose to give $HgCl_2 \cdot HgO \cdot 12H_2O$ on standing. When $Hg(ClO_2)_2$ is heated it is transformed into $HgCl_2 \cdot 4HgO$. The barium salt is obtained from lead chlorite by treatment of the latter with a suspension of barium carbonate.

A dilute solution of chlorous acid results when barium chlorite is treated with sulfuric acid:

$$Ba^{++} + 2ClO_2^- + 2H^+ + SO_4^= \rightarrow 2HClO_2 + BaSO_4$$

When chlorine dioxide and a chlorite are in intimate contact, there is a rapid exchange between the chlorine atoms. The occurrence of this process is proved by the use of radioactive chlorine. It is worthy of note that there is no such exchange between the chlorine atoms of chlorine dioxide and chlorates, perchlorates, free chlorine, or the chloride ion. Hypochlorous acid slowly oxidizes chlorine dioxide to a chlorate, during which reaction there is a slow exchange between the chlorine of ClO_2 and that of $HClO$.[137]

The hypochlorite and chlorite ions react alike in solution with most reagents. However, a violet oxidation product formed by chlorite ions with *o*-phenetidine is insoluble in diethyl ether, while the corresponding oxidation product formed by hypochlorite ions is soluble in this ether.[138]

3. *Chloric acid, $HClO_3$, and its salts.* Two metathetical reactions serve for the preparation of solutions of chloric acid:

I. $\quad Ba^{++} + 2ClO_3^- + 2H^+ + SO_4^= \rightarrow BaSO_4 + 2HClO_3$

II. $\quad 2H^+ + SiF_6^= + 2K^+ + 2ClO_3^- \rightarrow K_2SiF_6 + 2HClO_3$

[135] G. P. Vincent *et al.*, *J. Chem. Educ.* **22**, 283 (1945).
[136] C. A. Hampel, U. S. **2,433,622**, Dec. 30, 1947.
[137] H. Dodgen and H. Taube, *J. Am. Chem. Soc.* **71**, 2501 (1949).
[138] F. Gasser, *Österr. Chem. Ztg.* **50**, 78 (1949).

The concentrated acid is colorless and is stable as long as it is kept cool and in the dark. Its odor is not unlike that of nitric acid. There is no stable anhydride of chloric acid.

Although no intermediate equilibrium constants are available for verification, a mechanism for chlorate formation from hypochlorite is postulated as follows:[139]

$$2HClO \rightleftharpoons Cl_2O_2^= + 2H^+$$

(speed determining steps) $Cl_2O_2^= + (Cl^+Cl^-) \rightarrow$

$$Cl_2O_2^= + Cl_2 \rightarrow Cl_2O_2 + 2Cl^-$$
$$Cl_2O_2 \rightleftharpoons ClO_2^+ + Cl^-$$
$$O^= + ClO_2^+ \rightleftharpoons ClO_3^-$$

The infrared spectrum of potassium chlorate single crystals has been observed.[140] A band between 9.2 and 12μ is interpreted as due to frequencies $\nu_1 = 930$ cm^{-1} and $\nu_2 = 975$ cm^{-1} of the ClO_3^- ion combined with low frequency lattice oscillations.

Some chloric acid results when chlorine water or solutions of hypochlorous acid or sodium hypochlorite are exposed to sunlight. The yields of chlorate are higher if the solutions are heated, or exposed to ultraviolet light, or contain a small amount of hydrochloric acid. The photochemical reaction is reduced when the amount of HCl is increased, or if there are chlorides present. The *initiating* steps for the three starting solutions (Cl_2, HClO, ClO$^-$) just mentioned are:[141]

$$Cl_2 + h\nu \rightarrow 2Cl$$
$$Cl + H_2O \rightarrow H^+ + Cl^- + OH$$
$$OH + Cl_2 \rightarrow ClO + H^+ + Cl^-$$
$$HClO + h\nu \rightarrow Cl + OH$$
$$Cl + HClO \rightarrow ClO + H^+ + Cl^-$$
$$ClO^- + H_2O + h\nu \rightarrow Cl + OH + OH^-$$
$$OH + ClO^- \rightarrow ClO + OH^-$$

A chlorate is formed when clorine is passed into a caustic solution at an elevated temperature. It is assumed that the hypochlorite first formed is further oxidized to chlorate at the high temperature. Calcium chlorate which is low in chloride ion content may be prepared in this way. Calcium chloride, also produced in the reaction, is removed from the solution

[139] E. Abel, *Monatsh.* **82**, 751 (1951).
[140] A. K. Ramdas, *Proc. Indian Chem. Soc.* **35A**, 249 (1952).
[141] K. W. Young and A. J. Allmand, *Can. J. Research* **27B**, 318 (1949).

at a temperature above 35°C by the addition of calcium oxide to precipitate $CaCl_2 \cdot Ca(OH)_2 \cdot H_2O$. In this way the $CaCl_2$ content of the mixture of crystals, $Ca(ClO_3)_2, CaCl_2$, ordinarily obtained is reduced from 31 to 6 per cent.

In the Castner-Kellner type chlorine cell, sodium chlorate may be formed as an undesirable side product:

$$NaClO + 2HClO \rightarrow NaClO_3 + 2HCl$$

The formation of $NaClO$ and $HClO$ is attributed to a secondary reaction in the decomposition of the sodium amalgam.   If the brine source is high in calcium and magnesium ions, the formation of the chlorate ion in the cell is favored.   This condition is the case if the bottom of the anode chamber is not uniformly covered with mercury.[142]   The chlorate formed in an electrolytic caustic cell may be removed by hydrogen reduction if the caustic is to be used in the rayon industry where high purity caustic is essential.   Raney nickel is dispersed in 50 per cent caustic when the chlorate impurity may be as high as 0.1 per cent.   Hydrogen is introduced at 165 lb pressure at 165°C for one hour.[143]

Direct electrolytic production of alkali chlorates is accomplished by electrolyzing a chloride solution at a pH of 6.7 to 6.9.   Best results and yields are obtained at relatively high current densities and high alkali chloride concentrations.   Addition of a few grams of sodium dichromate favors high current efficiency.   The use of magnetite as an anode material decreases efficiencies unless the temperature is raised.   The potential drop is somewhat greater when magnetite is used at low temperatures, but the drop is less pronounced with an increase in temperature.[144]

Potassium chlorate is the most important salt of chloric acid.   It is best prepared from calcium chlorate and potassium chloride.   The solubility of potassium chlorate is only 3.1 g per 100 g of water at 0°C; therefore, it can be crystallized from the reaction mixture of chlorine and hot calcium hydroxide after the addition of potassium chloride.   On heating to moderate temperatures, potassium chlorate decomposes into oxygen and potassium chloride.   This decomposition is catalyzed by the addition of manganese dioxide.   If the heating is carried out carefully to minimize the evolution of oxygen, potassium perchlorate is formed:

$$4KClO_3 \rightarrow 3KClO_4 + KCl$$

In the thermal decomposition of $KClO_3$ according to this equation the

[142] V. La Pietra, *Chim. ind. agr. biol.* **18**, 155 (1942).
[143] T. S. Perrin and R. L. Annis, **Brit. 642,946**, Sept. 13, 1950.
[144] O. E. Salas S., *Bol. soc. chilena quím.* **4**, 43 (1952).

mechanism does not involve a transfer of oxygen from the chlorate to the chloride. Radiochlorine in KCl* in the presence of ordinary $KClO_3$ does not lead to labeled $KClO_4$. During the reaction there is no appreciable exchange between Cl^- and ClO_3^- or between Cl^- and ClO_4^-.[145]

Potassium chlorate is also prepared by passing chlorine into aqueous calcium hydroxide solution containing some $Ca(ClO_3)_2$, $CaCl_2$, and $Ca(ClO)_2$. The resulting reaction mixture containing calcium chlorate and small amounts of calcium hypochlorite and chlorine is treated with $Ca(SH)_2$. The hypochlorite and chlorine are thereby removed. The potassium salt, $KClO_3$, is precipitated by the addition of KCl to the $Ca(ClO_3)_2$ solutions.[146] Potassium chloride has been noted as having an unpredictable but definite effect on the thermal decomposition of potassium chlorate. The previous history of the potassium chloride controls the final product of the decomposition as to whether potassium perchlorate or oxygen is formed. Thus, samples of potassium chloride that are irradiated with weakly radioactive substances, that are prepared from potassium perchlorate decomposition, or that are taken directly from C. P. reagent grade stock have various catalytic effects on either reaction I or II:

$$\text{I.} \quad 2KClO_3 \rightarrow 2KCl + 3O_2$$
$$\text{II.} \quad 4KClO_3 \rightarrow 3KClO_4 + KCl$$

It may be that nascent oxygen is absorbed by certain of the potassium chloride samples. A $KClO_3$—KCl—$KClO_4$ mixture on heating results in the induced formation of $KClO_4$. It is suggested that an equilibrium is established in the various mixtures; that is, potassium perchlorate and chlorate are continuously formed and decomposed.[147]

At high temperatures potassium chlorate is an excellent oxidizing agent. With sulfur or organic material the reaction is explosive. Large amounts of potassium chlorate are used in the manufacture of matches, pyrotechnics, and certain explosive mixtures.

Chloric acid is a powerful oxidizing agent. It reacts explosively with organic matter. When the acid is formed by the direct addition of sulfuric acid to a chlorate, the nature of the reaction depends on the concentration of the acid and of the salt, if the latter be in solution. With 47 per cent $KClO_3$ solution and a drop of 95.5 per cent H_2SO_4, no explosion occurs; but with more dilute acid, there is a violent reaction. The explosion of the decomposition products of $HClO_3$ and the high heat of re-

[145] A. vanden Bosch and A. H. W. Aten, Jr., *J. Am. Chem. Soc.* **75**, 3835 (1953).
[146] E. Eguchi and J. Jinya, **Japan.** 424 ('52), Feb. 13.
[147] A. Glasner and L. Weidenfeld, *J. Am. Chem. Soc.* **74**, 2464 (1952).

action combine in making the reaction a violent one. When chlorine dioxide is added directly to a mixture of sulfur and a chlorate, no explosion occurs until the chlorine dioxide itself decomposes.[148]

The chlorate ion has an anodic effect in electrolytic oxidation even though it practically disappears from the anolyte during electrolysis. Apparently it is readily discharged at the anode and remains combined at the active centers of the electrode surface, thereby reducing the catalytic activity for the reaction $O + O \rightarrow O_2$. Thus the concentration of atomic oxygen is increased around the anode, and hence there is an increase in the oxidizing power and potential at the anode toward the solution. That the chlorate ion is much more effective in this process than is the perchlorate might be expected from the high oxidation level possessed by the chlorine atom in the latter radical.[149]

4. *Perchloric Acid, $HClO_4$, and its salts.* New uses developed during World War II boosted the demands for perchloric acid and perchlorates to new heights. The production capacity during the period 1941–45 was increased from 1000 to 20,000 tons per year in the United States.

One method for the preparation of perchloric acid requires the distillation of a mixture of sulfuric acid and a perchlorate. The reaction is not easily controlled. Anhydrous perchloric acid may be distilled from a mixture of 72 per cent $HClO_4$ and 20 per cent fuming sulfuric acid. The mixture serves as the reaction medium. The distillation is carried out at 1 mm pressure or less. At temperatures from 27 to 75°C the anhydrous acid is obtained in about 75 per cent yield. The product is completely recovered by chilling to dry ice temperature. A similar method is suitable for the preparation of hydronium (oxonium) perchlorate, H_3OClO_4.[150]

A second method for preparing the anhydrous acid is by the action of a mixture of nitric and hydrochloric acids on ammonium perchlorate. Chlorine dioxide, ClO_2, may be oxidized by freshly precipitated lead(IV) oxide hydrate with the ultimate formation of perchloric acid. The ClO_2 results from the autodecomposition of $HClO_3$. The PbO_2 is prepared as a paste with sulfuric acid and mixed with $KClO_3$. The decomposition of $KClO_3$ to ClO_2 takes place and the latter compound then reacts and is oxidized to $HClO_4$. The reaction mixture is refluxed until the $HClO_3$ is no longer in evidence as determined by starch-potassium iodide tests. On filtration and evaporation $KClO_4$ is formed in high yields.[151]

Perchloric acid may be produced by the electrolytic oxidation of hy-

[148] F. Taradoire, *Bull. soc. chim.* 9, 610, 615 (1942).
[149] A. Rius and J. O. Garcia, *Anals fis. y quím.* 40, 886 (1949).
[150] G. F. Smith, *J. Am. Chem. Soc.* 75, 184 (1953).
[151] E. Ott, *Chem. Ber.* 86, 1065 (1953).

rochloric acid using platinum anodes and either silver or copper cathodes. Twenty per cent concentration is possible in the anode compartment:

$$4H_2O + HCl \rightarrow HClO_4 + 8H^+ + 8e^-$$

Evaporation of the anode compartment acid follows to the usual 60 per cent commercial acid.

A common chemical preparation involves the acidification of concentrated sodium perchlorate solution with hydrogen chloride. Sodium chloride is separated by filtration and the filtrate containing $NaCl$, $NaClO_4$, $HClO_4$, and HCl is subjected to fractional distillation to give HCl and $HClO_4$. The concentration and purification of perchloric acid is achieved by further fractionations.[152]

As has been previously mentioned, potassium perchlorate is formed by the controlled thermal treatment of potassium chlorate. The lower solubility of potassium perchlorate over potassium chlorate or potassium chloride permits an easy separation of $KClO_4$ from solution. Chlorates may be oxidized to perchlorates by such agents as sodium bismuthate and peroxydisulfuric acid. The oxidizing agent used must be more powerful than the chlorate.

Sodium and potassium perchlorates are also prepared by the electrolytic oxidation of chlorides in much the same way as chlorates are formed. The highly hygroscopic sodium salt is often not separated as such, but is converted to the slightly soluble ammonium salt by the addition of ammonium chloride to a concentrated solution of sodium perchlorate.

A very high current efficiency is obtained in the electrolytic production of perchlorates through the use of lithium chloride rather than sodium, potassium, or magnesium chloride. This advantage must be related to, though not entirely explainable by, the small ionic radius of the lithium ion and its high heat of hydration.[153]

A mechanism by which perchlorates may be formed from chlorates in an electrolytic process is postulated. The first step is the discharge of the chlorate ion at the anode, $2ClO_3^- \rightarrow 2ClO_3 + 2e^-$, and hydrogen at the cathode, $2H^+ + 2e^- \rightarrow H_2$. The chlorate is then converted to perchloric acid through the intermediate, Cl_2O_6:

$$O_2ClO + OClO_2 \rightarrow O_2Cl-O-O-ClO_2$$

$$O_2Cl-O-O-ClO_2 + HOH \rightarrow O_2ClOOH + O_2ClOH$$

$$O_2ClOOH \rightarrow O_3ClOH$$

[152] J. C. Pernert, U. S. 2,392,861, Jan. 15, 1946; C. L. Mantell, *Industrial Electrochemistry*, McGraw-Hill Book Co., Inc., New York, 3rd Ed., 1949, p. 134.

[153] N. A. Izgaryshev and M. G. Khachaturyan, *Doklady Akad. Nauk, U.S.S.R.* **59**, 1125 (1948).

These reactions may all be summed up as

$$ClO_3^- + H_2O \rightarrow ClO_4^- + H_2$$

in which two Faradays are needed for the conversion. Loss of curren may be accounted for by the following reactions:

$$2Cl^- \rightarrow Cl_2 + 2e^-$$
$$HOH + Cl_2 \rightarrow H^+ + HClO + Cl^-$$
$$2HClO \rightarrow Cl_2 + \tfrac{1}{2}O_2 + H_2O$$

The anodes are made of sheet platinum and are operated at a curren density of 2 amps/sq cm. The sheets are perforated to gain greate contact surface and to eliminate channeling of the flow of electrolyt through the cell. A jacketed mild-steel cathode serves as the electrolyt container. In a typical run the electrolyte solution in a continuous first stage electrolysis contains 600 g/l of $NaClO_3$ at a pH of 6.1 to 6.4. Th perchlorate solution, withdrawn from the cell, contains approximatel 500 g/l of $NaClO_4$ and 90 to 110 g/l of $NaClO_3$. The cell temperature i maintained at 40–50°C. In a second-stage batch electrolysis, the chlorat concentration is lowered to about 5 g/l. Potassium perchlorate is pro duced from purified sodium perchlorate by treatment with KCl. Th product of this process analyzes from 99.0 to 99.5 per cent $KClO_4$. Th addition of sodium chromate or dichromate to the chlorate electrolyt protects the cathode by preventing the formation of hydrogen. An excess chlorate at the end of the electrolysis may be reduced by the addi tion of sulfur dioxide.[154]

Except for $KClO_4$, all the perchlorates crystallize from aqueous solu tion as hydrates. The thermal decomposition of the hydrates may pro ceed by one or the other of the two following mechanisms:

(1) Dehydration followed by decomposition to yield oxygen and chloride:

$$LiClO_4 \cdot 3H_2O \rightarrow LiClO_4 + 3H_2O$$
$$LiClO_4 \rightarrow LiCl + 2O_2$$

(2) Hydrolysis to form perchloric acid and an oxide or hydroxide:

$$Mg(ClO_4)_2 \cdot 6H_2O \rightarrow 2HClO_4 + Mg(OH)_2 + 4H_2O$$

The monohydrate of perchloric acid exists as a hydronium complex $H_3O^+[ClO_4^-]$, according to spectra taken on capillary thickness layers.[15]

[154] J. C. Schumacher, *Trans. Electrochem. Soc.* **92**, 45 (1947).
[155] D. E. Bethell and N. Sheppard, *J. Chem. Phys.* **21**, 1421 (1953).

Perchloric acid is somewhat more stable to organic agents than chloric acid, but violent explosions have occurred upon the slightest percussion. Procedures for the safe handling of $HClO_4$ have been worked out.[156] An explosion in Los Angeles in 1947 involved 150 gallons of perchloric acid and 50–60 gallons of acetic anhydride. Seventeen persons were killed and some 116 buildings were wrecked. It is now recognized that a mixture of perchloric acid and pure acetic anhydride (for use in electropolishing baths) in a ratio of 68 volumes of the former to 32 volumes of the latter has marked explosive characteristics. Mixtures containing less than 55 per cent of perchloric acid by volume are relatively safe to handle. Mixtures of the two components having a density less than 1.50 have no explosive properties. Such a solution may consist of 37 volumes of 65 per cent perchloric acid, 63 volumes of acetic anhydride, and 8 volumes of water. Small traces of organic matter do not increase the danger of explosion in such a system. Massive quantities of such matter would, however, especially if the bath is hot. An obvious precaution is the refrigeration of the bath to prevent loss of acetic acid by volatilization, and thereby the increase of the perchloric acid content to the danger point.[157]

The industrial uses of perchloric acid and potassium perchlorate are numerous and varied. They include the manufacture of explosives and matches; the electropolishing of steel, stainless steel, brass, nickel, copper, and certain other metals; and the bright-dipping of cadmium and zinc plates. The acid is used as a cathode-treating agent in the electrodeposition of copper powder, and as a catalyst in the acetylation of cellulose.

A perchloric acid cell has been designed which permits a relatively high current density to be drawn because of the solubility of the discharge product, $Pb(ClO_4)_2$. The cell contains plated positive plates, metallic negative plates, and aqueous perchloric acid as the electrolyte. The cell operates efficiently at temperatures as low as $-20°C$. The reaction occurring on discharge is:[158]

$$PbO_2 + Pb + 4HClO_4 \rightleftharpoons 2Pb(ClO_4)_2 + 2H_2O$$

Sodium perchlorate is safe to use for weed extermination. A substantial tonnage of the potassium salt is used annually for blasting and in the manufacture of railroad fusees.

[156] "Preliminary Chemical Safety Data Sheet SD-11 on Perchloric Acid Solution," Manufacturing Chemists Assn., Washington, D. C.
[157] A. Jaquet, *Metal Finishing* **47**, No. 11, 62 (1949).
[158] J. C. White *et al.*, *Trans. Electrochem. Soc.* **91**, 73 (1947).

The Oxyacids of Bromine and Their Salts. Both HBrO and HBrO$_3$ are known. Possibly, HBrO$_2$ also exists.

1. *Hypobromous acid, HBrO, and its salts.* The tendency of bromine to hydrolyze is much less marked than for chlorine. The concentration of hypobromous acid in bromine water is thus much lower than hypochlorous acid in a corresponding solution of chlorine water. When bromine water is agitated with mercury(II) oxide, hypobromous acid is formed. With continued addition of mercury(II) oxide to bromine water, the concentration of HBrO may be increased to 6 per cent:

$$2Br_2 + 2HgO + H_2O \rightarrow 2HBrO + HgBr_2 \cdot HgO$$

The acid is very unstable and decomposes readily to the bromide and bromate ions. It is intermediate in stability between hypochlorous acid and hypoiodous acid. Its very weak acid properties show the increasing basic nature of the halogens with increasing atomic weight. The pK value for HBrO is reported as 8.70 at 25°C[159] by electrometric titrations. This value is in poor agreement with the value, 2×10^{-11}, for k_{HBrO} obtained from decomposition rate measurements.[160] Some information on the nature of hypobromous acid is given by studying the hydrolysis of bromine in solutions of soluble silver salts: $Br_2 + H_2O + AgR \rightarrow AgBr + HBrO + HR$ (where R may be acetate, nitrate, sulfate/2, or bromate). The oxidizing power of the resulting solution (in terms of the As$_2$O$_3$ reaction) which is initially (a) molar in bromine, and (b) molar in AgR in an alkaline medium decreases with time. The rate of decrease is greater when R is the anion of a weak acid than when that of strong acid. The pH of the solution also decreases when R is the anion of a weak acid, but remains constant when R is the anion of a strong acid. The rate of decrease is a minimum when $b/a = 1$, increasing with an increasing concentration of the silver ion. The change may be due to the oxidation of BrO$^-$ to BrO$_3{}^-$, the latter ion precipitating as AgBrO$_3$. The dissociation constant determined as a result of these experiments at 15–22°C is given as $1.6 \pm 0.4 \times 10^{-9}$. The kinetics of the BrO$^-$ to BrO$_3{}^-$ oxidation is indicated as initially third order with $k = 800 \pm 100$ at 20°C, but after 6–8 hours reducing to a second order reaction.[161]

The conversion of bromine to hypobromite is nearly complete when bromine is passed into cold concentrated alkali solution:

$$Br_2 + 2OH^- \rightarrow BrO^- + Br^- + H_2O$$

[159] L. Farkas and M. Lewin, *J. Am. Chem. Soc.* **72**, 5766 (1950).

[160] A. Skrabal, *Z. Elektrochem.* **48**, 314 (1942). For a more concordant result with the first, see E. Shilov and J. N. Gladtchikova, *J. Am. Chem. Soc.* **60**, 490 (1938).

[161] G. Sourisseau, *Ann. chim.* **8**, 349 (1953).

Bromine and "dry" calcium hydroxide react to give a product corresponding to bleaching powder. This reaction product yields $HBrO_3$ when treated with nitric acid.

The addition of 90 per cent of the calculated amount of bromine to a 40 per cent sodium hydroxide or to a 53 per cent postassium hydroxide solution at $-5°C$ gives a supersaturated solution of the corresponding alkali hypobromite. On cooling to $-3°C$, 90 per cent pure $NaBrO \cdot 5H_2O$ is formed; on cooling to $-7°C$, 99 per cent pure $NaBrO \cdot 7H_2O$ is formed; and on cooling to $-40°C$, 90 per cent pure $KBrO \cdot 3H_2O$ is formed. The impurities are largely alkali bromides and bromates.[162]

Metal hypobromites are stable, but undergo autoxidation-reduction to bromide and bromate. This reaction is favored by an increase in temperature.

The reactivity of bromide-free hypobromous acid with organic compounds is much greater than is that of free bromine in a mineral acid medium. Such compounds as malic acid, benzene, and benzoic acid are readily brominated by hypobromous acid in fairly strong nitric and sulfuric acids. The reactivity is in accord with the view that the ion Br^+ or $[H_2OBr]^+$ is present as a result of the equilibrium

$$H_3O^+ + HBrO \rightarrow Br^+ + 2H_2O$$

or

$$HBrO + H_3O^+ \rightarrow H_2OBr^+ + H_2O$$

An active brominating solution can be produced by treating bromine water with an ion such as silver(I) or lead(II). In this way the bromide ion is removed from the solution.[163]

2. *Bromous acid, $HBrO_2$, and its salts.* Bromous acid is unknown. There is evidence that in the decomposition of hypobromites some bromite ions are formed:

$$2BrO^- \rightarrow BrO_2^- + Br^-$$

The acid may be present to a small extent in a solution of bromine and silver nitrate.

3. *Bromic acid, $HBrO_3$, and its salts.* Bromic acid is obtained only in solution; the maximum concentration obtainable is 50 per cent. The solution is a colorless liquid and a powerful oxidizing agent. It decomposes readily into oxygen and bromine according to the equation:

$$4HBrO_3 \rightarrow 2H_2O + 2Br_2 + 5O_2$$

---

[162] R. Scholder and K. Kraus, *Z. anorg. u. allgem. Chem.* **268**, 279 (1952).
[163] D. H. Derbyshire and W. A. Waters, *Nature* **164**, 446 (1949).

Potassium and sodium bromates are readily formed by passing bromine into hot solutions of the alkali hydroxides:

$$3Br_2 + 6OH^- \rightarrow 5Br^- + BrO_3^- + 3H_2O$$

This reaction has been used to recover bromine from brines and sea water after chlorine treatment. The difference in solubility between potassium bromide and bromate permits the ready crystallization of the less soluble bromate.

Active oxidizing agents such as hypochlorites, nitric acid, hydrogen peroxide, and chlorine convert bromine or the bromide ion to bromate:

$$6ClO^- + Br_2 \rightarrow 2BrO_3^- + 4Cl^- + Cl_2$$

and

$$3Cl_2 + Br^- + 6OH^- \rightarrow BrO_3^- + 6Cl^- + 3H_2O$$

Silver bromate is unstable. It is easily prepared by the addition of silver nitrate to potassium bromate. Bromic acid can in turn be prepared from silver bromate by adding bromine to a suspension of the latter salt:

$$3Br_2 + 5AgBrO_3 + 3H_2O \rightarrow 5AgBr + 6H^+ + 6BrO_3^-$$

Bromates undergo very vigorous reduction at room temperature by sulfur, selenium, or tellurium in the presence of water.[164] The stoichiometric equation for the reaction with sulfur is:

$$2S + 2KBrO_3 \rightarrow K_2SO_4 + Br_2 + SO_2$$

In the presence of an excess of $KBrO_3$, selenium reacts to yield a solution which contains bromine and the K^+, H^+, Br^-, and $SeO_4^=$ ions.

The heat of reduction with bromide and iodide as well as the heat of solution for $KBrO_3$ have been measured calorimetrically at 25°C. For the last process,

$$KBrO_3 \rightleftarrows K^+ + BrO_3^-$$

the value for ΔH^0 is 9.76 ± 0.05 kcal/mol. For the iodide reduction of $KBrO_3$ in an acid solution,

$$KBrO_{3(c)} + 9I^- + 6H^+ \rightarrow 3I_3^- + K^+ + Br^- + 3H_2O$$

the value for ΔH^0 is −122.26 ± 0.8 kcal/mol. For the bromide reduction of $KBrO_3$,

$$KBrO_3 + 8Br^- + 6H^+ \rightarrow 3Br_3^- + K^+ + 3H_2O$$

[164] F. Taradoire, *Bull. soc. chim.* **12**, 445–450 (1945).

the value of ΔH^0 is -42.17 ± 0.3 kcal/mol. Using these three results and other thermodynamic data,[165] ΔH_f^0 and ΔF_f^0 for the bromate ion are calculated as -18.3 and 2.1 kcal/mol, respectively.[166]

The nature of the thermal decomposition of bromates varies depending on the cation. In contrast to chlorates, there is no evidence for the formation of perbromates. The potassium, mercury, and silver bromates decompose to give bromide ion and oxygen; magnesium, zinc, and aluminum bromates give the metal oxide, bromine, and oxygen; lead(II) and copper(II) bromates give the metal oxide and the bromide ion.[167]

Sulfur reacts with bromic acid to give sulfur monobromide, S_2Br_2. No sulfur dioxide or oxides of bromine are noted in the reaction mixture. The sulfur monobromide reacts with bromates to give bromine and the sulfate ion. Explosive reactions are obtained when sulfur is mixed with potassium bromate, barium bromate, or silver bromate and then treated with sulfuric acid, sulfur dioxide, sulfur monobromide, or bromine. The mixture of sulfur and potassium bromate needs a drop of water before an explosion takes place.[168]

Bromine exchange in the system Br^-—BrO_3^-—$HBrO$ has been studied using $Na^{82}Br$ as a tracer.[169] Solvent (benzene) extraction methods were used to determine bromine concentrations. Three reactions are suggested:

$$HBr + HBrO_3 \rightarrow HBrO_2 + HBrO$$
$$HBr + HBrO_2 \rightarrow 2HBrO$$
$$HBrO + HBr \rightarrow Br_2 + H_2O$$

The bromine-bromate exchange rate is inversely proportional to the concentration of HBrO. The isotopic exchange rate of $Na^{82}BrO_3$ is given by

$$R = k[Br_2]^m[BrO_3^-]^n[H^+]^p$$

where k is 0.023 mol$^{-2.1}$l$^{2.1}$hr^{-1}; m is 0.3 ± 0.05; n is 1.7 ± 0.05; and p is 1.1 ± 0.05.

The Oxyacids of Iodine and Their Salts. Hypoiodous, iodic, and periodic acids and their salts are known.

1. *Hypoiodous acid, HIO, and its salts.* Some hypoiodous acid along with hypoiodite and iodide ions are formed when iodine is dissolved in cold dilute alkali. The solution has oxidizing properties which are lost

[165] F. D. Rossini *et al.*, *Natl. Bur. Standards (U.S.) Circ.* No. **500**, 1266 pp. (1952).
[166] H. C. Mel *et al.*, *J. Am. Chem. Soc.* **75**, 3827 (1953).
[167] Partington, J. R., *A Textbook of Inorganic Chemistry*, Macmillan and Co., Ltd., London, 1937, p. 361.
[168] F. Taradoire, *Bull. soc. chim.* **12**, 93, 97 (1945).
[169] R. H. Betts and A. N. Mackenzie, *Can. J. Chem.* **29**, 655 (1951).

on standing or on heating due to the decomposition of the hypoiodite ion to the more stable iodate ion. Higher concentrations of the acid are attainable by using the method of preparation analogous to that for hypobromous and hypochlorous acids:

$$2HgO + 2I_2 + H_2O \rightarrow HgI_2 \cdot HgO + 2HIO$$

The amphiprotic character of hypoiodous acid is represented by the equilibria: $HIO \rightleftharpoons H^+ + OI^- \rightleftharpoons OH^- + I^+$. The weakness of HIO as an acid is emphasized by the value, 2×10^{-10}, for the ionization constant.[170] The existence of the $[I^+]$ ion is reasonable in view of the fact that a series of salts of the hypothetical base $I(py)OH$ and $I(py)_2OH$ have been prepared (py represents the pyridine molecule). From the behavior of these compounds, there is no doubt but that the iodine is positive and univalent. The following salts have been prepared in the crystalline state: $I(py)NO_3$, $I(py)_2NO_3$, $I(py)_2ClO_4$, and $I(py)OAc$. When dissolved in sodium hydroxide containing potassium iodide, solutions of these salts upon acidification liberate iodine. With potassium chloride and potassium bromide, a reaction takes place with the formation of the interhalogen complexes such as $ICl \cdot py$ and $IBr \cdot py$. Direct treatment of the nitrate with sodium hydroxide liberates the bases $I(py)_2OH$ and $I(py)OH$. These bases are unstable and immediately go to their respective anhydrides, $I(py)_2$—O—$(py)_2I$ and $I(py)$—O—$(py)I$.[171]

2. *Iodic acid, HIO_3, and its salts.* Sodium iodate is found in Chile saltpeter. The acid is best prepared by oxidizing iodine with concentrated nitric acid. Iodic acid is very insoluble in nitric acid and separates as a white solid along with iodine pentoxide during the course of the reaction. Colorless rhombohedral crystals of iodic acid separate if the white solid is dissolved in a minimum of warm water and the solution is cooled:

$$I_2 + 8H^+ + 10NO_3^- \rightarrow 2IO_3^- + 10NO_2 + 4H_2O$$

Iodic acid is highly soluble in water and comparatively stable. At 170°C it decomposes into its anhydride, I_2O_5, and water. It is more stable than either chloric or bromic acid.

Chlorine and potassium chlorate as well as the hypochlorite ion oxidize iodine or the triiodide ion, I_3^-, to iodic acid according to the equations:

$$I_2 + 5Cl_2 + 6H_2O \rightarrow 2IO_3^- + 10Cl^- + 12H^+$$
$$5ClO_3^- + 3I_3^- + 3H_2O \rightarrow 6H^+ + 6IO_3^- + 5Cl^- + 3I^-$$

[170] M. L. Josien and G. Sourisseau, *Bull. soc. chim. France* 1950, 255; *cf.* Ref. 160.
[171] J. Kleinberg, *J. Chem. Educ.* 23 (11), 559 (1946).

and

$$I_2 + 5ClO^- + H_2O \rightarrow 2IO_3^- + 5Cl^- + 2H^+$$

Three potassium salts are known. They are the normal salt, KIO_3, the monobasic salt, $KH(IO_3)_2$ (extensively used both as an acid and oxidizing primary standard in volumetric analysis); and the dihydrogen salt, $KIO_3 \cdot 2HIO_3$ or $KH_2(IO_3)_3$. There is no evidence for periodate formation when these salts are thermally decomposed. Potassium iodate thermally decomposes into the iodide and oxygen. Calcium iodate, on the other hand, decomposes into calcium oxide, iodine, and oxygen.

The oxidizing character of iodic acid is pronounced. It bleaches litmus shortly after turning it red. The iodide ion is converted to iodine. Two half reactions best show the iodide ion and then iodine to be the reduction product of iodic acid:

$$5H^+ + HIO_3 + 6e^- \rightarrow I^- + 3H_2O$$
$$3(2I^- \rightarrow I_2 + 2e^-)$$
$$\overline{}$$
$$5H^+ + HIO_3 + 5I^- \rightarrow 3I_2 + 3H_2O$$

Sulfur dioxide and hydrogen sulfide are oxidized to sulfate and sulfur, respectively, by iodic acid. The oxidizing action of the solid acid with charcoal, phosphorus, sulfur, and organic material is vigorous.

The exchange of iodine atoms between iodine and iodate using ^{131}I as a tracer in solutions of $HClO_4$ and $LiClO_4$ follows the equation

$$R = k[I_2]^{0.6}[IO_3^-]^x[H^+]^y[H_2O]^z$$

where x is 0.80 at varying $[IO_3^-]$ and constant $[H^+]$ concentrations, and y is 1.8 at constant $[IO_3^-]$ and varying $[H^+]$ concentrations.[172]

3. *The periodic acids and their salts.* Periodic acid may be formed by the electrolytic oxidation of iodic acid; however, it is more conveniently formed when chlorine is passed into a 10 per cent sodium hydroxide solution containing iodine. A white precipitate of sodium paraperiodate, $Na_2H_3IO_6$, is formed:

$$3I_2 + 6OH^- \rightarrow IO_3^- + 5I^- + 3H_2O$$
$$2Na^+ + IO_3^- + 3OH^- + Cl_2 \rightarrow Na_2H_3IO_6 \downarrow + 2Cl^-$$

To this suspension of the paraperiodate, boiling silver nitrate is added to form a black precipitate of silver dimesoperiodate, $Ag_4I_2O_9$. The salt is suspended in water and subjected to a current of chlorine. The silver is

[172] R. E. Connick and Z Z. Hugus, Jr., *Brookhaven Conf. Rept.* BNL-C-8 *Chem. Conf. No.* 2164–70 (1948).

converted to insoluble silver chloride, which is removed by filtration. The filtrate is concentrated on a water bath at 60–70°C, and finally desiccated over calcium chloride. Monoclinic deliquescent crystals of the paraperiodic acid, H_5IO_6, are formed. After standing there is evidence of ozone formation by this substance. The thermal decomposition of disodium paraperiodate proceeds according to the equation:

$$4Na_2H_3IO_6 \rightarrow 4Na_2O + 2I_2 + 6H_2O + 7O_2$$

The para acid, H_5IO_6, is partially converted to the meta acid, HIO_4, by vacuum desiccation below 100°C. In addition to the meta acid, dimesoperiodic acid, $H_4I_2O_9$, is also formed in the desiccation. The disilver paraperiodate, $Ag_2H_3IO_6$, behaves as if it were a hydrated salt of the dimesoperiodic acid, $Ag_4I_2O_9 \cdot 3H_2O$, since three molecules of water are readily lost from the former according to the following equation:[173]

$$2Ag_2H_3IO_6 \rightarrow Ag_4I_2O_9 \cdot 3H_2O \xrightarrow{\text{heat}} Ag_4I_2O_9 + 3H_2O$$

Metaperiodic acid coordinates with Nb_2O_5 and Ta_2O_5 to form heteropoly acids of the formulas, $Nb_2O_5 \cdot 2HIO_4 \cdot 8H_2O$ and $Ta_2O_5 \cdot 2HIO_4 \cdot 2H_2O$. The coordination number of iodine in these complexes is 6. All the compounds are acid to litmus and liberate iodine from KI with the addition of further amounts of acid. Similar heteropoly acids are formed with iodic acid.[174] A copper(III) complex is also known, $Na_7[Cu(IO_6)_2] \cdot 20H_2O$.[175]

A study of the phase diagram of Ag_2O—HIO_4—H_2O at 35°C shows the existence of three silver salts. A deep black crystalline powder of composition $5Ag_2O \cdot I_2O_7$ exists in aqueous solution containing I_2O_7 in the concentration range between 0.00 to 0.065 per cent; chocolate brown crystals which turn deep red, when powdered, of composition $2Ag_2O \cdot I_2O_7$ between 0.065 and 50.83 per cent I_2O_7; and deep yellow $Ag_2O \cdot I_2O_7$ between 50.83 and 63.80 per cent I_2O_7.[176]

A very comprehensive study of the various silver periodates formed by precipitation at various pH values has been reported. When silver nitrate is added at 17°C to buffered solutions of alkali periodates, Ag_5IO_6 (brown-black) is precipitated at pH > 3. At 2 < pH < 3, $Ag_2H_3IO_6$ (lemon-yellow) is precipitated initially but a transformation takes place

[173] J. R. Partington and R. K. Bahl, *J. Chem. Soc.* **1934**, 1086.
[174] D. Sen and P. Rây, *J. Indian Chem. Soc.* **30**, 250 (1953).
[175] M. W. Lister, *Can. J. Chem.* **31**, 638 (1953).
[176] B. P. Gyani, *J. Phys. Colloid Chem.* **55**, 1111 (1951).

eversibly to Ag_5IO_6 in the presence of excess silver ion. At the temperaure of 58°C the following precipitations take place at the pH values adicated:

Compound	pH
Ag_5IO_6	>3.1
Ag_5IO_6 and $Ag_3H_2IO_6$(black) (mixed crystals)	$>1.9 < 3.1$
$Ag_3H_2IO_6$	$>1 < 1.9$
$Ag_2H_3IO_6$	<1

Vhen $Ag_2H_3IO_6$ is heated to 58°C in contact with solutions with pH = 1, he compound is transformed irreversibly into $Ag_2H_3IO_6$. At 15°C \gIO_4(orange), which is stable only in contact with very strong HNO_3, ransforms irreversibly (in 2-7N HNO_3) into $Ag_2H_3IO_6$ which in turn ransforms irreversibly into Ag_2HIO_5(vermilion). At 60°C this transiion occurs in 1N HNO_3. The compound Ag_5IO_6, from all observations nade on the nature of the precipitates and pH of solutions from which the salt is precipitated, is pentabasic and not a salt represented by the ormula $AgIO_4 \cdot 2Ag_2O$.[177]

The $H_4IO_6^-$ ion is prepared by the action of iodate on a base in the presence of elemental chlorine as represented by the equation

$$IO_3^- + H_2O + 2OH^- + Cl_2 \rightarrow H_4IO_6^- + 2Cl^-$$

In a potassium hydroxide medium a mixture of KH_4IO_6 and $K_2H_3IO_6$ is ormed unless the $K^+ : H_4IO_6^-$ ratio is 4 or greater.[178] Potassium metaperiodate, KIO_4, is prepared according to the following reactions:

$$2KIO_3 + 2Cl_2 + 6KOH \rightarrow K_4I_2O_9 + 4KCl + 3H_2O$$
$$K_4I_2O_9 + 2HNO_3 \rightarrow 2KIO_4 + 2KNO_3 + H_2O$$

The products of the second reaction are separated by fractional crystallization.[179]

The formula of solid potassium periodate is perhaps better represented as a dimeso salt, $K_4I_2O_9$, than as KIO_4 (the metaperiodate), in spite of the fact that in solution there is no evidence for the $I_2O_9^{-4}$ ion.[180] Barium paraperiodate, $Ba_5(IO_6)_2$ is stable and is prepared by heating barium

[177] P. Souchay and A. Hessaby, *Bull. soc. chim. France* 1953, 599.
[178] A. A. Bombelli, *Anales assoc. quim. Argentina* 39, 3–10 (1951).
[179] Staff Report, *Ind. Eng. Chem.* 42, 9 (1950).
[180] P. Souchay, *Bull. soc. chim. France* 1948, 463.

iodate to redness:

$$5Ba(IO_3)_2 \rightarrow Ba_5(IO_6)_2 + 4I_2 + 9O_2$$

An interesting periodate is a complex in which Ni(IV) is present. The oxidation of a solution containing nickel(II) sulfate and an alkali-metal periodate with an alkali-metal peroxysulfate yields a salt as $Na[Ni(IO_6)]$ The bonds between Ni and O, and I and O are said to be chiefly covalent.[181]

Raman spectra[182] of aqueous solutions of $NaIO_4$ and H_5IO_6 are reported and give some information as to the structure of each, and the equilibrium between the two substances. Sodium metaperiodate $NaIO_4$, exhibits lines at 791 cm^{-1} (A_1), 853 (F_2), 256 (F), and 325 (F_2) These lines are expected of an XY_4^- type molecule of symmetry T_h plus one extra line at 636 cm^{-1}. The molecule H_5IO_6 exhibits the same four lines shown by $NaIO_4$ plus those at 632 (A_{1g}), 594 (E_g), and 387 (F_{2g}) The last three lines are those expected for an octahedral molecule of symmetry O_h. It may be concluded from these data that there is an equilibrium,

$$H_5IO_6 \rightleftharpoons IO_4^- + H^+ + 2H_2O$$

with a K equilibrium value of 2.3×10^{-2}. The structure of the H_5IO_6 molecule is postulated to be $(HO)_5I \rightarrow O$, with the iodine atom having 12 electrons in its outer shell. The IO_4^- ion is assumed to be a resonant molecule with an average valence of 1.5 for the oxygen atoms. Force constants for the two molecules are $f_{(IO_4^-)} = 5.73$ millidynes/A and $f_{(H_5IO_6)} = 3.69$ millidynes/A.[182]

Magnetic susceptibility measurements of the periodates and periodic acid indicate that in the solid state and in solution, H_5IO_6 exists as $HIO_4 \cdot 2H_2O$. This formulation need not be considered as being contrary to the chemical properties exhibited by H_5IO_6. The magnetic susceptibilities of KIO_4, $Na_2H_3IO_6$, and H_5IO_6 are -66.7×10^{-6}, -70.3×10^{-6}, and -71.4×10^{-6}, respectively.[183]

The values for the activity dissociation constants, K_a' and K_a'', of H_5IO_6 at various temperatures are noted in Table 7.7. The values of K_a' and K_a'' are calculated from the dissociation constants K_c' and K_c'' which are, in turn, defined by $[H^+][H_4IO_6^-]/[H_5IO_6]$ and $[H^+][H_3IO_6^-]/[H_4IO_6^-]$, respectively. The third dissociation constant of H_5IO_6 is

[181] P. Rây and B. Sarma, *Nature* **157**, 627 (1946).
[182] H. Siebert, *Z. anorg. u. allgem. Chem.* **273**, 21 (1953).
[183] S. L. Aggarwal and S. J. Singh, *J. Indian Chem. Soc.* **22**, 158 (1945).

eported as 2.5×10^{-13}. The fourth and fifth dissociation constants are oo small to be measured by potentiometric methods.[184]

The periodic acids and their salts are powerful oxidizing agents. The oxidation of manganese(II) ion or manganese dioxide to permanganate is eadily accomplished by KIO_4 in an acid solution. Advantage is taken of his reaction in the colorimetric determination of manganese in steel or ores. When periodic acid and fluorine react, water is first removed from he acid, and HF, O_2, and some OF_2 are formed. With a short reaction ime, oxygen difluoride formation is favored. As the reaction progresses, $_2O_5$ is formed and finally, at 250°C, iodine pentafluoride, IF_5, is formed.[185]

TABLE 7.7. ACTIVITY DISSOCIATION CONSTANTS OF H_5IO_6*

Temperature °C	$K_a' \times 10^8$	$K_a'' \times 10^9$
10	5.89	9.77
20	6.17	9.77 (9.8 maximum at 15°C)
30	6.31 (maximum)	9.55
40	6.17	9.12
50	6.03	8.51

* N. F. Ivanova and M. B. Neiman, *Doklady Akad. Nauk. U.S.S.R.* **60**, 1005 (1948).

The oxidizing capacity of periodates and periodic acid is indicated in their reaction with polyhydric organic compounds.[186] Potassium periodates, KIO_4 and $K_4I_2O_9$, oxidize glycerol completely in a period of less than three minutes. The $K_4I_2O_9$ is more effective due to its greater solubility over that of KIO_4. The kinetics of the oxidation of α-glycol, $(CH_2OH)_2$, suggest that the reaction mechanism includes a singly charged cyclic intermediate.[187]

$$\left[\begin{array}{c} CH_2{-}O \\ | \\ | \\ CH_2{-}O \end{array} \quad IO_4H_2 \right]^{-}$$

The kinetics of the reaction represented by

$$5IO_4^- + I_2 + H_2O \rightarrow 7IO_3^- + 2H^+$$

[184] P. Souchay and H. Hessaby, *Bull. soc. chim. France* **1953**, 614.
[185] G. H. Rohrback and G. H. Cady, *J. Am. Chem. Soc.* **70**, 2603 (1948).
[186] L. Hartman, *J. Appl. Chem.* **3**, 308 (1953).
[187] G. J. Buist *et al.*, *Research* **6**, Suppl. No. 1, 45–55 (1953).

follow the equation

$$\frac{d(IO_4)}{dt} = \frac{-d[I_2]}{dt} = 1.37 \times 10^7 \cdot (10)^{\sqrt{\mu}} \cdot A \cdot [IO_4^-][I_2] \cdot [H^+]^{\frac{1}{2}}$$
$$\times e^{-19,000/RT} \text{ mol } l^{-1}t$$

where μ is the ionic strength, and A is a constant dependent upon th dielectric constant of the medium. A is equal to 1 where solutes ar absent that appreciably change the dielectric constant of water. In a acetic acid-acetate buffer solution, the activation energy of the iodide periodate reaction falls to 12,000 cal/mol and the equation followed is

$$\frac{d[IO_4^-]}{dt} = 2.1 \times 10^9 [IO_4^-][I^-] e^{-12,000/RT} \text{ mol } l^{-1}t^{-1}$$

at $\mu = 0$.[188]

[188] D. Peschanski, *J. chim. phys.* **48**, 489 (1951).

CHAPTER 8

POSITIVE HALOGENS, INTERHALOGEN, AND POLYHALIDE ANIONIC COMPLEXES

POSITIVE HALOGENS

The electronegativity of the halogens, as stated, decreases with tomic weight, and their electromerism

$$X_2 \rightleftharpoons X^+ + X^-$$

ncreases in the same order. In fluorine, the electropositive character is educed to a minimum. The so-called "hypofluorites" (pp. 28, 31), such s FNO_3 and $FClO_4$, are gaseous compounds in which the fluorine is nked by highly covalent bonds to the oxygen atom. There is little kelihood that any ionic forms of positive fluorine will ever be isolated. he electropositive character is probably most pronounced in astatine. he positive character of the halogens in oxycompounds (with the possible xception of fluorine) is well established. Although the stability of the ree X^+ ion in solution must be extremely low,[1] a mechanism of the haloenation of organic compounds by either the free element or a hypohalite nvolves its use. The mechanism for chlorination by the Cl^+ ion from IClO is claimed to be inconsistent with kinetic data. Thus, the rate aw for the reaction between HClO and sodium alkyl sulfonates shows no lependence on the hydrogen ion concentration. Hence, the equilibrium

$$HClO + H^+ \rightleftharpoons Cl^+ + H_2O$$

nust be of little or no consequence.[2]

Exchange resins have been utilized to accomplish the exchange of H^+ vith I^+ of INO_3 and Br^+ of $BrNO_3$.[3] It is suggested that these positive ıalogens are stabilized on the resin. A typical procedure in the fixation ıf I^+ is to pass a solution of 0.5 g of iodine in 100 ml of absolute alcohol hrough Amberlite IR100H resin.

$$H^+ + Res^- + I_2 \rightarrow I^+ \, Res^- + HI$$

[1] Ph. Fresenius, *Angew. Chem.* **64**, 470 (1952).
[2] E. A. Shilov, *Doklady Akad. Nauk, S.S.S.R.* **84**, 1001 (1952); P.B.D. De la Mare *t al., Research* (London) **3**, 192, 242 (1950).
[3] H. Brusset and T. Kikindai, *Compt. rend.* **232**, 1840 (1951); T. Kikindai and M. Cassel, *ibid.* **232**, 1110 (1951).

The formation of HI causes a measurable decline in the pH of the solution. The amount of positive iodine in the resin is determined by passing a saturated solution of KI through the exchange column and titrating the liberated iodine with thiosulfate:

$$I^+ \, Res^- + KI \rightarrow K^+ \, Res^- + I_2$$

Approximately 0.02 to 0.03 g of I^+ is said to be fixed upon the resin by this method. Solutions of I_2SO_4 and INO_3 are obtained by passing a solution of H_2SO_4 and of HNO_3, respectively, in absolute alcohol through the exchanger containing the positive, I^+, ion. The salts of positive iodine and bromine may be prepared from the corresponding acid if the solutions are completely anhydrous and the activity of the hydrogen ion is great enough to effect the change.

Electrolytic-cell reactions have been used to prove the ionic migration of the Br^+ ion. A solution of HBrO is placed in the middle compartment of an electrodialyzing apparatus having sodium fluoresceinate solution in the electrode compartments. The formation of eosin after prolonged electrolysis is suggested as proof of the migration of the positive halogen.[4] In highly acid solutions of HBrO, eosin is formed in the cathode compartment; and in an alkaline solution, eosin is formed in the anode compartment. It is claimed that the eosin formation in acid medium is due to the electrophoretic migration of the Br^+ ion and not to simple diffusion. Studies on the I^+ and Cl^+ by similar techniques are inconclusive. If the Br^+ ion does exist in highly acid solution, its concentration is likely to be less than 10^{-10}.[5]

Equilibrium constants have been calculated for the two reactions represented by the following equations:

$$X_2(aq) \rightleftharpoons X^+(aq) + X^-(aq) \qquad (I)$$

and

$$H_2O(liq) + X_2(aq) \rightleftharpoons X(H_2O)^+(aq) + X^-(aq) \quad (II)$$

When X is Cl, Br, and I, respectively, the K values for reaction (I) are reported as 10^{-60}, 10^{-50}, and 10^{-40}. For reaction (II) and the same sequence of halogens the values of K are 10^{-30}, 10^{-20}, and 10^{-10}, respectively. It is again concluded that the species X^+ does not exist in appreciable quantities in aqueous solution. The hydrated ion, as $I(H_2O)^+$, may however exist in larger concentrations. The free energy of ionization of iodine at 25°C is reported as 15 kcal/mol, a value in agreement with the

---

[4] K. Gonda-Hunwald *et al.*, *Magyar Kém. Folyóirat* **56**, 203 (1950); *Nature* **166**, 68 (1950).

[5] F. Korosy and G. Szekely, *Nature* **168**, 77 (1951); *Magyar Kem. Folyóirat* **57**, 110 (1951).

ree energy calculated for the reaction

$$I_2 + H_2O \rightleftharpoons I(H_2O)^+ + I^-$$

The I^+ waves have been characterized in a voltametric study of the oxidation of iodide ion at the rotating platinum electrode.[6] The half-wave potentials *vs.* the saturated calomel electrode in $HClO_4$, dilute HCl, 0.05M HCN + 0.1M $HClO_4$, and 0.1M pyridine in a pH 6 buffer are +1.1 v, +0.75 v, +0.5 v, and +0.56 v, respectively.

When iodine[7] dissolves in water, a variety of reactions probably takes place. A few are represented by the following equilibria:

$$I_2 + H_2O \rightleftharpoons H_2OI^+ + I^- \qquad (1)$$
$$H_2OI^+ + H_2O \rightleftharpoons HOI + H_3O^+ \qquad (2)$$
$$3HOI + 3H_2O \rightleftharpoons IO_3^- + 2I^- + 3H_3O^+ \quad (3)$$
$$I_2 + I^- \rightleftharpoons I_3^- \qquad (4)$$

The formation of hydrated I^+ ion is favored by reducing the I^- concentration, a condition which would, however, repress the forward reaction of (4). The equilibrium constants of reactions (1) and (2) are reported as $\times 10^{-11}$ and 3×10^{-2}, respectively. It must be emphasized that the cation present is not the simple I^+ but a hypoiodous acidium ion, H_2OI^+.[8]

The positive character of certain of the combined halogens has been definitely established.[9] Hypoiodous acid has the properties of a very labile base, IOH, as substantiated by the preparation of a number of salts of the hypothetical bases IpyOH and $Ipy(OH)_2$. There seems to be no doubt that the iodine exists in the unipositive state in these compounds.[10]

Among the crystalline compounds of $I(py)^+$ are $I(py)NO_3$, $I(py)_2NO_3$, $(py)_2ClO_4$, $I(py)_2C_2H_3O_2$, as well as a series of $I(py)^+$ salts of some thirty organic acids.[11] The reactions of these salts indicate that the halogen is unipositive. All the salts liberate free iodine from acidified potassium iodide solutions. A number of the reactions of $I(py)_2NO_3$ are summarized. Other salts of this type behave in a similar fashion:

a. Hydrolysis proceeds slowly:

$$I(py)_2NO_3 + HOH \rightarrow I(py)OH + py \cdot HNO_3$$
$$5I(py)OH \rightarrow 2I_2 + py \cdot HIO_3 + 2H_2O + 4py$$

[6] I. M. Kolthoff and J. Jordan, *J. Am. Chem. Soc.* **75**, 1571 (1953).

[7] H. Carlsohn, *Über eine neue Klasse von Verbindungen des positiv einwertigen Iods.*, Verlag, J. Hirzel, Leipzig (1932).

[8] R. P. Bell and E. Gelles, *J. Chem. Soc.* **1951**, 2734–2740.

[9] J. Kleinberg, *J. Chem. Educ.* **23**, 559 (1946).

[10] H. Carlsohn, *Angew. Chem.* **46**, 747 (1933); *Ber.* **68**, 2209 (1935).

[11] R. Zingaro, J. Goodrich, J. Kleinberg, and C. Vander Werf, *J. Am. Chem. Soc.* **1**, 575 (1949).

b. Treatment with sodium hydroxide gives the bases I(py)OH an
I(py)$_2$OH. These bases revert to their respective anhydrides and may
be isolated as such:

$$2I(py)_2OH \rightarrow I(py)—O—I(py) + HOH$$

c. Reaction with phenol produces iodophenols:

$$C_6H_5OH + 3I(py)_2NO_3 \rightarrow C_6H_2I_3OH + 3HNO_3 + 6py$$

d. Noble metals are dissolved by chloroform solutions of the iodine
pyridine complexes:

$$3I(py)_2NO_3 + Au \rightarrow Au^{+3} + 3NO_3^- + 3/2I_2 + 6py$$

The results of this reaction are in agreement with the position of I$^+$ in th
electromotive force series. According to the position occupied by I$^+$ i
should oxidize noble metals.[12]

e. Electrolysis of I(py)$_2$NO$_3$ in chloroform or methanol produce
iodine at the cathode:

$$I^+ + 1e^- \rightarrow \tfrac{1}{2}I_2$$

Interhalogens, as iodine chloride and iodine bromide, contain uni
positive iodine, as is evidenced by hydrolysis followed by autoxidatio
reactions.[13] Electrolysis of cyanogen halides likewise gives evidence fc
a positive cyano as well as a positive halogen ion.[14]

Numerous compounds of tripositive iodine (other than interhalogens
have been prepared. The following table includes several of these com
pounds and their preparation.[15]

TABLE 8.1. SOME COMPOUNDS OF IODINE(III)*

Compound	Method of Preparation
IPO$_4$	I$_2$ + H$_3$PO$_4$ + (CH$_3$CO)$_2$O + concentrated HNO$_3$
I(COOCCl$_3$)$_3$	I$_2$ + CCl$_3$COOH + (CH$_3$CO)$_2$O + fuming HNO$_3$
I(COOCHCl$_2$)$_3$	I$_2$ + CHCl$_2$COOH + (CH$_3$CO)$_2$O + fuming HNO$_3$
I(COOCH$_2$Cl)$_3$	I$_2$ + CH$_2$ClCOOH + (CH$_3$CO)$_2$O + fuming HNO$_3$
I(COOCH$_2$Br)$_3$·I(IO$_3$)$_3$	I$_2$ + CH$_2$BrCOOH + (CH$_3$CO)$_2$O + fuming HNO$_3$
I(SO$_3$CH$_3$)$_3$	I(COOCH$_3$)$_3$ + CH$_3$SO$_3$H
I(COCCl$_3$)$_3$·I(IO$_3$)$_3$	I$_2$ + CCl$_3$COOH + O$_3$

* J. Kleinberg, *J. Chem. Educ.* **23**, 561 (1946).

These iodine-containing compounds have limited thermal stability
Their hydrolysis is illustrated by that of the phosphate, IPO$_4$:

$$5IPO_4 + 9H_2O \rightarrow I_2 + 3HIO_3 + 5H_3PO_4$$

[12] V. Finkelstein, *Z. physik. Chem.* **124**, 285 (1926).
[13] K. J. Orton and W. L. Blackmann, *J. Chem. Soc.* **77**, 830 (1900).
[14] R. H. Clark and H. R. L. Streight, *Trans. Roy. Soc. Canada* **3**, 22, 323 (1928).
[15] J. Kleinberg, *J. Chem. Educ.* **23**, 561 (1946).

Electrolysis of iodine (III) acetate yields iodine in strict conformance with Faraday's laws, and thereby gives further proof of the tripositive state of iodine. Tripositive iodine in certain polyhalide complexes is considered later.

General Considerations. The differences in electronegativity among members of the halogen family make possible the combination of one halogen with another to form an interesting series of compounds known as the interhalogens. The strong oxidizing action of fluorine, as well as the small size of the fluoride ion, results in an extensive series of halogen fluorides, certain members of which have commercial potentialities. No interhalogens in which more than two halogens are combined have been prepared. The maximum number of covalently bound atoms in the interhalogen series increases with the size of the oxidized atom. The maximum values are three for chlorine, five for bromine, and seven for fluorine. Only one atom of the heavier (less electronegative) halogen is present. Combinations of halogens and halide ions are also common.

Figs. 8.1 and 8.2 relate graphically the boiling and melting points of the interhalogens with their respective molecular weights. The free halogens are included for comparison.[16] The melting and boiling points of each member of the AB class are intermediate between those of the two free halogens involved.

The structures of the interhalogens are difficult to determine for several reasons. Electron diffraction measurements do not locate fluorine atoms because of their low refraction. The extreme reactivity and instability of most of the interhalogens preclude measurements. The purity of most of the interhalogens is also questionable.

The order of treatment of the interhalogens is according to the ratio in which the halogen atoms are combined—AB, AB_3, AB_5, and AB_7.

Type AB. The members of this group are iodine monochloride, ICl, iodine monobromide, IBr; bromine monochloride, BrCl; chlorine monofluoride, ClF; and bromine monofluoride, BrF. They can all be prepared by mixing equimolecular portions of the respective halogens. The reaction between iodine and chlorine goes to completion but mixtures of iodine and bromine, as well as those of bromine and chlorine, form equilibrium mixtures which do not favor the interhalogen compound formation. Bromine monofluoride and iodine monofluoride have never been isolated and only impure samples of bromine monochloride have been produced

---

[16] E. Fessenden, *J. Chem. Educ.* **28**, 619 (1951).

by fractional distillation of chlorine and bromine mixtures at low temperatures.

The interhalogen molecules of the AB type are linear with interatomic distances being approximately equal to the average of the two elements involved.[17]   The absorption spectra of the molecules ClF, ICl, and IBr have been reported and all three spectra have similar forms.

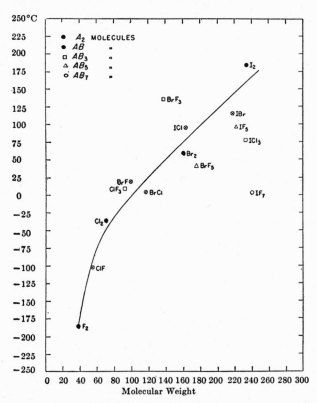

FIG. 8.1.   Boiling points of the interhalogen compounds.
From J. Chemical Education, 28(12), 619 (1951).

Classification and characterization of interhalogens are possible using as a basis their relative Lewis acid strength.   Acid strength decreases in the order

$$\text{ICl} \gg \text{BrCl} > \text{IBr} \gg \text{I}_2 > \text{Br}_2 \gg \text{Cl}_2$$

The halogens are included for comparison.   The classification agrees with

[17] C. M. Beeson and D. M. Yost, *J. Am. Chem. Soc.* **61**, 1432 (1939).

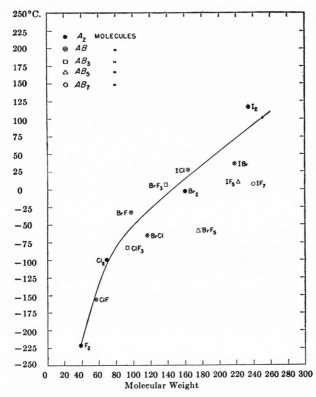

FIG. 8.2.   Melting points of the interhalogen compounds.
From J. Chemical Education, 28(12), 619 (1951).

TABLE 8.2.   FREE ENERGIES OF TRIHALIDE FORMATION FROM THE
AB + X⁻ → ABX⁻ REACTION

Base → Acid	$\Delta F°$ in Kcal/Mol at 25°		
	$I^-(aq)$	$Br^-(aq)$	$Cl^-(aq)$
ICl(aq)	−11.6	−5.9	−3.02
BrCl(aq)	—	(−3.8)*	?
IBr(aq)	−8.85	−3.49	−2.23
I₂(aq)†	−3.89	−1.46	−0.44
Br₂(aq)†		−1.67	−0.19
Cl₂(aq)†			+2.7

* Uncertain because the value depends upon an estimate of the standard free energy
of a solution of BrCl(aq).
† The halogens are included for comparison with interhalogens.

relative acidities from measurements on halogen complexes with aromatic hydrocarbons.

Thermodynamic data are reported[18] for the complex formation of certain of the interhalogens of the AB class according to Lewis acid-base reactions: $AB + Aq \rightleftarrows AB(aq)$ and $AB + X^- \rightleftarrows ABX^-$. Tables 8.2 and 8.3 include the ΔF^0 of several of these reactions.

TABLE 8.3. FREE ENERGIES OF COMPLEX FORMATION IN THE ACID-BASE REACTIONS $AB(g) + X^- \rightarrow ABX^-(Aq)$ AND $AB(g) + Aq \rightarrow AB(Aq)$

Base → Acid	ΔF^0 in Kcal/Mol at 25°C			
	$I^-(aq)$	$Br^-(aq)$	$Cl^-(aq)$	$H_2O(liq)$
$ICl(g)$	−14.3	−8.6	−5.7	−2.7
$BrCl(g)$	—	−5.78	?	(−2.0)
$IBr(g)$	−10.66	−5.30	−4.04	−1.81
$I_2(g)*$	−4.59	−2.16	−1.14	−0.70
$Br_2(g)*$		−1.44	+0.04	+0.226
$Cl_2(g)*$			+4.4	+1.65

* Halogens are included for comparison.

From the free energy data of Tables 8.2 and 8.3, the nonexistence of trihalide ions in which one or both of the outside atoms is heavier than the central atom is explainable. The free energies are given for the isomerization equilibria:

$$\Delta F^0, \text{kcal}$$
$$[I\text{—}Br\text{—}Cl]^-_{(aq)} \rightarrow [Br\text{—}I\text{—}Cl]^-_{(aq)} \qquad -16$$
$$[I\text{—}Br\text{—}Br]^-_{(aq)} \rightarrow [Br\text{—}I\text{—}Br]^-_{(aq)} \qquad -18$$
$$[I\text{—}Cl\text{—}Cl]^-_{(aq)} \rightarrow [Cl\text{—}I\text{—}Cl]^-_{(aq)} \qquad -32$$
$$[Br\text{—}Cl\text{—}Cl]^-_{(aq)} \rightarrow [Cl\text{—}Br\text{—}Cl]^-_{(aq)} \qquad -14$$

In each case, the free energy favors the forward "reaction."

A summary of some thermodynamic data on interhalogens of the class AB at 298.16°K is given in Table 8.4.[19]

1. *Iodine monofluoride, IF.* As already stated this compound has never been isolated. Evidence for IF is reported[20] from the spectrum of methyl iodide burning in an atmosphere of fluorine. The spectrum from this source is identical to that arising when fluorine gas is caused to

[18] R. L. Scott, *J. Am. Chem. Soc.* **75**, 1551 (1953).

[19] L. G. Cole and G. W. Elverum, Jr., *J. Chem. Phys.* **20**, 1543 (1952); data also given to 2000°K.

[20] R. H. Durie, *Proc. Phys. Soc.* (*London*) **63A**, 1292 (1950).

TABLE 8.4. SUMMARY OF THERMODYNAMIC DATA ON INTERHALOGENS
OF THE CLASS AB

Interhalogen	C_p^0 Cal Mol^{-1} Deg^{-1}	Entropy, S^0 Cal Mol^{-1} Deg^{-1}	Free Energy $-(F^0 - E_0^0)/T$ Cal Mol^{-1} Deg^{-1}	Heat Constant $(H^0 - E_0^0)/T$ Cal Mol^{-1} Deg^{-1}
ClF	7.669	52.080	44.936	7.143
BrF	7.869	54.703	47.474	7.229
IF	7.996	56.454	49.155	7.293
BrCl	8.384	57.339	49.783	7.556
ICl	8.492	59.123	51.468	7.655
IBr	8.721	61.752	53.809	7.943

impinge on the surface of iodine crystals. A detailed study of the red-degraded spectral bands (from 4300 to beyond 6900 A) leads to the conclusion that the IF band system arises from the corresponding states in the IF molecule. There is a distinct similarity between the rotational structure of the IF spectrum and the $^3\pi_0^+ \leftarrow {}^2\Sigma$ system of ICl.

2. *Iodine monochloride, ICl.* This compound is prepared in solution from potassium iodate, potassium iodide, and concentrated hydrochloric acid:

$$6H^+ + IO_3^- + Cl^- + 4e^- \rightarrow ICl + 3H_2O$$
$$2(I^- + Cl^- \rightarrow ICl + 2e^-)$$

$$6H^+ + IO_3^- + 3Cl^- + 2I^- \rightarrow 3ICl + 3H_2O$$

Any iodate or iodide in excess at the end of the reaction is titrated with dilute iodide or iodate solution, respectively, to attain a stoichiometric ratio of the reactants. The solution of iodine monochloride is commonly used as a catalyst in the oxidation of arsenic(III) oxide by cerium(IV) sulfate.

Iodine monochloride is known to exist in two allotropic modifications. The alpha or stable modification takes the form of red cubic needles, melting at 27°C to a dark red oily liquid. A second and less stable beta modification appears as red-brown, rhombic, six-sided plates melting at 14°C. On direct combination of the elements, a dark red liquid forms which solidifies to the beta form. On standing the more stable alpha form results. Either alpha or beta crystals may separate from a mixture of chlorine and iodine below 14°C, depending upon whether alpha or beta seed crystals are added. On cooling to −10°C, the beta form is obtained. At the boiling point of ICl (97°C), only the alpha form may exist. The parachor of iodine monochloride is reported as 135.83, a value expected of a compound of the formula ICl.[21]   The molecular dipole moment of the molecule ICl is approximately 0.65×10^{-18} esu as determined from intensity measurements.   The bond in ICl appears to be about 8 per cent ionic.[22]

Iodine monochloride reacts with the elements potassium, aluminum, and white phosphorus with explosive violence to form chlorides.   (See also Tables 8.5 and 8.6).   The elements Mg, Ge, S, Ca, Ba, Ni, Cu, Ag, Bi, Se, Co, Ni, Zn, red P, Fe, Sn, Ti, As, Sb, and Te react with ICl to form chlorides with increasing intensity in the order named.   Heat is required to cause a reaction with Au, Hg, In, V, and Mn.   The elements Cd, B, C, Si, Pb, Zr, Nb, Ta, Cr, Mo, W, and Pt do not react with ICl.[23]

Iodine monochloride reacts by disproportionation with acetamide according to the equation

$$CH_3CONH_2 + ICl \rightarrow CH_3CONH_2\text{-}ICl \rightarrow (CH_3CONH_2I^+) + Cl^-$$

Under the stress of an electric current the acetamide moves to the cathode and the reaction occurring at this electrode is

$$(CH_3CONH_2I^+) + e^- \rightarrow CH_3CONH_2 + I$$

The general tendency of ICl to react with acid amides to form complexes is shown by viscosity isotherms, coefficients of viscosity, cryoscopic, and conductivity physicochemical data.[24]   The reactions appear to take place in the amide form rather than in the tautomeric imide form.   Other amide complexes reported are $PhCONEt_2 \cdot ICl$, $(PhCONEt_2I)^+(ICl_2)^-$, and $(PhNHAc \cdot I)^+(ICl_2)^-$.

A disproportionation of ICl also occurs with pyridine.   During electrolysis of a pyridine solution of iodine monochloride, the reactions occurring at the electrodes are:[25]

$$2(C_5H_5NI)^+ + 2e^- \rightarrow 2C_5H_5N + I_2$$

and

$$2Cl^- \rightarrow Cl_2 + 2e^-$$

Although iodine monochloride is used as an iodinating reagent for organic compounds, there is always some chlorination.   The latter reaction may be minimized by removing the hydrogen chloride as it is formed or by the proper choice of solvents for a reaction medium.

[21] C. P. Agarwal, *Z. physik. Chem.* **200**, 302 (1952).
[22] C. E. Townes *et al.*, *Phys. Rev.* **73**, 1334 (1948).
[23] V. Gutmann, *Z. anorg. u. allgem. Chem.* **264**, 169 (1951).
[24] Ya. A. Fialkov and I. D. Muzyka, *J. Gen. Chem. U.S.S.R.* **21**, 905 (1951).
[25] *Ibid.*, **18**, 802, 1205 (1948); **19**, 1416 (1949).

The solvent plays an important role in controlling whether chlorination or iodination takes place. Solvents of high dielectric constant favor a homolytic fission of bonds. Salicylic acid (solid) undergoes chlorination by ICl vapor; in carbon tetrachloride the reaction is largely iodination, whereas in nitrobenzene the reaction is exclusively iodination.[26]

Iodine monochloride undergoes exchange reactions with organic halides. The reaction mechanism suggested for the formation of benzyl halides (RCH_2X) is

$$RCH_2X + ICl \rightarrow RCH_2X \cdot ICl$$

followed by

$$RCH_2X \cdot ICl + ICl \xrightarrow[k_1]{\text{slow}} \text{various benzyl halides} + IX$$

The latter is the rate determining step,[27] following the rate law $d(IX)/dt = k_1(RCH_2X)(ICl)$. With isopropyl iodide the reaction is represented by

$$(CH_3)_2CHI + 2ICl \rightarrow C_3H_6ICl + I_2 + HCl$$

Iodine monochloride may be hydrolyzed in two ways, with the formation of either hypoiodous acid or iodic acid. As is expected from the unit positive charge on the iodine, iodine monochloride is an oxidizing agent. The reduction product may be either iodine or iodide ion, depending on the strength of the reducing agent:

$$ICl + 2e^- \rightarrow I^- + Cl^-$$
$$ICl + 1e^- \rightarrow \tfrac{1}{2}I_2 + Cl^-$$

The conductivity of ICl at several temperatures is shown in Table 8.5. It will be noted that the value of k falls with rise in temperature after a maximum value is reached over the 50–70°C range. This behavior is probably due to the dissociation of iodine monochloride into iodine and chlorine and the formation of ICl_3. A maximum has also been reported at 40°C with a slightly different value of 4.64×10^{-3} ohm^{-1}cm^{-1}. The degree of ionization is in the order of 1 per cent at 35°C.[28]

The electrolysis of iodine monochloride in nitrobenzene, using a silver electrode, indicates that both the chlorine and iodine are deposited at the anode—chlorine in the amount of 1.5 equivalents per faraday and iodine in less than one equivalent per faraday. The concentration of the unipositive iodine atom decreases as evidenced by the test $ICl_2^- + KI \rightarrow$

[26] F. W. Bennett and A. G. Sharpe, *J. Chem. Soc.* **1950**, 1383.
[27] R. N. Keefer and L. J. Andrews, *J. Am. Chem. Soc.* **75**, 543 (1953).
[28] M. N. Greenwood and H. J. Emeléus, *J. Chem. Soc.* **1950**, 987.

TABLE 8.5. CONDUCTIVITY OF IODINE MONOCHLORIDE*

Specific Electrical Conductance $(k) \times 10^3$ $(ohm^{-1}cm^{-1})$	Temperature, °C
4.52	35
4.70	40
5.14 (maximum)	50–70
4.75	80
4.16	90
3.49	97

* Ya. A. Fialkov and O. I. Shor, *J. Gen. Chem. U.S.S.R.* 18, 14 (1948).

$KCl + I_2 + Cl^-$. Some potassium is deposited at the cathode. The existence of the ion ICl_2^- has been proved by transference studies of ICl and KCl mixtures in nitrobenzene. Iodine monochloride in aluminum chloride gives a complex of the formula $I^+[AlCl_4]^-$. The aluminum atom is part of the anion and the iodine is deposited at the cathode under the stress of an electrical current.[29]

The spectrum of ICl (as well as IBr) is entirely one of continuous bands and atomic lines, most of which are identical with those of iodine. Discrete bands of iodine and chlorine are absent from the excited spectrum.[30] The origin of certain of the continuous bands arising from the emission spectrum of ICl (and IBr) is explained as being due to transitions from stable electronic states to a number of repulsive states. The latter arise from a combination of normal and $^2P_{\frac{1}{2}}$ excited states of the individual halogen atoms.

The system $SbCl_5$—ICl shows enhanced conductivity due to the ionization $ISbCl_6 \rightleftharpoons I^+ + SbCl_6^-$. Addition of KCl to equimolecular proportions of $SbCl_5$ and KCl reduces the conductivity to a minimum. Addition of further quantities of KCl gives a marked increase in conductivity due to the formation of $KICl_2$. The following equilibrium is suggested:[31]

$$I^+[SbCl_6]^- + K^+[ICl_2]^- \rightleftharpoons KSbCl_6 + 2ICl$$

Conductometric titrations are possible in iodine monochloride as a solvent using $SbCl_5$ and related chlorides as acids and alkali metal chlorides as bases. Among the neutralizations reported are $SbCl_5$—RbCl; $NbCl_5$—KCl; VCl_4—KCl; $TiCl_4$—CsCl; $SnCl_4$—NH_4Cl; $AlCl_3$ and $SiCl_4$—KCl. The neutralization curves indicate that the reaction proceeds by the formation of ionized compounds with the solvent, as $I^+ SbCl_6^-$

[29] Ya. A. Fialkov and Ya. K. Koganskaya, *J. Gen. Chem. U.S.S.R.* 11, 910 (1941); 18, 289 (1948); 19, 235 (1949).
[30] R. K. Asundi and P. Venkateswarlu, *Indian J. Phys.* 21, 76 (1947).
[31] V. Gutmann, *Research* 3, 337 (1950).

nd Rb^+ ICl_2^-, which in turn react to give the neutral salts. The solvent properties of ICl also make it useful in the preparation of certain salts, as $KSbCl_6$ by heating $SbCl_5$ and KCl in an iodine monochloride medium. Excess solvent is easily removed from a reaction mixture by extraction with carbon tetrachloride.[32]

3. *Iodine monobromide, IBr.* The solid-liquid curves for the system iodine-bromine indicate a continuous series of solid solutions (similar to the bromine-chlorine system); however, at 50 mol per cent, the curves meet, indicating the existence of a compound, IBr.[33] A further indication of compound formation is the increase in the dielectric constant of iodine from 3.082 to 3.724 when bromine is added. The density of the mixture increases from 3.1135 to 3.1855 on standing. The heat of formation of $IBr_{(g)}$ is low, as expected, 2.30 kcal.

Iodine monobromide crystals have the color of solid iodine. They melt at 42°C, forming a nearly black liquid boiling at 116°C. Vapor of IBr appears red and is partially dissociated (8 per cent at 25°C). In carbon tetrachloride solution IBr is dissociated to about 9.5 per cent.[34]

Iodine monobromide reacts rapidly with phenol with the immediate evolution of hydrogen bromide and the appearance of an iodine color. Half the oxidizing power of IBr disappears at the completion of the reaction, and half the bromine (but no iodine) enters the aromatic nucleus. The reaction of IBr with aniline appears to involve the thermal decomposition of IBr followed by the fast reaction between bromine and aniline. A slower reaction then occurs between iodine and aniline.[35]

Iodine monobromide added to certain polymers, such as starch, appears to incorporate itself into the polymer to form a linear polymeric molecule. Absorption spectra and diffraction data indicate straight chains of halogen atoms. The I-Br bond distance is 2.90 A, a value less than that found for unbound or free IBr (3.90 A). The former value is greater than the distance for single intramolecular bonds (2.70 A). It is probable that the IBr molecule is directly bonded in the polymer by forces weaker than single covalent bonds but stronger than van der Waals forces.[36]

Table 8.6 includes several physical constants of iodine monobromide in both the gaseous and solid states at 25°C.[37]

[32] V. Gutmann, *Z. anorg. u. allgem. Chem.* **264**, 151 (1951).
[33] P. C. E. Meerum-Terwagt, *Z. anorg. Chem.* **47**, 209 (1905).
[34] D. M. Yost, *J. Am. Chem. Soc.* **55**, 552 (1933).
[35] A. G. Sharpe, *J. Chem. Soc.* **1953**, 3713.
[36] C. D. West, *J. Chem. Phys.* **17**, 501 (1949).
[37] J. McMorris and D. M. Yost, *J. Am. Chem. Soc.* **53**, 2630 (1931).

TABLE 8.6. THERMODYNAMIC CONSTANTS OF IODINE MONOBROMIDE

Substance	Reference Substances	Free Energy	Heat Content	Entropy	Heat of Sublimation
$IBr_{(g)}$	$I_{2(g)}$, $Br_{2(g)}$	−1790	−1270	60.6	—
$IBr_{(g)}$	$I_{2(s)}$, $Br_{2(l)}$	903	9963	—	—
$IBr_{(s)}$	$I_{2(s)}$, $Br_{2(l)}$	ca. −1830	2470	ca. 31.8	12,433
$IBr_{(g)}$	$I_{(g)}$, $Br_{(g)}$	−36,105	−41,570	60.6	—

Iodine monobromide behaves as an acid in an iodine solution, as illustrated by the neutralization reaction:

$$IBr + KI \xrightarrow{I_2} KBr + I_2$$
$$\text{acid} \quad \text{base} \quad \text{solvent} \quad \text{salt} \quad \quad \text{solvent}$$

In the molten state, IBr acts as a solvent. The conductivity of IBr is reported as 4.0 to 7.23 × 10^{-6} ohm^{-1} cm^{-1} at 55°C. The alkali (except Li) and ammonium bromides are good conductors; molybdenum(V), tungsten(II), antimony(III), zinc, and aluminum bromides are moderately good conductors. Niobium(V), tantalum(V) bromides, iodine monochloride, and thionyl chloride are nonconductors. The reaction in which the compound PBr$_5$·IBr functions as a base in IBr solvent is

$$PBr_5 \cdot IBr \xrightarrow{IBr} PBr_4^- + IBr_2^+$$

The reactions represented by

$$2MIBr_2 + SnBr_4 \xrightarrow{IBr} M_2SnBr_6 + 2IBr$$

and

$$2MIBr_2 + I_2SnBr_6 \rightarrow M_2SnBr_6 + 4IBr$$

(where M may be K$^+$, NH$_4^+$, Rb$^+$, or Cs$^+$) are illustrative of neutralizations carried out in IBr as a solvent.[38] Very few acids would be expected in the iodine monobromide system due to the general instability of complex bromides. The chlorides and bromides of the heavier alkali metals are basic anhydrides in the solvent IBr (and in ICl), while the corresponding tin, antimony, and phosphorus halides behave as acid anhydrides. The ionization of IBr and two metal bromide reactions with IBr are

[38] V. Gutmann, *Monatsh.* **82**, 156 (1951).

represented by the equations

$$2IBr \rightleftharpoons I^+ + IBr_2^-$$
$$RbBr + IBr \rightleftharpoons Rb^+ IBr_2^-$$
$$SnBr_4 + IBr \rightleftharpoons (I^+)_2 SnBr_6^=$$

The behavior of a large number of elements in IBr as well as ICl and I_2 is described in Table 8.7.

4. *Bromine monochloride, BrCl.* The definite existence of red-yellow bromine monochloride was proved in 1928 by spectrophotometric measurements. Bromine-chlorine phase curves are not indicative of compound formation unless the existence of a partially dissociated compound is assumed since the three substances are of the same type. A continuous

TABLE 8.7. BEHAVIOR OF ELEMENTS IN THE SOLVENTS I_2, ICl, AND IBr

Element	Solubility or Compound Formed* in		
	I_2	ICl	IBr
Na		NaCl	NaBr
K		$KICl_2$	KBr-$KIBr_2$
Cu	insol.	$CuCl_2$	$CuBr_2$
Ag	insol.	AgCl	AgBr
Au		$AuCl_3$	$AuBr_3$
Mg	insol.	$MgCl_2$	$MgBr_2$
Ca		$CaCl_2$	$CaBr_2$
Ba		$BaCl_2$	$BaBr_2$
Zn	insol.	$ZnCl_2$	$ZnBr_2$
Cd	insol.	insol.	insol.
Hg		$HgCl_2$	$HgBr_2$
B		insol.	insol.
Al	AlI_3	$AlCl_3$	$AlBr_3$ (?)
In		$InCl_3$ (?)	(surface react.)
Ti		$TiCl_4$	$TiBr_4$ (?)
Zr		insol.	insol.
C		insol.	insol.
Si		insol.	insol.
Ge		$GeCl_4$ (?)	$GeBr_4$ (?)
Sn	SnI_4	$SnCl_4$	$SnBr_4$
Pb	insol.	insol.	insol.

* Underlined compounds formed in yields equal to or greater than 50 per cent.

TABLE 8.7.—*Continued*

Element	Solubility or Compound Formed* in		
	I_2	ICl	IBr
V		VCl_3	VBr_3
Nb		insol.	insol.
Ta		insol.	insol.
P		PCl_5	PBr_5-$PBr_5 \cdot IBr$
As	AsI_3	$AsCl_3$	$AsBr_3$
Sb	SbI_3	$SbCl_5$	$SbBr_3$
Bi	BiI_3	$BiCl_3$	$BiBr_3$
Cr	insol.	insol.	insol.
Mo		insol.	insol.
W		insol.	insol.
S	soluble	S_2Cl_2 (?)	S_2Br_2 (?)
Se	soluble	$SeCl_4$ (?)	$SeBr_4$ (?)
Te	soluble	$TeCl_4$	$TeBr_4$
Mn		$MnCl_2$	$MnBr_2$
Fe	FeI_3	$FeCl_2$-$FeCl_3$	$FeBr_2$
Co		$CoCl_2$	$CoBr_2$
Ni	insol.	$NiCl_2$	$NiBr_2$
Pt	insol.	insol.	insol.

series of solid solutions is possible in the system bromine-bromine mono-chloride-chlorine.[39] Additional evidence for compound formation in a mixture of bromine and chlorine is noted in the fact that the mixture reacts with unsaturated acids and esters more rapidly than either elementary chlorine or bromine.

It is doubtful that physical data can be accurately reported since, at ordinary temperatures, the compound is constantly changing into its elements. The boiling point is about 5°C and the melting point about $-54°$C.[40] A solid hydrate, $BrCl \cdot 4H_2O$, of moderate stability is reported as separating when chlorine is passed into bromine under water.[41]

Some thermodynamic data are available for bromine monochloride.[42]

[39] B. J. Karsten, *Z. anorg. Chem.* **53**, 365 (1907); C. R. Lebeau, *Compt. rend.* **143**, 589 (1906); K. H. Butler and D. McIntosh, *Proc. Nova Scot. Inst. Sci.* **17**, 23 (1927).
[40] H. Lux, *Ber.* **63**, 1156 (1930).
[41] S. A. Ullah, *J. Chem. Soc.* **1932**, 1176.
[42] A. I. Popov and J. J. Mannion, *J. Am. Chem. Soc.* **74**, 222 (1952).

'he dissociation of BrCl in carbon tetrachloride is reported as 43.2 ± 1 er cent. The K equilibrium value for the reaction represented by

$$2BrCl \rightleftharpoons Br_2 + Cl_2$$

n CCl_4 is 0.145 ± 0.0006. For the system

$$\tfrac{1}{2}Br_{2(CCl_4)} + \tfrac{1}{2}Cl_{2(CCl_4)} \rightarrow BrCl_{(CCl_4)}$$

he values of $\Delta H^0{}_{298}$, $\Delta F^0{}_{298}$, and $\Delta S^0{}_{298}$ are -312 cal, -572 cal, and $+0.872$ cal/deg mol, respectively.

The complex equilibrium constants of molecules of bromine, chlorine, nd bromine monochloride over a wide temperature range are given in Table 8.8. The values are theoretical calculations from vapor pressure lata of the bromine-chlorine system.

TABLE 8.8. COMPLEX EQUILIBRIUM CONSTANT OF THE
BROMINE-CHLORINE SYSTEM*

	K_{298}	K_{500}	K_{1000}	K_{2000}	K_{3000}
BrCl → $\tfrac{1}{2}$Br$_2$ + $\tfrac{1}{2}$Cl$_2$	0.13	0.22	0.33	0.40	0.42
Br$_2$ → 2Br	4.74×10^{-29}	2.22×10^{-15}	3.27×10^{-5}	4.934	304
BrCl → Br + Cl	2.99×10^{-34}	1.439×10^{-18}	6.70×10^{-7}	0.793	68.74
Cl$_2$ → 2Cl	1.17×10^{-37}	1.97×10^{-20}	1.46×10^{-7}	0.519	87.6

* K. V. Butkow, *Rec. trav. chim.* **67**, 551 (1948).

5. *Chlorine monofluoride, ClF.* When fluorine is subjected to a spark lischarge in the presence of chlorine at room temperature, more than one product is produced:

$$Cl_2 + 2F_2 \rightarrow ClF + ClF_3$$

If the volume ratio is one to one, the predominant product is chlorine nonofluoride. Unless moisture is carefully avoided in the reaction vessel, an explosion is likely. Either a flame-heated silica tube or an oil-heated copper container is a suitable reaction vessel. Purification is achieved by fractional condensation and distillation of the products. Cooling them to -95 to $-105°C$ removes both excess chlorine and chlorine trifluoride. Final condensation is achieved in a trap at $-150°C$. Excess fluorine (bp $-188°C$) passes through this trap. Chlorine monofluoride is a colorless gas with an odor different from either fluorine or chlorine. At $-154 \pm 0.5°C$, the gaseous chlorine monofluoride (bp $-100.8°C$) condenses to a yellowish liquid. In the temperature range -150 to $-105°C$, the vapor pressure follows the relationship:

$$\log p = 15.738 - 3109/T + 1.538 \times 10^5/T^2$$

The calculated critical temperature of the monofluoride is about $-14°C$, and the latent heat of vaporization is 2.27 kcal per mol.[43]

The heat of reaction for $\frac{1}{2}F_2 + \frac{1}{2}Cl_2 \rightarrow ClF$ is 15 ± 0.5 kcal (exothermic) as computed from the two reactions:

$$NaCl + ClF \rightarrow NaF + Cl_2 + 24.5 \pm 0.1 \text{ kcal } 18°C$$

and

$$NaCl + \tfrac{1}{2}F_2 \rightarrow NaF + \tfrac{1}{2}Cl_2 + 39 \pm 0.5 \text{ kcal } 18°C$$

A lower value for the heat of formation of chlorine monofluoride as determined by direct combination of the elements is reported as 11.6 ± 0.4 kcal.[44] From the band spectrum, the heats of dissociation of chlorine monofluoride are 60.3 ± 0.5 or 58.9 ± 0.5 kcal, respectively, depending on whether the optical transition leads to excited fluorine and normal chlorine or to excited chlorine and normal fluorine.[45]

The bond energy for ClF, calculated from the general formula $\frac{1}{2}(A—A)$ $+ \frac{1}{2}(B—B)$ where A—A and B—B are the bond energies of the individual halogens) compared with the bond energies of Cl_2 and F_2, indicates about 30 per cent ionic character for the molecule.[46] Other calculations indicate that the ionic nature may be somewhat less (only 20 per cent).[47]

The infrared spectrum of chlorine monofluoride has been reported. A grating spectrometer was used in resolving the vibrational-rotational fine structure of the fundamental and first overtone. The values found for ω_e and $\chi_e\omega_e$ for $^{35}Cl^{19}F$ and $^{37}Cl^{19}F$ are 786.34 and 6.23, and 778.82 and 6.11 cm^{-1}, respectively.[48]

6. *Bromine monofluoride, BrF.* Bromine monofluoride is a pale redbrown gas at ordinary temperatures. On cooling, a dark red liquid first forms followed by leaflet crystals with the red-orange color of potassium dichromate. Due to the instability of BrF, the physical constants are of questionable accuracy. The boiling point is about 20°C as estimated by the extrapolation of the vapor pressure curve. The melting point is about $-33°C$. At 50°C, BrF decomposes spontaneously to BrF_3, BrF_5, and Br_2. The monofluoride is more reactive than the tri- or pentafluoride.

The heat of dissociation for bromine monofluoride is calculated to be either 59.9 or 50.3 kcal (± 1 per cent), depending on whether normal fluorine and excited bromine or normal bromine and excited fluorine are

[43] E. B. Maxted, *op. cit.*, p. 149.

[44] E. Wicke, *Nachr. Akad. Wiss. Gottingen. Math.-physik Klasse,* **1946**, 89.

[45] H. S. Schumacher *et al., Anales Asoc. quím. argentina* **38**, 98 (1950); A. G. Sharpe, *Quart. Revs., (London)* **4**, 115 (1950).

[46] L. Pauling, *The Nature of the Chemical Bond*, 2nd Ed., Cornell Univ. Press, Ithaca, N. Y., 1942.

[47] D. A. Gilbert *et al., Phys. Rev.* **76**, 1723 (1949).

[48] A. H. Nielsen and E. A. Jones, *J. Chem. Phys.* **19**, 1117 (1951).

formed.[49] The bond energy is approximately 60.6, indicating a smaller ionic character for BrF than for ClF. An absorption band at 3250 A indicates a vibrational fine structure. Electron diffraction data indicate a distance of 1.78 A for the Br-F atoms. This figure is somewhat less than the value of 1.81 A calculated from the sum of atomic radii.[50]

Bromine monofluoride reacts with all massive metals; however, the intensity of the reaction depends on the stability of the fluoride coating. Hydrogen reacts if first heated. Elemental bromine and iodine react with ClF to form a mixture of the interhalogen compounds, BrF_3 and IF_5. Sulfur reacts slowly while phosphorus burns vigorously. Ozone and oxygen are formed when chlorine monofluoride is added to water. Carbon monoxide and sulfur dioxide react with the monofluoride on warming.

Type AB₃. The known members of this group of interhalogens are chlorine trifluoride, ClF_3, bromine trifluoride, BrF_3, and iodine trichloride, ICl_3. Some evidence is offered for iodine tribromide, IBr_3. The first of these compounds is the most important of the interhalogens from an industrial standpoint. All the trifluorides are oxidizing agents. Their oxidizing power increases in the order $I^{+3} < Br^{+3} < Cl^{+3}$, which is the reverse of the order of the stabilities of their compounds. The trivalent halogen is reduced either to a free halogen or to a halide ion. The existence of IBr_3 is indicated, but the compound has not been isolated.[51]

1. *Chlorine trifluoride, ClF_3.* This compound is produced in rather low yields by the direct combination of the elements. Three volumes of fluorine and two volumes of chlorine combine to form one volume of the trifluoride and four volumes of the monofluoride. The separation of the trifluoride (bp 11.3°C) from the monofluoride (bp −100.8°C) is accomplished by cooling the vapors of the reaction product to about −80°C. Hydrogen fluoride, as an impurity, is removed by passing the ClF_3 vapor over sodium fluoride pellets. Final purification is accomplished by fractional distillation. Gaseous ClF_3 is colorless, the liquid is pale green, and the solid (mp −83°C) is white. The vapor pressure of the liquid follows the relationship $\log p = 7.42 − 1.292 \times 10^3/T$. The calculated critical temperature is 153.5°C. The density of liquid ClF_3 under its own vapor pressure over the temperature range −5° to +46°C is represented by the equation:[52]

$$d_4{}^t = 1.8853 − 2.942 \times 10^{-3}\, t − 3.79 \times 10^{-6} t^2$$

[49] H. Schmitz and H. J. Schumacher, *Z. Naturforsch.* **2a**, 359 (1947).
[50] M. T. Rogers *et al.*, *Abstracts, 111th Meeting of the American Chemical Society*, April, 1947, p. 21P.
[51] J. H. Faull and G. S. Forbes, *J. Am. Chem. Soc.* **55**, 1820–1830 (1933).
[52] A. A. Banks and A. J. Rudge, *J. Chem. Soc.* **1950**, 191.

The surface tension values of chlorine trifluoride as determined by the method of capillary rise over the temperature range 0 to 50°C are expressed by the equation

$$\nu_t = 26.7 - 0.16t \pm 0.2 \text{ dyne/cm}$$

The parachor for ClF_3 is 111.5.   The viscosity at 20°C is 4.35 millipoise.[ˡ]

The Raman and infrared spectra indicate the association of chlorine trifluoride to $(ClF_3)_2$ at pressures of 300 to 800 mm.[54]   Light absorption for chlorine trifluoride begins at 4700 A and slowly increases with decreasing wave lengths. A sharp rise in absorption begins at 2600 A. No maximum occurs at wave lengths over 2200 A.[55]

Vibrational assignments have been reported in conformance with a pyramidal structure; however, microwave data are not in accord with such a structure.   Reasonable assignments for the Cl-F stretching from microwave data are 508, 644, and 750 cm^{-1}; planar bendings are 316 and 428 cm^{-1}; out of the plane bending is 395 cm^{-1}.[56]   Among the structures assigned is a planar "T" with the chlorine atoms at the intersection of two arms.   The two similar Cl-F bonds (1.70 A) are longer than the unique Cl-F bond (1.56 A).   The moments of inertia are reported for I_1, I_2, and I_3 as 61.0×10^{-40}, 182.0×10^{-40}, and 243.0×10^{-40} g cm respectively, with a symmetry number of $\sigma = 2$.[57]   It is doubtful that the molecule is either planar or pyramidal.   It may be asymmetrical or associated in the liquid state.[58]   X-ray analysis[59] on a single crystal of ClF_3 has added to the knowledge of structure of this compound.   The crystal is reported as being orthorhombic with a, b, and c distances of 8.825 ± 0.01, 6.09 ± 0.01, and 4.52 ± 0.01 A, respectively.   The planar point group symmetry is mm. The chlorine atom is bonded to one fluorine atom at 1.621 A and to two fluorine atoms at 1.716 A.   The F—Cl—F bond angle from the x-ray data is 86°59'.   These x-ray data are not in complete accord with the microwave data just noted nor with somewhat more recent microwave data. The short Cl—F distance by this latter method is reported as 1.598 A and the two long Cl—F$^-$ bonds are 1.698 A. The bond angle (F—Cl—F) is 87°29'.[60]

[53] A. A. Banks et al., J. Chem. Soc. 1953, 732.

[54] E. A. Jones et al., J. Chem. Phys. 17, 501 (1949); K. Schafer and E. Wicke, Z. Elektrochem. 52, 205 (1948).

[55] H. Schmitz and H. J. Schumacher, Z. Naturforsch. 2a, 363 (1947).

[56] A. Weber and S. Ferigle, J. Chem. Phys. 20, 1497 (1952).

[57] M. D. Scheer, J. Chem. Phys. 20, 924 (1952).

[58] A. G. Sharpe, Quart. Revs., (London) 4, 115 (1950); E. A. Jones et al., J. Chem. Phys. 17, 501 (1949).

[59] R. Burbank and F. N. Bensey, J. Chem. Phys. 21, 602 (1953).

[60] D. F. Smith, J. Chem. Phys. 21, 609 (1953).

A reported value of the Trouton constant (20.8) is not in accord with any high degree of dimerization in the liquid state. Dimerization in the gaseous state is known, and the Trouton constant need not be a true indiation of the state of aggregation. Dielectric constant measurements at 400 Mc/sec are reported with a dimer molar polarization of 49.8 cc (no dipole moment being assumed). The monomer molar polarization is epresented (in cc) by

$$P = 15.944 + 1882.0/T$$

correcting for the amount of dimer and assuming a dipole moment of 1.554D.[61]

Assuming that the ICl_3 molecule dissociates into the ICl_2^+ and ICl_4^- ons, structures may be assigned in terms of analogous ions with similar inpaired electron systems. The unshared pair (or pairs) may be conidered as occupying one or more of the corners in polyhedral structures. Thus, in an ion, such as ICl_4^-, the four chlorine atoms may be located at he corners of a square and the iodine in the center. Two unshared pairs of electrons, one pair above and one pair below the plane, complete an octahedron. A trigonal bipyramid is suggested for the ion $ClICl^+$, in which three unshared pairs of electrons are involved.[62] The structure of chlorine trifluoride molecule with its three pairs of shared and two pairs of unshared electrons may be developed from similar considerations:

Some thermodynamic numerical data have been reported on chlorine trifluoride.[63]

The heats of dissociation at 0°C and 298°C for the reaction $ClF_3 \rightarrow ClF + F_2$ are calculated from Raman data to be $\Delta H_0^0 = 25.5 \pm 0.5$ and $\Delta H^0{}_{298} = 26.5 \pm 0.5$ kcal/mol. The heat of reaction for $2ClF_3 \rightarrow (ClF_3)_2$ is calculated as 3.3 ± 0.5 kcal. The equilibrium constants for he system $K = p_{ClF} \cdot p_{F_2}/p_{ClF_3}$ are 2.98×10^{-4}, 24×10^{-4}, and 143×10^{-4}, respectively, at 200, 300, and 350°C.[64]

[61] D. W. Magnuson, *J. Chem. Phys.* 20, 229 (1952).

[62] Fessenden, *loc. cit.* (Ref. 16); Pauling, *op. cit.* (Ref. 46); W. G. Palmer, *Endeavour* 2, 124 (1953).

[63] Scheer, *loc. cit.*

[64] Schmitz and Schumacher, *loc. cit.*, p. 363.

TABLE 8.9. SOME THERMODYNAMIC PROPERTIES OF CHLORINE TRIFLUORIDE

$T^\circ K$	Free Energy $-(F^0 - E_0^0/T)$	S^0	C_p^0
284.91 (bp)	56.04	66.90	15.09
298.16	56.54	67.58	15.38
600	65.39	79.51	18.36
1000	73.16	89.16	19.29
1500	79.92	97.07	19.61

Complete exchange between $H^{18}F$ and liquid ClF_3 (as well as liqui
BrF_3, BrF_5, and IF_7) is reported after a 10-minute contact time. Fo
gaseous ClF_3 (as well as gaseous BrF_5 and IF_5), the exchange with H^{18}]
is complete within a contact time of 3 minutes at room temperature an
atmospheric pressure. No exchange is noted between ClF_3 and F_2 a
room temperature.[65]

At ordinary temperatures, chlorine trifluoride reacts with every ele
ment but nitrogen, the rare gases, and possibly platinum, palladium
chromium, and V2A steel. At elevated temperatures even the protectiv
fluoride coatings on metal surfaces do not prevent further reaction. I
this respect, the trifluoride is comparable to elementary fluorine. I
effect, the difficulties in shipping elemental fluorine are overcome by usin
chlorine trifluoride. The latter is easily liquefied. A steel cylinde
which would normally hold 4 lb of fluorine at 400 psi will hold 100 lb o
chlorine trifluoride. This amount of ClF_3 is equivalent to 61.7 lb o
available fluorine. The pressure is relatively low for ClF_3, decreasing th
safety precautions needed. The German High Command during Worl
War II recognized the potentialities of chlorine trifluoride, and advise
its use in incendiary warfare to neutralize "fireproof" fortifications.

The reaction between ClF_3 (as well as ClF) and gaseous hydrocarbon
is sufficiently stoichiometric that gas phase titrations are possible with
precision of 3 per cent[66] at the 95 per cent confidence interval. This ga
phase titration technique has been applied to ClF_3—F_2 mixtures, F_2
Cl_2—F_2, methane, and olefins in hydrocarbon mixtures with the describe
precision of 3 per cent.

Sulfur dioxide, hydrogen sulfide, and ammonia all ignite in chlorin
trifluoride. No reaction occurs at ordinary temperatures with oxides suc
as ZnO, HgO, SiO_2, ZrO_2, and ThO_2, nor with salts such as NaCl, K_2SO_4

[65] M. T. Rogers and J. J. Katz, *J. Am. Chem. Soc.* 74, 1375 (1952); R. B. Bernstei
and J. J. Katz, *J. Phys. Chem.* 56, 885 (1952).
[66] S. Katz and J. I. Barr, *Anal. Chem.* 25, 619 (1953).

KNO_3, $HgSO_4$, and $HgCl_2$. Pure ClF_3 does not attack Pyrex glass. Selenium dioxide is converted to selenium oxyfluoride, $SeOF_2$, and selenium tetrafluoride, SeF_4. The compound SOF_4 is prepared from SO_2 and ClF_3. The fluorides AgF and CoF_2 are converted to AgF_2 and CoF_3, respectively. Chlorine trifluoride converts $CoCl_2$, $NiCl_2$, and AgCl to CoF_3, NiF_2, and AgF_2, respectively.[67] These three salts and HgF_2 are important organic fluorinating agents. At elevated temperatures, HgF_2, CuF_2, TiF_3, PbF_2, and PtF_4 are reported as being formed from their respective metals. Grey selenium gives SeF_4 (bp 102°C) and SeF_6.[68]

2. *Bromine trifluoride*, BrF_3. Bromine trifluoride is prepared by the direct combination of its elements. The gaseous product is condensed at 10°C, at which temperature bromine monofluoride and fluorine are not trapped. Purification from bromine is achieved by fractional distillation or by merely allowing the two liquids to separate; BrF_3 forms the upper layer. It also is formed when the bromides of certain metals are fluorinated:

$$MBr + 2F_2 \rightarrow MF + BrF_3$$

Liquid BrF_3 (bp 127.6°C) is colorless to greenish-yellow when it is free from bromine. It fumes in air and solidifies to greenish-yellow crystals at 8.8°C. The densities of the liquid and the solid are, respectively, 3.23 and 2.843 g/ml.

Certain physical measurements are reported on bromine trifluoride of 0.91 mole per cent purity.[69] The molal heat capacity in cal/deg changes from 1.279 at 15.32°K to 23.90 at 273.51°K. The heat of fusion is 2874.6 ± 3 cal/mol at 281.93°K (the triple point of BrF_3). Vapor pressure values up to 1800 mm follow the equation

$$\log p_{mm} = 7.74853 - 1685.8/(t + 220.57)$$

The calculated heat of vaporization at 125.75°C (the boiling point[70] of BrF_3) is 10,235 cal/mol. At 25°C the value increases to 11,370 cal/mol. The entropy of vaporization at 125.75°C is 13.14 cal/deg mol. The entropy of the liquid and ideal gas at 25°C are 42.57 ± 0.10 and 71.57 cal/deg mol, respectively.

Evidence is offered for both a planar and pyramidal structure of bromine trifluoride. The molecule, according to electron diffraction data, is pyramidal with a F—Br—F bond angle of 86°. The F—Br

[67] E. G. Rochow and I. Kukin, *J. Am. Chem. Soc.* **74**, 1615 (1952).
[68] W. Hückel, *Nach. Akad. Wiss., Göttingen, Math.-physik. Kl.* 1946, 36; **1949**, 55.
[69] G. D. Oliver and J. W. Grisard, *J. Am. Chem. Soc.* **74**, 2705 (1952).
[70] The boiling point of BrF_3 is also reported as 127.6°C (see Fig. 8.1).

distance is 1.78 A.[71]   The ionic species suggested from conductivity measurements are BrF_2^+ and BrF_4^-.   The former is angular rather than linear; the latter has been suggested as being planar with unshared electron pairs above and below the plane and perpendicular to it.[72]   The BrF_4^- ion, although similar to ClF_4^-, is probably smaller.   Evidence for a pyramidal structure is found in the Zachariasen rule.   An AB_3 molecule should be planar if the total number of outer electrons of all sharing atoms equals two or three times the number of electrons in the outer shell of the B atom following the inert gas.   If such is not the case, a pyramidal structure is expected.   Thus, for BrF_3 there are 28 such electrons, a number neither twice nor three times 21.

Elemental bromine dissolves in BrF_3.   The bromine in this solvent reacts quantitatively with gaseous fluorine.   An estimation of the latter is based upon this reaction.[73]

Bromine trifluoride is assumed to undergo autoionization.   This phenomenon is compatible with the high value for the Trouton constant (253).   In this respect it resembles water and ammonia:

$$Acid \qquad Base$$
$$2H_2O \rightleftharpoons H_3O^+ + OH^-$$
$$2NH_3 \rightleftharpoons NH_4^+ + NH_2^-$$
$$2BrF_3 \rightleftharpoons BrF_2^+ + BrF_4^-$$

The specific conductivity of BrF_3 at 25°C is 8.0×10^{-3} ohm^{-1} cm^{-1} in contrast to 10^{-6} for ClF_3 and 2×10^{-5} for IF_5.

The tetrafluobromides (e.g., $AgBrF_4$, $Ba(BrF_4)_2$ and $KBrF_4$) would be base analogs in this BrF_3 solvent system.   Corresponding acids containing the BrF_2^+ cation have been prepared.   Typical compounds (acids) containing this cation are BrF_2SbF_6, BrF_2NbF_6, and $(BrF_2)_2SnF_6$. Conductometric titrations of these acids with bases such as $AgBrF_4$ and $KBrF_4$ have been reported.[74]

$$BrF_2SbF_6 + AgBrF_4 \rightarrow AgSbF_6 + 2BrF_3$$
$$BrF_2NbF_6 + KBrF_4 \rightarrow KNbF_6 + 2BrF_3$$
$$(acid) \quad + \quad (base) \rightarrow (salt) + (solvent)$$

The gold analog, BrF_2AuF_6, of the acid, BrF_2SbF_6, has been prepared. Its decomposition at 180°C results in the formation of the previously un-

[71] Rogers *et al.*, *loc. cit.* (Ref. 50).

[72] Pauling, *op. cit.*; E. B. R. Prideaux, *J. Chem. Soc.* **89**, 316 (1906).

[73] H. H. Hyman and J. J. Katz, *Anal. Chem.* **25**, 1877 (1953).

[74] A. A. Woolf and H. J. Emeléus, *J. Chem. Soc.* **1949**, 2865.

known gold(III) fluoride, AuF_3. The acid, BrF_2AuF_4, undergoes a neutralization reaction represented as follows:

$$AgBrF_4 + BrF_2AuF_4 \rightarrow AgAuF_4 + 2BrF_3$$

Neutralizations involving anhydrides[75] are also reported:

$$VF_5 + AgBrF_4 \rightleftharpoons AgVF_6 + BrF_3$$
$$\text{acid anhydride} + \text{base} \rightleftharpoons \text{salt} + \text{solvent}$$
$$BrF_2TaF_6 + LiF \rightleftharpoons LiTaF_6 + BrF_3$$
$$\text{Acid} + \text{basic anhydride} \rightleftharpoons \text{salt} + \text{solvent}$$
$$VF_5 + LiF \rightleftharpoons LiVF_6$$
$$\text{acid anhydride} + \text{basic anhydride} \rightleftharpoons \text{salt}$$

The bromine trifluoride may act as a fluoride ion donor or acceptor in an acid-base type solvent system, in which the fluoride ion plays a role similar to that of the proton in water but of reverse charge. The solubility of alkali metal fluorides increases as the atomic size of the cation increases. As the oxidation state increases in a given series of the periodic table, the effective nuclear charge increases, and thus the tendency to lose fluoride ions decreases. A corresponding decrease in solubility of the metal fluoride occurs. For those metal fluorides which can act as fluoride ion acceptors, a rise in solubility is noted. Such is the case for Group V fluorides, MF_5, which dissolve in BrF_3 to give strongly conducting solutions.

Bromine trifluoride may serve as an inert solvent rather than as an ionizing solvent. Group VI fluorides as SF_6, MoF_6, and WF_6 appear to dissolve in BrF_3 in relation to their melting points.

The solubility of a few representative metal fluorides in BrF_3 are noted in Table 8.10.[76]

The solubilities of a large number of halides in bromine trifluoride as well as in I_2, ICl, and IBr are included in Table 8.11.

Two solvation type reactions involving BrF_3 are represented as

$$KPF_6 + BrF_3 \rightarrow KBrF_4 + (PF_5)$$
$$(PF_5) + BrF_3 \rightarrow (BrF_2PF_6)$$

[75] V. Gutmann, *Angew. Chem.* **62A**, 312 (1950); A. G. Sharpe and H. J. Eméleus, *J. Chem. Soc.* **1948**, 2135.
[76] I. Sheft, H. H. Hyman, and J. J. Katz, *J. Am. Chem. Soc.* **75**, 5221 (1953).

The compounds in parentheses are actually intermediate in the complete fluorination of potassium metaphosphate, the third step being

$$(BrF_2PF_6) + KBrF_4 \rightarrow KPF_6 + 2BrF_3$$

Another solvolysis is represented by

$$2KBrF_4 + (BrF_2)_2TiF_6 \rightleftarrows K_2TiF_6 + 4BrF_3$$

Nitronium compounds, containing the NO_2^+ group, result when bromine trifluoride and nitrogen(IV) oxide are mixed with tin(IV) fluoride or arsenic(III) oxide. The products in the two cases are $(NO_2)_2$-SnF_6 and NO_2AsF_6, respectively.[77]

TABLE 8.10. THE SOLUBILITY OF SOME METAL FLUORIDES IN BrF_3 AT 25°C

Type	Solubility ($g/100\ g\ BrF_3$)
Type MF	
LiF	0.125 ± 0.003
NaF	$2.08\ \pm 0.2$
AgF	$3.22\ \pm 0.3$
Type MF_2	
CaF_2	0.017 ± 0.0009
CuF_2	0.002
BaF_2	$3.53\ \pm 0.2$
Type MF_3	
AlF_3	0.0195 ± 0.0002
LaF_3	0.02
Type MF_4	
ZrF_4	0.0005
ThF_4	0.001
Type MF_5	
NbF_5	15.7 ± 0.01

There are many unusual reactions in BrF_3 resulting in the preparation of nitrosyl and nitronium complex fluorides and various fluosulfonates. Table 8.12 illustrates the scope of these reactions.[78]

Bromine trifluoride fluorinates such halides as CdI_2, $LiCl$, $AlCl_3$, and $FeCl_3$. With $CuCl$, $TlCl$, $PbCl_2$, and $CoCl_2$ a mixture of the higher and lower fluorides is obtained. Solid uranium compounds are converted quantitatively to volatile UF_6. Since no other naturally occurring element with an atomic number greater than 80 forms a volatile

[77] H. J. Eméleus, *European Scientific News, Office of Naval Research*, Jan. 15, 1950; A. A. Woolf and H. J. Eméleus, *J. Chem. Soc.* 1950, 1050.

[78] A. A. Woolf, *J. Chem. Soc.* 1951, 1053.

compound with BrF_3 in this way, a useful method of analyzing mixtures of uranium decay products is suggested. A possible exception is bismuth, whose oxide, Bi_2O_3, is fluorinated to a volatile compound.

A number of oxides and oxyacids react with BrF_3 (Table 8.13). Oxygen is liberated from CuO, B_2O_3, Tl_2O_3, SiO_2, GeO_2, TiO_2, As_2O_3, SeO_2, Sb_2O_3, and I_2O_5. Bromine is liberated and metal fluorides are formed in essentially complete reactions. Reactions are incomplete with BrF_3 and BeO, MgO, ZnO, CdO, HgO, CaO, Al_2O_3, SnO_2, PbO_2, and ThO_2. It would appear as if a volatile fluoride or a reagent-soluble

TABLE 8.11. SOLUBILITY OF HALIDES IN IODINE AND IN INTERHALOGEN SOLVENTS

Cation	Iodide in I_2	Chloride in ICl	Bromide in IBr	Fluoride in BrF_3
Li^+	soluble	slightly sol.	very sl. sol.	slightly sol.
Na^+	soluble	slightly sol.	very sl. sol.	soluble
K^+	soluble	very soluble	very soluble*	soluble
Rb^+	soluble	very soluble	very soluble	soluble
Cs^+	soluble	very soluble	very soluble	soluble
NH_4^+	soluble	very soluble	very soluble	
Cu^{+2}				insoluble
Ag^+		insoluble		soluble
Ag^{+2}				insoluble
Au^{+3}				soluble
Be^{+2}	insoluble			insoluble
Mg^{+2}	insoluble			insoluble
Ca^{+2}	insoluble			very sl. sol.
Sr^{+2}	insoluble	insoluble	mod. soluble	
Ba^{+2}	insoluble	insoluble	mod. soluble	
Zn^{+2}			mod. soluble	insoluble
Cd^{+2}				insoluble
Hg^{+2}	soluble			insoluble
B^{+3}				soluble
Al^{+3}	soluble	soluble	mod. soluble	insoluble
Ga^{+3}				insoluble
In^{+3}				insoluble
Tl^+	soluble			
Tl^{+3}				insoluble
Ti^{+4}		mod. soluble		soluble
Zr^{+4}				insoluble
Ce^{+3}				insoluble
Ce^{+4}				soluble
Th^{+4}				insoluble

* KI also very soluble.

TABLE 8.11—*Continued*

Cation	Iodide in I_2	Chloride in ICl	Bromide in IBr	Fluoride in BrF_3
Si^{+4}		soluble		soluble
Ge^{+4}				soluble
Sn^{+4}	soluble	soluble	very sl. sol.	
Pb^{+2}	soluble (?)			insoluble
Pb^{+4}				insoluble
V^{+4}		soluble		
V^{+5}				soluble
Nb^{+5}		soluble	insoluble	soluble
Ta^{+5}			insoluble	soluble
P^{+3}	soluble	soluble	very soluble	
P^{+5}		soluble	very soluble	soluble
As^{+3}	soluble			
As^{+5}				soluble
Sb^{+3}	soluble		mod. soluble	
Sb^{+5}		slightly sol.		soluble
Bi^{+3}	soluble			insoluble
Bi^{+5}				soluble
Cr^{+3}				insoluble
Mo^{+2}			mod. soluble	
W^{+2}			mod. soluble	
SO^{+2}		soluble†	insoluble	
Mn^{+2}				insoluble
Mn^{+3}				insoluble
Fe^{+3}	soluble			insoluble
Co^{+2}				insoluble
Co^{+3}				insoluble
Ni^{+2}			insoluble	insoluble

† Miscible in all proportions.

fluoride must be formed if the reaction is to go to completion.[79] Compounds of vanadium, chromium, and manganese are fluorinated by BrF_3. Thus $K_2Cr_2O_7$ and $Ag_2Cr_2O_7$ form $KCrOF_4$, and $AgCrOF_4$. Potassium permanganate reacts to form either $KMnF_5$ (pink) or $KMnF_6$ (yellow). Both of these fluocomplexes react with water to form MnO_2. Vanadium(V) oxide reacts with a mixture of NOCl and BrF_3 to form $NOVF_6$, a white powder reacting rapidly with water at 60°C.[80]

A violent reaction takes place between BrF_3 and NH_4F, NH_4Cl, KBr, or KI. Potassium fluoride reacts to form $KBrF_4$; AgCl and AgF give

[79] H. J. Eméleus and A. A. Woolf, *J. Chem. Soc.* **1950**, 164.
[80] A. G. Sharpe and A. A. Woolf, *J. Chem. Soc.* **1951**, 798.

TABLE 8.12. PREPARATION OF NITROSYL AND NITRONIUM COMPLEX FLUORIDES AND FLUOSULFONATES IN BrF_3*

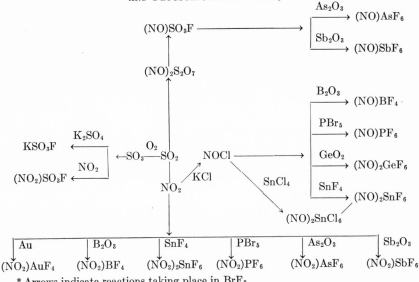

* Arrows indicate reactions taking place in BrF_3.

$AgBrF_4$; $BaCl_2$ yields $Ba(BrF_4)_2$. All of these polyfluocomplexes are stable at room temperature but decompose above 280°C. The compound $Ca(BrF_4)_2$ is so unstable it cannot be isolated in the free state. The complex $KBrF_4$ apparently is not a double salt of KF, since no lines

TABLE 8.13. BEHAVIOR OF OXIDES IN BrF_3

Oxide	Compound Formed	Per Cent Yield
BeO	BeF_2	20
MgO	MgF_2	25–30
HgO	HgF_2	7
ZnO	ZnF_2	23
CdO	CdF_2	30
B_2O_3	BF_3	100
Al_2O_3	AlF_3	7
Tl_2O_3	TlF_3	100
PbO_2	PbF_4	70–90
SnO_2	SnF_4	20
ZrO_2	ZrF_4	13
Sb_2O_3	$SbF_5 \cdot BrF_3$	100
As_2O_3	AsF_5	100
Bi_2O_3	BiF_3	41–87
SeO_2	SeF_6	100
I_2O_5	IF_5	100
MoO_3	MoF_6	100

attributable to KF are noted in the x-ray pattern. With water, $KBrF_4$ forms bromine, bromic acid, hydrogen fluoride, and oxygen. Platinum yields a brown solid which reacts with water to form K_2PtF_6. Iodine reacts with BrF_3 to form iodine pentafluoride and bromine. Sulfur forms a number of polyfluorides and polybromides (SF_x and SBr_x). On hydrolysis, BrF_3 is converted to a mixture of hydrogen fluoride, hydrobromic acid, and bromic acid. With dilute sodium hydroxide the products are oxygen, sodium bromide, and sodium fluoride. Lamp black burns readily in an atmosphere of BrF_3. Organic molecules are fluorinated by both BrF_3 and ClF_3 in a more easily controlled reaction than they are by fluorine. The present-day importance of the perfluorocarbons makes this reaction worthy of note.

Potassium metaphosphate reacts with BrF_3 yielding the hexafluorophosphate. The coordination number of phosphorus is increased from four to six. Potassium peroxysulfate and pyrosulfate give potassium fluosulfonate. The reaction with carbon tetrachloride yields the partly fluorinated products, trichlorofluoromethane and dichlorodifluoromethane. No iodofluoromethanes are obtained in the reaction between carbon tetraiodide and BrF_3.[81]

Metallic platinum[82] is not attacked by BrF_3 at room temperature; but, if the metal is converted into its tetrachloride, a vigorous reaction takes place on the addition of the reagent. A product of the empirical formula $PtBr_2F_{10}$ is formed. Rhodium tetrafluoride and palladium trifluoride yield complex fluorides; however, they are unstable toward water and have not been obtained in the pure state. Treatment of potassium tetrachloropalladate(II) or hexachloropalladate(IV) with BrF_3 gives a compound of the composition $K_2PdF_6 \cdot 0.1BrF_3$.[83] Rubidium and cesium chloropalladates under similar conditions with BrF_3 yield the pure compounds $RbPdF_6$ and Cs_2PdF_6, respectively. Gold dissolves readily on warming in bromine trifluoride with the evolution of bromine. A compound of empirical formula $AuBrF_6$ results on evaporation.

3. *Iodine trichloride, ICl_3.* This compound is also formed by the direct union of its elements. A solution of ICl_3 in HCl, stable for over a six-month period of time, has been prepared according to the reaction:[84]

$$KI + 2KIO_3 + 12HCl \rightarrow 3ICl_3 + 3KCl + 6H_2O$$

In the solid state the compound exists as lemon-yellow crystals which sublime at temperatures below 0°C. No accurate values for the melting

[81] H. J. Eméleus, *J. Chem. Soc.* 1948, 2188.
[82] A. G. Sharpe, *J. Chem. Soc.* 1949, 2901.
[83] A. G. Sharpe, *ibid.* 1953, 197.
[84] Ya. A. Fialkov and F. E. Kagan, *Ukrain. Khim. Zhur.* 18, 55 (1952).

and boiling points of ICl$_3$ have been reported because of the ease with which the compound decomposes to the monochloride and chlorine. Iodine trichloride is soluble in most organic solvents and dissolves in water with decomposition.

The high and nearly identical conductivities of both liquid and solid ICl$_3$ (8.4 × 10^{-3} ohm^{-1}cm^{-1}) indicate true electronic conduction probably attributable to the ICl$_2^+$ and ICl$_4^-$ ions. X-ray diffraction measurements prove the I—Cl distance in KICl$_4$ to be 2.34 A.[85] The structures of the ICl$_2^+$ ion and ICl$_3$ molecule are probably both planar. The latter molecule is suggested as planar with two pairs of electrons above and below the plane of the iodine and chlorine atoms.[86]

The velocity of the ICl$_3$ oxidation of H$_3$PO$_3$ to H$_3$PO$_4$ is comparable to that of the iodine oxidation of H$_3$PO$_3$. One mole of iodine trichloride in 15 liters of water is 76 per cent hydrolyzed and 83 per cent hydrolyzed in 100 liters of water.[87]

The conductivity of solid and liquid iodine trichloride has been measured over a range of 70 to 150°C. The conductivity of the solid increases rapidly with temperature. No marked discontinuity is found at the melting point. The maximum conductivity for the liquid is 9.6 × 10^{-3} ohm^{-1}cm^{-1} at 111°C. The ions accounting for the conductivity are probably ICl$_2^+$ and ICl$_4^-$.[88]

4. *Iodine tribromide, IBr$_3$*. A mixture of iodine and bromine in a stoichiometric ratio of 1:3 is used medicinally under the name "iodine tribromide." There is some electrometric evidence for at least a portion of the iodine and bromine being chemically combined in an IBr$_3$ molecule. Certainly most of the iodine is combined as the IBr molecule.[89] Iodine tribromide is described as a dark-brown liquid, soluble in water and alcohol.

Type AB$_5$. Two halogen pentahalides are known, BrF$_5$ and IF$_5$. In each molecule there are five pairs of shared electrons and one unshared pair.

1. *Bromine pentafluoride, BrF$_5$*. Bromine trifluoride may be used as a starting material in the preparation of the pentafluoride. A mixture of the trifluoride and fluorine is passed through a platinum tube at 200°C. The danger of explosion is greater by this method, however, than it is by the direct combination of bromine and fluorine in a copper tube at 200°C.

[85] W. G. Palmer, *Valency, Classical and Modern*, Cambridge Univ. Press, New York, 1948; *Endeavour* 12, 124 (1953).
[86] E. Fessenden, *loc. cit.* (Ref. 16).
[87] B. V. Soldatov and S. A. Voznesendkiï, *Khim. Referat. Zhur.* 4, No. 4, 32 (1941).
[88] M. N. Greenwood and H. J. Emeléus, *loc. cit.* (Ref. 28).
[89] J. H. Faull and G. S. Forbes, Jr., *J. Am. Chem. Soc.* 55, 1820 (1933).

Both the pentafluoride and trifluoride are formed in the latter process, but the differences in volatility are great enough to allow the more volatile pentafluoride (bp 40.5°C) to be separated from the trifluoride (bp 127.6°C) by low-pressure fractional distillation. A quartz apparatus serves for the distillation if the temperature of the distilling column is kept at 0°C. Excess fluorine is condensed in a trap cooled with liquid air.

The nearly colorless liquid BrF_5 freezes at -61.3°C. The vapor pressure of the liquid is related to the temperature according to the relationship $\log p = 8.0716 - 1,627.7/T$. The heat of vaporization is 7.443 kcal/mol. The density at the melting point is 3.09 g/ml and varies with the temperature according to the relationship, $d = 3.946 - 0.00346\ T$. The pentafluoride is stable toward heat. There is evidence of dissociation up to 400°C (about 0.1 per cent) from exchange studies.[90]

The rather high Trouton constant, 23.7, is indicative of some association; however, no association is noted in the vapor form from density measurements.

Raman measurements on purified liquid BrF_5 at λ4358 excitation show nine frequencies designated as fundamentals. Three of these frequencies are very strong. Infrared data are reported on the gas only. Two structural models are possible—one, a tetragonal pyramid; and the other, a trigonal bipyramid. The former is in accord with the nine Raman frequencies.[91]

Bromine pentafluoride is highly reactive, converting such oxides as WO_3, MoO_3, Cr_2O_3, P_2O_5, I_2O_5, As_2O_5, SiO_2, and MgO to the fluorides. It is likely, then, that any metal or nonmetal oxide might react. Sodium chloride and potassium bromide react to form chlorine and bromine, respectively. Bromine pentafluoride reacts with water to form $BrOF_3$ and HF.

2. *Iodine pentafluoride, IF_5.* This compound is one of the earliest known interhalogens. It was prepared in 1871 according to the reaction represented by the equation:

$$5AgF + 3I_2 \xrightarrow[\text{heat}]{\text{red}} IF_5 + 5AgI$$

Iodine burns in a fluorine atmosphere to form iodine pentafluoride as the predominant product, $I_2 + 5F_2 \rightarrow 2IF_5$. In an excess of fluorine, the pentafluoride is further fluorinated to IF_7. Fluorine reacts with metal iodides and hydrogen iodide to form iodine pentafluoride and either a

[90] Bernstein and Katz, *loc. cit.* (Ref. 65).
[91] T. G. Burke and E. A. Jones, *J. Chem. Phys.* **19**, 1611 (1951)

metal fluoride or hydrogen fluoride. The pentafluoride is purified by distillation in fused quartz. In the liquid state the compound is colorless and boils at 98°C. The freezing point is 9.6°C. The vapor pressures of the solid and liquid states are related to temperature according to the equations $\log p$ (solid) $= 11.764 - 3035/T$ and $\log p$ (liquid) $= 8.83 - 2205/T$, respectively. The density at 0°C is 3.75 g/ml. The heats of formation of liquid and gaseous IF_5 have been calculated from the heat of aqueous hydrolysis of IF_5 and heats of formation of HF, H_2O, and HIO_3. For $IF_5(l)$ the value is 204.7 kcal and for $IF_5(g)$, 194.6 kcal. A slightly different value (204.2 kcal) is found for the heat of formation for $IF_5(l)$ if the heat of alkaline hydrolysis is used:[92]

$$6KOH + IF_5 \rightarrow 5KF + KIO_3 + 3H_2O + 118.8 \text{ to } 119.0 \text{ kcal}$$

From vibrational spectra, the IF_5 molecule is assumed to be a tetragonal pyramid. Four fluorine atoms are at corners of the square base and the iodine atom and the odd fluorine atoms are on the fourfold axis normal to the base.[93] Compositions of bonds have been calculated for IF_5 leading to five tetragonal pyramidal bonds and seven pentagonal bipyramidal bonds. There are in all 21 configurations consistent with an established C_{4v} symmetry. Only the following satisfy all the symmetry requirements: sp^3d, fsp^3, sp^2d^2, fsp^2d, and fp^3d.[94]

Iodine pentafluoride is generally less reactive than the other interhalogens. It decomposes on heating to iodine and the heptafluoride, $7IF_5 \rightarrow I_2 + 5IF_7$. Silver, magnesium, copper, iron, mercury, and chromium are only slightly attacked by IF_5. Finely divided molybdenum and tungsten burn in it. Massive alkali metals undergo surface attack only in the cold but explode when hot. There is no reaction with dry hydrogen or oxygen at 100°C. Sulfur is converted to the hexafluoride. Phosphorus burns in an atmosphere of IF_5 forming iodine and phosphorus trifluoride. Chlorine and bromine do not react in the cold. On hydrolysis, iodic acid and hydrogen fluoride are formed according to the equation:

$$6H_2O + 2IF_5 \rightarrow 2HIO_3 + 10HF$$

The reactions of iodine pentafluoride with a number of inorganic substances have been investigated.[95] Iodine(V) oxide, I_2O_5, when boiled with IF_5 gives white crystals of IOF_3. These crystals decompose at 110°C to give IF_5 and IO_2F. The latter compound is a white, stable,

[92] A. A. Woolf, *J. Chem. Soc.* **1951**, 231.
[93] R. C. Lord *et al.*, *J. Am. Chem. Soc.* **72**, 522 (1950).
[94] R. L. Scott, *J. Chem. Phys.* **18**, 1420 (1950); W. G. Palmer, *Endeavour* **12**, 124 (1953).
[95] E. E. Aynsley *et al.*, *J. Chem. Soc.* **1953**, 623.

nonhygroscopic solid which slowly evolves HF in moist air and hydrolyzes in water to HIO_3 and HF.   When refluxed with IF_5, iodine dioxyfluoride gives IOF_3.   The oxide I_2O_4 dissolves in IF_5 to form IOF_3 and some iodine.

The oxides P_2O_5, V_2O_5, Sb_2O_5, Cr_2O_3, and WO_3 dissolve in hot IF_5 to give POF_3, VOF_3, $SbF_5 \cdot IO_2$, CrO_2F_2, and $WO_3 \cdot 2IF_5$, respectively.

Neither CO nor SO_2 reacts with IF_5.   Nitrogen(IV) oxide dissolves readily in IF_5 to give a cream colored crystalline solid, $IF_5 \cdot NO_2$.   This compound sublimes when gently heated but decomposes at elevated temperatures.   The addition compounds $KIO_4 \cdot IF_5$, $Ba(NO_3)_2 \cdot 2\frac{1}{2}IF_5$, $AgNO_3 \cdot 1/10\ IF_5$, and $Hg(IF_5)_2$ have been prepared.   Elemental silver is unaffected by IF_5.

Iodine pentafluoride is partially soluble in dry 1,4 dioxane.   An excess of the pentafluoride causes the precipitation of a complex, IF_5—$C_4H_8O_2$, which hydrolyzes immediately on contact with moist air.

Acid-base reactions are possible in iodine pentafluoride as a solvent. Two such reactions are indicated:[96]

$$SbF_5 + IF_5 \to SbIF_{10} \xrightarrow{\ KF\ } KSbF_6 + IF_5$$

and

$$BF_3 + KF \xrightarrow{\ IF_5\ } KBF_4$$

Sulfur trioxide and iodine pentafluoride form a constant boiling mixture with an approximate composition of $(IF_5) \cdot (1.17\ SO_3)$.   Neither IF_5 nor ClF_3 give polyhalide complexes in hydrogen fluoride.

The specific conductivity of IF_5 in HF at 25°C is reported as 1.53×10^{-5} ohm^{-1}cm^{-1} indicating some degree of ionization.   A positive temperature coefficient also indicates ionization:

$$2IF_5 \rightleftharpoons IF_6^- + IF_4^+$$

Potassium iodohexafluoride, $K[IF_6]$ is prepared by adding KF to boiling IF_5.   The complex is decomposed at its melting point (200°C) to give KF.   The hydrolysis reaction is represented by

$$K[IF_6] + 3H_2O \to K^+ + 6F^- + IO_3^- + 6H^+$$

Below a pressure of 1 mm the complex dissociates to IF_5 and KF.

The IF_6^- ion is suggested as having a valency shell of 14 electrons involving $5s^2 5p^6 5d^4 6s^2$ orbitals with but sixfold coordination.   Thus, the structure would be octahedral.[97]

[96] A. A. Woolf, *J. Chem. Soc.* 1950, 3678.
[97] H. J. Eméleus and A. G. Sharpe, *J. Chem. Soc.* 1950, 2206–2208.

Type AB$_7$. The sole representative of this type of halogen is iodine heptafluoride, IF$_7$. This compound is unique in that it is the only neutral, *simple* binary compound in which 7-coordination is shown. Thus, the iodine atom is large enough to accommodate seven groups of the size of the fluoride ion and to form seven single covalent bonds. Such a system is geometrically most unusual. Two fluorines are readily lost on heating. The existence of the resulting pentafluoride can be explained by available iodine orbitals. It is logical to assume a high degree of ionic contribution for both the penta- and heptafluoride molecules.[98]

Iodine heptafluoride is prepared by fluorinating the pentafluoride at 280–290°C.[99] The colorless gas, IF$_7$, has a musty odor. On cooling, colorless crystals are formed which melt under slight pressure at 5–6°C. The liquid has a density of 2.75 g/ml (at the melting point). The latent heat of vaporization is 7.33 kcal. The vapor pressure of the solid is related to temperature by the equation $\log p$ (solid) $= 8.6604 - 1602.6/T$. The vapor density is normal; however, the relatively high Trouton constant (26.4) points to some association. The values for $\Delta H°$ and $\Delta S°$ for the reaction IF$_7 \rightleftarrows$ IF$_5$ + F$_2$ are 28.5 ± 2.0 kcal and 43.5 ± 3.0 eu, respectively.[100]

The IF$_7$ molecule appears to have the structure of a pentagonal bipyramid. The iodine atom is situated at the center of a regular pentagon formed by five fluorine atoms. The remaining fluorine atoms are equally spaced above and below the plane on the fivefold axis through the iodine atoms.[101] The IF$_7$ molecule uses all the valence electrons for bonding (no unshared pairs). Of eight configurations allowed for D_{5h} symmetry, only two, dp^3d^3 and f^2sp^3d, utilize fully the 5s and 5p orbitals. Energetically any reasonable configuration should make complete use of these orbitals in preference to 5d or 4f. Both the dp^3d^3 and f^2sp^3d configurations are consistent with the structures of ZrF$_7^{-3}$ and TaF$_7^{-2}$, two experimentally observed arrangements with seven coordination.[102]

The heptafluoride reacts with all metals except the platinum group. The extent of reaction depends on the stability of the fluoride coating. Sodium, potassium, barium, magnesium, aluminum, and tin react vigorously. Sulfur reacts at room temperature to form polyfluorides. Selenium and tellurium require heat for their reactions with IF$_7$. Arsenic, phosphorus, boron, and silicon react at room temperature. The alkali

[98] E. B. Maxted, *op. cit.*, p. 154; G. C. Hampson and L. Pauling, *J. Am. Chem. Soc.* 60, 2702 (1930).

[99] W. C. Schumb and M. A. Lynch, Jr., *Ind. Eng. Chem.* 42, 1383–1386 (1950).

[100] R. B. Bernstein and J. J. Katz, *J. Phys. Chem.* 56, 885 (1952).

[101] R. C. Lord, *et al., loc. cit.* (Ref. 93).

[102] R. L. Scott, *loc. cit.* (Ref. 94).

hydroxides react to form iodates and oxygen or periodates depending on the thermal conditions. Water reacts to form periodic acid and the fluoride ion. Iodine reduces the heptafluoride to the pentafluoride. This action is essentially the reverse of the one by which the heptafluoride is formed:

$$\underset{I_2}{\overset{F_2}{IF_5 + F_2 \rightleftharpoons IF_7}}$$

Chlorine gives a mixture of ICl, ICl_3, and ClF but bromine gives no appreciable reaction. Hydrogen does not react at low temperatures, but explodes at elevated ones. Carbon monoxide burns in an atmosphere of iodine heptafluoride.

No stable compounds of the type $M(IF_8)$ are formed by the interaction of NaF, KF, or RbF with IF_7. Freon-12 (CCl_2F_2) reacts with IF_7 in the presence of an HgF_2 catalyst to form $CClF_3$ in 4–9 per cent yields.[103]

Exchange between IF_7 (as well as BrF_5) and F_2 is reported as being essentially zero at room temperature. At 300°C there is exchange. The equilibrium rate is represented by $-(1/t) \ln(1-f)m^{-1}$, where t is the time and f is the fraction exchanged.[104]

Polyhalide Anionic Complexes

The ability of halide ions to associate with one another, with one or more halogen molecules, or with an interhalogen molecule to form polyhalide anionic complexes has long been recognized. Alkali metal iodides associate with a molecule of iodine to form a soluble complex triiodide ion:

$$I^- + I_2 \rightleftharpoons I_3^-$$

Higher orders of complexes are also known up to I_9^-. A general classification of the complexes is suggested in the number of halogen atoms involved, as A_n^-, AB_n^-, and ABC_n^- where A, B, and C represent different halogen atoms. A partial list of representative members of these classes is found in Table 8.14.[105]

Some general properties are common to all polyhalides. Most of the complexes hydrolyze readily. The covalent-polar nature is manifest in their solubility in solvents of high dielectric constant, as alcohols and

---

[103] W. C. Schumb and M. A. Lynch, Jr., *Ind. Eng. Chem.* **42**, 1383 (1950).

[104] Bernstein and Katz, *loc. cit.*

[105] T. Moeller, *Inorganic Chemistry*, John Wiley and Sons, Inc., New York, 1952, p. 454.

TABLE 8.14. SOME POLYHALIDE COMPLEX COMPOUNDS

Type A_n^-	*Type AB_n^-*	*Type ABC_n^-*
$KI_3 \cdot H_2O$	NH_4IBr_2	$CsFIBr$
RbI_3	$KICl_2$	$RbFICl_3$
CsI_3	$RbICl_2$	$KClIBr$
CsI_4	$RbBrCl_2$	$CsClIBr$
NH_4I_5	$CsICl_2$	
$(C_2H_5)_4NI_7$	$CsClBr_2$	
$(CH_3)_4NI_9$	$(CH_3)_4NIBr_2$	
$KI_9 \cdot 3C_6H_6$	$HICl_4 \cdot 4H_2O$	

ketones. If the dissociation pressure is low, solubility in water is not unusual. Crystallization may be accomplished from this solvent. When a complex of the type MAB_n is decomposed by heat, the metal halide formed is usually the one with the highest lattice energy. Thus, the dissociation of $CsICl_2$ results in the formation of $CsCl$ rather than CsI.

Thermal stability of polyhalide anions is a function of symmetry. Comparing four such ions as $ClICl^-$, $BrIBr^-$, $ClIBr^-$, and $BrII^-$, the first would be the least, the last the most stable, and the others of intermediate stability. Size of the metal ion associated with a polyanionic group also influences thermal stability. In the alkali metal sequence, complexes of cesium are more stable than those of sodium.

The stability of the polyhalide anions formed in the solution of iodine in iodides, bromides, and chlorides decreases in the order: $[I_3^-] >$ $[BrI_2^-] > [ClI_2^-]$, with average values for K of 1.16×10^{-3}, 8×10^{-2}, and 2.9×10^{-1}, respectively. Table 8.15 includes the K values for a series of polyhalide anionic complexes $(X_2 + Y^- \rightleftarrows X_2Y^-)$.

Although a halogen molecule may be added to a polyhalide molecule (e.g., $KICl_2 + Cl_2 \rightarrow KICl_4$), it is not possible to add an interhalogen molecule to a polyhalide complex (e.g., $CsICl_2 + IBr \rightarrow CsIBrCl_3$). The latter reaction is not feasible, since the addition involves a change in sign of the more electropositive group. Specifically, a change of I^+ of IBr to I^- in the complex

$$Cs\left[\begin{array}{c} Cl^- \\ Cl^-I^+ \quad I^- \\ Br^- \end{array}\right]$$

takes place.

The equilibrium product formed when a halogen or interhalogen is added to a monohalide should depend upon the total composition of the system. The thermodynamics of two systems are considered:[106]

$$KBr + IBr \rightleftarrows KIBr_2 \quad (1)$$

[106] H. W. Cremer and D. R. Duncan, *J. Chem. Soc.* **1933**, 182.

and

$$KI + Br_2 \rightleftarrows KIBr_2 \quad (2)$$

A general classification of types is made on the basis of whether or not the starting materials are identical with the substances formed by spontaneous dissociation of the polyhalide. Since the lattice energy of KBr is greater than that of KI, the dissociation of $KIBr_2$ should result in the formation of KBr and IBr rather than KI and Br_2. In the reaction represented by (1), the polyhalide is readily formed if the pressure of the substance to be added exceeds the dissociation pressure of unchanged monohalide. Also the rate of formation of the polyhalide is approximately

TABLE 8.15. K VALUES OF POLYHALIDE ANIONIC COMPLEXES*

Formula of Complex	Value for K	Remarks
Br_2I^-	0.073	Very constant
ClI_2^-	0.28–0.30	Rises with increasing KCl or NaCl concentration
Br_2Br^-	No value	
Br_5^-	0.05	From the system $KBr + 2Br_2$
Br_5^-	0.031	From the system $NaBr + 2Br_2$
Br_5^-	0.37	From the system $SrBr_2 + Br_2$
Cl_2Br^-	0.83	
I_3^-	1.33×10^{-3}	
BrI_2^-	0.085	From the system $NaBr + I_2$
BrI_2^-	0.073	From the system $KBr + I_2$
ClI_2^-	0.30	From NaCl Rise with increasing NaCl or KCl concentration
ClI_2^-	0.28	From KCl

* I. M. Korenman, *J. Gen. Chem. U.S.S.R.* **17**, 1608 (1947).

proportional to the quantity of unchanged monohalide. The monohalide is assumed to be in a finely divided state. Surface formation of polyhalide on the monohalide has an adverse effect on the equilibrium. Small amounts of water have an effect on the velocity. Rising temperature increases the rate of formation up to that point at which decomposition of the polyhalide takes place.

The action of bromine (as well as chlorine) on alkali metal iodides varies depending upon the alkali metal ion. In the case of CsI, a direct addition takes place as represented by the equation:

$$CsI + Br_2 \rightarrow CsIBr_2$$

For other alkali iodides a substitution occurs, followed by a combination of products:

$$2MI + Br_2 \rightarrow 2MBr + I_2$$
$$I_2 + Br_2 \rightarrow 2IBr$$
$$MBr + IBr \rightarrow MIBr_2$$

The difference in mechanism is attributed to the high velocity of formation of $CsIBr_2$ and its low dissociation pressure.

A general classification of types of reaction between halogens on polyhalide ions has been suggested:[107]

1. A more electronegative halogen may replace a less reactive one in a polyhalide as $KIBr_2 + Cl_2 \rightarrow KICl_2 + Br_2$. In general, no intermediate products are formed. The reaction proceeds smoothly.

2. A more electropositive halogen may replace a less electropositive one in a polyhalide as $MBr_3 + I_2 \rightarrow MIBr_2 + IBr$. It is doubtful that the reaction is as simple as represented. Dissociation of MBr_3 to Br_2 and MBr is likely followed by a combination of Br_2 and I_2 to form IBr and finally the combination $MBr + IBr \rightarrow MIBr_2$ takes place.

3. A polyhalide may be converted into a monohalide without being influenced by the added halogen. The latter may merely act as an inert atmosphere.

4. A halogen or interhalogen may replace a halogen or halogen halide formed by dissociation of a polyhalide complex. An example is $MClIBr + ICl \rightarrow MClICl + IBr$. This reaction may pass through an intermediate stage (differentiating it from class 1): $MClIBr \rightarrow MCl + IBr$. Thermodynamically unfavorable reactions may be caused to proceed by an appropriate choice of solvent in which one or another of the products is insoluble.

5. A halogen may add directly to a polyhalide as $KICl_2 + Cl_2 \rightarrow KICl_4$. Interhalogens do not add directly to polyhalides (see p. 215).

6. Polyhalides may dissolve in liquid halogens or interhalogens to form solutions from which the original polyhalide crystallizes on evaporation. The polyhalides $KIBr_2$, NH_4IBr_2, and $RbIBr_2$ form a liquid solution in bromine. Conversely, $KICl_4$, $CsIBr_2$, $CsIBrI$, $CsBr_2$, $CsBr_3$, and $CsICl_2$ are unaffected in an atmosphere of bromine.

Isomerism in polyhalides does not appear to occur. The several instances reported wherein two forms of the same compound were formed depending upon the mode of formation are not valid.[108] Differences in

---

[107] H. W. Cremer and D. R. Duncan, *loc. cit.*

[108] H. L. Wells and S. L. Penfield, *Z. anorg. Chem.* 1, 83 (1892); F. Ephraim, *Ber.* 50, 1069 (1917).

color for two forms of $CsIBr_2$, for example, have been shown to arise only from differences in crystal size.

Principles of molecular orbital bondings (see also p. 213) have been applied to the polyhalide ions such as A_3^-, AB^-, ABC^-, and HF_2^- (where A, B, and C are halogen atoms). Molecular orbitals are formed from linear combinations of $np\sigma$ halogen orbitals and the 1s hydrogen orbital. Formation of an additional covalent bond in the A_3^- group provides an excess of electrons over the number required to fill the outermost fully occupied p orbitals of the X_2 group. At least one orbital of higher energy must be utilized.

X-ray studies of trihalide salts have been made for $CsICl_2$, $N(CH_3)_4$-ICl_2, NH_4I_3, and NH_4ClIBr.[109] The trihalide group is linear, although the I_3^- group may deviate from linearity by a few degrees. The central iodine atom does not appear to be equidistant from the end iodine atoms.[110]

Considerable data pertinent to the polyiodides are available. The triiodide of thallium is prepared from thallium(I) iodide, iodine, and hydrogen iodide. The triiodide decomposes to thallium(I) iodide and iodine through the intermediate phase Tl_3I_4. Dissociation pressures of certain polyiodides increase along the series: $Tl_3I_4 < CsI_3 < RbI_3 < KI_3$. The calculated standard free energy of $TlI_4^-(aq)$ is 40,340 cal.[111]

Two complex ammine polyiodides, $[Zn(NH_3)_4]I_2 \cdot I_x$ and $[Cd(NH_3)_4]$-I_2,I_x, have been investigated by thermal and electrical conductivity methods. The conclusions reached concerning the formation of these complexes are: (1) that the value of x is either 8 or 12 (that is, $(I_2)_4$ or $(I_2)_6$); (2) electrolytic characteristics of these two systems depend on the electrolytic dissociation of monomers and associated molecules of the polyiodides; (3) comparison of complex ammine iodide salts of Ni, Zn, and Cd with simple iodides of these elements shows the ability of iodine atoms to coordinate molecules of iodine in the formation of polyiodides.[112]

Iodine-iodide solutions have been studied by distribution measurements between carbon tetrachloride and water. Equilibrium constants for the reaction represented by: $I_2 + I^- \rightleftharpoons I_3^-$ are 768 ± 2 at 25.0°C, 590 ± 2 at 38°C, 490 ± 3 at 49°C, and 411.5 ± 2 at 63.05°C. Increase in heat content associated with the formation of I_3^- is markedly heat dependent. The heat content (ΔH) at 31.69°C is 3645 cal/g ion. Next to

[109] R. C. L. Mooney, Z. Krist. (A) 100, 519 (1939).
[110] G. C. Pimentel, J. Chem. Phys. 19, 446 (1951).
[111] A. G. Sharpe, J. Chem. Soc. 1952, 2165.
[112] Ya. A. Fialkov and F. D. Shevchenko, Zhur. Obshcheĭ Khim. 22, 1101; J. Gen. Chem. U.S.S.R. 22, 1143 (1952).

the triiodide formation, the $I_6^=$ ion formation assumes importance according to the equilibrium

$$2I_2 + 2I^- \rightleftharpoons I_6^=$$

The equilibrium constants are 6.2×10^{-5} at $25°C$, 3.8×10^{-5} at $38.38°C$, and 2.2×10^{-5} at $49.65°C$. The heat content of the $I_6^=$ ion is -7200 ± 600 cal/g ion.[113]

A polyiodide complex of the approximate composition KI_4 results when potassium iodide and iodine (in large excess) are agitated together for a long period. Radio-exchange studies prove that all the iodine atoms in the complex are exchangeable with the iodine of potassium iodide.[114]

Tetramethylammonium pentaiodide is prepared by slowly cooling a saturated alcohol solution of $N(CH_3)_4I$ to which a two- or threefold excess of iodine has been added. If larger quantities of iodine are added, $N(CH_3)_4I_3$ precipitates. Purification of the pentaiodide is accomplished by glacial acetic acid as a solvent. The pentaiodide possesses an end-centered monoclinic structure. Two I—I distances within each ion are 2.93 and 3.14, compared with 2.67 in the iodine molecule. The I_5^- ion bears no resemblance to the ICl_4^- ion. The I_5^- ion should be planar. It is suggested that the I^- does not use its d orbitals above the valence shell for covalent bonds. The I_5^- probably results from the interaction of iodide ions with polarizable iodine molecules.[115] The polyiodide phases Me_4NII_3, Me_4NII_5, and Me_4NII_{11} (where Me represents CH_3^-) were found to be stable in toluene at $6°C$ and at $25°C$. The phase Me_4NII_{10} was stable at $6°C$ and Me_4NII_9 stable at $25°C$.[116] An equation has been derived which permits the calculation of the value of n in a general reaction represented by

$$nMX + X_2 \rightleftharpoons M_nX_{n+2}$$

where M is an alkali metal or hydrogen and X is a halogen. It is

$$n = \frac{\log[(b-a)/(b'-a)]}{\log c/c'}$$

The term a represents the solubility of the halogen in water; b represents the solubility of the halogen in an RX solution of concentration c; and b' represents the solubility of the halogen in MX solution of concentration

[113] M. Davies and E. Gwynne, *J. Am. Chem. Soc.* **74**, 2748 (1952).
[114] D. Peschanski, *Compt. rend.* **230**, 85 (1950).
[115] R. J. Hach and R. E. Rundle, *J. Am. Chem. Soc.* **73**, 4321 (1951).
[116] H. W. Foote and M. Fleischer, *J. Phys. Chem.* **57**, 122 (1953).

c'. Experimental measurements have confirmed the validity of the equation for the system KI and I_2 to form KI_3 as well as KBr and Br_2 to form KBr_3.[117]

Although chaining is not expected of the halogens from their electronic structure, polyiodides of the formulas $[I_4^-]$, $[I_5^-]$, $[I_7^-]$, and $[I_9^-]$[118] appear to be formed by this mechanism. The cesium compound for which the formula CsI_4 has been written is diamagnetic. Therefore, the substance is more probably Cs_2I_8. The structure $Cs^+[I_3^- - I_2 - I_3^-]Cs^+$ is proposed.[119]

A positive trivalent iodine atom exists as part of the polyhalide complex $HICl_4 \cdot 4H_2O$. This compound is obtained when iodine is suspended in concentrated hydrochloric acid and treated with chlorine. The salts $KICl_4$ and $RbICl_4$ are prepared by the addition of the appropriate chloride. The ion ICl_4^- is one of the more stable of the polyhalide anions. This stability is attributed to the fact that iodine is surrounded by chlorine atoms—a large electropositive atom surrounded by small electronegative atoms. Phosphorus pentachloride interacts with iodine in solution to form a polyhalide complex of the formula PCl_6I as evidenced by an increase in the electrolytic conductance. The complex is assigned the structure $[PCl_4^+][ICl_2^-]$. The PCl_5 is assumed to oxidize iodine to the weakly polar interhalogen, ICl. The interaction of PCl_5, or $[PCl_4]Cl$, with ICl forms the complex $[PCl_5 \cdot ICl]$. Iodine does not form compounds with PCl_3, PBr_3, P_2I_4, or PI_5. The electrical conductivity of PCl_3—I_2 and PBr_3—I_2 mixtures is actually less than that of fused iodine.[120]

The dissociation of $[ICl_4^-]$ into $[ICl_2^-]$ is well established. The latter ion is relatively stable in aqueous and acidic solutions. A large number of transition-metal coordination complexes have been prepared in which both the $[ICl_4^-]$ and $[ICl_2^-]$ groups are ionically associated. Among these complexes are cis and trans $[Co(en)_2Cl_2][ICl_4]$, $[Co(py)_4Cl_2][ICl_4]$, cis and trans $[Co(en)_2Cl_2][ICl_2]$, trans $[Co(NH_3)_4Cl_2][ICl]$, and $[Co(NH_3)_6][ICl_2][IO_3]_2$.[121]

Compounds of the type $PX_5 \cdot IY$ (where X and Y are two different halogens) can be synthesized either by fusion or from PX_5 and IY in solution in such a solvent as carbon tetrachloride. Specifically, the compound $PBr_5 \cdot ICl$ is prepared by the latter method as cherry-red needle-

[117] A. K. Dey, *J. Indian Chem. Soc.* 24, 207 (1947).
[118] G. Bentruello, *Gazz. chim. ital.* 68, 394 (1938).
[119] S. S. Hubbard, *J. Phys. Chem.* 46, 227 (1942).
[120] Ya. A. Fialkov and A. A. Kuz'menko, *J. Gen. Chem. U.S.S.R.* 19, 812 (1949).
[121] P. Spacu and F. Popea, *Analele Acad. Rep. Populare Române, Ser. Mat., Fiz., Chim.* 3, *Mem.* 4, 38 pp. (1950).

shaped crystals of melting point 112.5°C. The compound is stable in sealed tubes, soluble in benzene, nitrobenzene, and carbon tetrachloride. Solutions in benzene and carbon tetrachloride are nonconducting and nonassociated. In nitrobenzene the compound is dissociated. A 2 to 4.6 per cent solution in nitrobenzene has an electrical conductivity of the order of 10^{-4} ohm^{-1}cm^{-1}. The complexes $[PBr_4^+][BrICl^-]$ and $PCl_5 \cdot IBr$ (a yellow substance of mp 140°C) have also been reported.[122]

When phosphorus trichloride is added to iodine monochloride, an intense exothermal reaction takes place. Analysis of the reaction mixture gives iodine and a yellow-orange product identical with the compound formed from iodine and phosphorus pentachloride, PCl_6I or $[PCl_4^+][ICl_2^-]$. The reaction can be represented by the stages,

$$PCl_3 + 2ICl \rightarrow PCl_5 + I_2$$
$$PCl_5 + ICl \rightarrow PCl_6I$$

or

$$PCl_3 + 3ICl \rightarrow PCl_6I + I_2$$

Electrical conductivity measurements again confirm the existence of the $[PCl_4^+][ICl_2^-]$ polyhalide complex. A similar complex, PBr_6I or $[PBr_4^+][IBr_2^-]$, is formed when iodine monobromide reacts with phosphorus tribromide:

$$PBr_3 + 3IBr \rightarrow PBr_6I + I_2$$

The same compound, PBr_6I, is obtained on mixing solutions of phosphorus pentabromide and iodine monobromide in carbon disulfide. Electrical conductivity measurements prove that iodine is transported to the anode while phosphorus goes to the cathode in accordance with the representation $[PBr_4^+][IBr_2^-]$. It appears, then, as if the systems PX_5—I_2 and PX_3—IX are conjugated.[123] Spectrophotometric studies of the PCl_6I and PBr_6I polyhalides complexes show the following dissociations in the nonpolar solvent, carbon tetrachloride:

$$PCl_6I \rightleftharpoons PCl_5 + ICl$$

and

$$PBr_6I \rightleftharpoons PBr_3 + IBr + Br_2$$

[122] I. D. Muzyka and Ya. A. Fialkov, *Doklady Akad. Nauk, S.S.S.R.* **83**, 415 (1952).
[123] Ya. A. Fialkov and A. A. Kuz'menko, *J. Gen. Chem. U.S.S.R.* **19**, 1645 (1949); *ibid.*, 797, 997 (1949).

In a polar solvent as methyl nitrile, the ionic dissociations

$$PCl_6I \rightleftharpoons PCl_4^+ + ICl_2^-$$

and

$$PBr_6I \rightleftharpoons PBr_4^+ + IBr_2^-$$

take place. A solvated complex $PBr_5 \cdot 2CCl_4$ forms when PBr_3 is mixed with bromine in carbon tetrachloride.[124]

The system $SbCl_5$ and iodine forms two compounds—$SbCl_5 \cdot 2ICl$ and $SbCl_5 \cdot 3ICl$. Electrolysis of nitrobenzene solutions of each of these complexes leads to the transfer of iodine to the cathode and antimony as well as chlorine to the anode. The ICl compounds with $SbCl_5$ are given the structures $I[SbCl_6] \cdot nICl$ where n may be 1 or 2. Fusion diagrams show no evidence for compounds of $SbCl_3$ and I_2.[125]

[124] A. I. Popov and E. H. Schmorr, *J. Am. Chem. Soc.* **74**, 4672 (1952).
[125] Ya. A. Fialkov and I. L. Abarbarchuk, *Ukrain, Khim. Zhur.* **15**, 372 (1949).

CHAPTER 9

THE PSEUDOHALOGENS (HALOGENOIDS) AND RELATED COMPOUNDS

General Considerations. A pseudohalogen is defined as "any univalent chemical aggregation, composed of two or more electronegative atoms, which shows in the free state certain characteristics of the free halogens, and which combines with hydrogen to form an acid and with silver to form a salt insoluble in water."[1] Cyanogen, $(CN)_2$, was the first example of a group which meets the above definition. It was isolated in 1815 by Liebig, who defined it as an "inorganic radical." Other examples of pseudohalogens which stimulated interest in this class of compounds are thiocyanogen, $(SCN)_2$, selenocyanogen, $(SeCN)_2$, oxycyanogen, $(OCN)_2$, azidocarbon disulfide, $(SCSN_3)_2$, and the azide ion N_3^-.[2]

The similarities between the pseudohalogens and the halogens are as follows:

1. They are in general fairly volatile.

2. They show affinity for metals, with which they combine directly to form salts.

3. The silver, lead, and mercury(I) salts are insoluble in water.

4. They form hydroacids some of which are highly ionized.

5. They are capable of forming interhalogenoid compounds such as $CN \cdot SCN$, CNN_3, etc.

6. They are prepared, in general, by chemical or electrochemical oxidation of the hydroacids or their salts, or by decomposition of the perhalides.

7. They form polyhalogenoid and polyhalogen-halogenoid complexes, such as $Cs(SeCN)_3$, $K(SeCN)I_2$.

From electrical conductivity measurements an activity series has been developed which permits a comparison with the halide ions. The stability[3] decreases from F^- to $TeCN^-$:

$$F^-, ONC^-, OCN^-, Cl^-, N_3^-, Br^-, CN^-, SCN^-,$$
$$SCSN_3^-, I^-, SeCN^-, TeCN^-$$

[1] L. Birckenbach and K. Kellermann, *Ber.* **58B**, 786, 2377 (1925); G. B. L. Smith *et al.*, *J. Am. Chem. Soc.* **56**, 1116 (1939).

[2] E. Soderback, *Ann.* **419**, 217 (1919).

[3] Birckenbach and Kellermann, *loc. cit.*; A. A. Woolf, *Chemistry and Industry* **1953**, 868.

The order suggested has little other experimental evidence as justification. Since iodine appears to be a stronger oxidizing agent than azidocarbon disulfide, the order of I^- and $SCSN_3^-$ should probably be reversed.

The position of the cyanogen radical has been determined in terms of the behavior of various cyanogen halides and the way in which these compounds ionize. The use of solvents can alter the order in the case of CNBr, due to solvation energy effects. It is estimated that the CN radical is between bromine and iodine in agreement with the order just noted. The interpseudohalogen halide, CNCl yields a positive cyanogen ion when it ionizes. Several pieces of evidence are offered for this ionization: (1) Although CNCl forms compounds with halides analogous to nitrosyl salts (as $CNCl \cdot AuCl_3$ and $CNCl \cdot BCl_3$), the high dissociation energy of CNCl and the high ionization potential of the cyanogen radical indicate that these compounds are unlikely to be salts in the solid state. These compounds, however, enhance the conductivity of CNCl, and that this increased conductance is not due to ionization of the halide itself in CNCl as a solvent is shown by the nonionization of the compound $AsCl_3$ which forms no compound with the solvent. (2) Electrolysis of $AlCl_3$ and $FeCl_3$ in CNCl results in anionic transference of the metal. (3) Cyanogen can be introduced into aromatic nuclei with $CNCl \cdot AlCl_3$. Cyanogen bromide behaves similarly, although exact data are difficult to obtain due to the ready polymerization of the compound in presence of the $AlCl_3$. The examination of CNI cannot be made in the absence of solvents due to the decomposition to iodine at elevated temperatures. In solvents the ionization is to positive iodine and negative cyanogen, or as iodine cyanide, $I^+ CN^-$.

Certain other reactions involving the formation and reactions of pseudohalogens are mentioned to illustrate the similarity between pseudohalogens and the halogens. Both substances add across the double bond of ethylenic compounds:

$$\begin{array}{ccc} \underset{|}{\overset{H}{\underset{|}{C}}}=\underset{|}{\overset{H}{\underset{|}{C}}} + (SCN)_2 \rightarrow & \underset{SCN}{\overset{H}{\underset{|}{C}}}-\underset{SCN}{\overset{H}{\underset{|}{C}}} \end{array}$$

"Hypopseudohalites" are formed by the action of a pseudohalogen on an alkali as represented by

$$(CN)_2 + 2OH^- \rightarrow CN^- + OCN^- + H_2O$$

The "hypopseudohalite" in this instance is the cyanate ion and may be likened to the hypochlorite or hypobromite ion. Certain of the heavy metal (in their high oxidation states) pseudohalides undergo thermal decomposition in an analogous fashion to heavy metal chlorides and bromides. An example is the decomposition of lead(IV) thiocyanate, $Pb(SCN)_4$, to lead(II) thiocyanate and thiocyanogen.

A possible reason for the similarity between the halogens and the halogenoids is found in a comparison of their electronic structures. The valence electrons of all the atoms in a halogenoid group can be arranged in saturated shells of eight electrons and an additional shell of seven electrons. Examples of such an arrangement are as follows:

$$N_3 = (5 + 5 + 5) \text{ or } 8 + 7 = 15$$
$$SeCN = (6 + 4 + 5) \text{ or } 8 + 7 = 15$$
$$CS_2N_3 = (4 + 12 + 15) \text{ or } 8 + 8 + 8 + 7 = 31$$

Oxidation potentials in acid medium are listed in Table 9.1 for certain of the pseudohalides and pseudohalogens. A few halogens, polyhalides, and halides are included for comparison.[4]

TABLE 9.1. OXIDATION POTENTIAL COUPLES IN ACID SOLUTION

Couple	E_o
$N_3^- \rightleftarrows \frac{3}{2}N_2 + e^-$	3.09*
$SCSN_3^- \rightleftarrows \frac{1}{2}(SCSN_3)_2 + e^-$	−2.75*
$HCN \rightleftarrows \frac{1}{2}(CN)_2 + H^+ + e^-$	−0.37
$2I^- \rightleftarrows I_2 + 2e^-$	−0.5355
$3I^- \rightleftarrows I_3^- + 2e^-$	−0.536
$2SCN^- \rightleftarrows (SCN)_2 + 2e^-$	−0.77
$2Cl^- + \frac{1}{2}I_2 \rightleftarrows ICl_2^- + e^-$	−1.06
$2Br^- \rightleftarrows Br_2(l) + 2e^-$	−1.0652
$2Cl^- \rightleftarrows Cl_2 + 2e^-$	−1.3595
$2F^- \rightleftarrows F_2 + 2e^-$	−2.65

* T. Moeller, *Inorganic Chemistry*, John Wiley & Sons, New York, 1952, pp. 466, 587.

The preparation, properties, and reactions of the pseudohalogens as well as certain of the pseudohalide ions are discussed.

Thiocyanogen, (SCN)₂. Thiocyanogen is best prepared by the oxidation of lead thiocyanate by bromine:[4a]

$$Pb(SCN)_2 + Br_2 \rightarrow (SCN)_2 + PbBr_2$$

[4] W. Latimer, *Oxidation Potentials*, 2nd Ed., Prentice Hall, New York, 1952, Appendix 1.
[4a] H. S. Booth, *Inorganic Syntheses*, McGraw-Hill Book Co., Inc., New York, 1939, p. 84.

Solutions of thiocyanogen may be prepared by oxidation of the free acid with MnO_2:

$$4HSCN + MnO_2 \rightarrow 2H_2O + Mn(SCN)_2 + (SCN)_2$$

Such a reaction is analogous to the preparation of chlorine by the action of HCl on MnO_2. Thiocyanates may be electrolytically oxidized to cyanogen at the anode in an alcoholic solution.[5]

In solutions less than one normal, thiocyanogen is dimeric, $(SCN)_2$. In higher concentrations there are higher polymeric forms. Solid thiocyanogen melts at -2 to $-3°C$. The liquid may be supercooled to a temperature as low as $-30°C$.

A solution of thiocyanogen in ether or carbon disulfide liberates iodine from iodides, oxidizes copper from the copper(I) to the copper(II) state, combines directly with metals, reacts with mercury diphenyl to form phenyl mercury(II) thiocyanate, reacts with unsaturated hydrocarbons to form addition products $[C_2H_4 + (SCN)_2 \rightarrow C_2H_4(SCN)_2]$, and with amines to form compounds analogous to the chloramines $[(SCN)_2 + 2NHR_2 \rightarrow NCSNR_2 + NHR_2HSCN]$.

Thiocyanogen is formed by the reaction of thiocyanates (either alkali metal thiocyanates or silver thiocyanate) with nitrosyl chloride in liquid sulfur dioxide at $-30°C$. An intermediate compound, nitrosyl thiocyanate, NOSCN, is formed first, $SCN^- + NOCl \rightarrow Cl^- + NOSCN$, but decomposes on distilling (to remove excess sulfur dioxide) the reaction mixture to form $(SCN)_2$. Purification of thiocyanogen is achieved by dissolving the reaction mixture (containing thiocyanogen) in liquid sulfur dioxide. A second distillation removes sulfur dioxide and leaves pure $(SCN)_2$. The thiocyanogen polymerizes on heating to form $(SCN)_x$. The compound $K(SCN)_3$ can be prepared by treating two moles of nitrosyl chloride with 3 moles of KSCN.[6]

An interpseudohalogen, cyanothiocyanogen, CNSCN, is formed by the interaction of thiocyanogen and mercury(II) cyanide.[7] Of the two tautomeric structures for thiocyanogen

$$
\begin{array}{ccc}
S-C\equiv N & & C\equiv N \\
| & \text{and} & \diagup \\
S-C\equiv N & & S=S \\
& & \diagdown \\
& & C\equiv N \\
\text{(a)} & & \text{(b)}
\end{array}
$$

[5] R. P. Cook and P. L. Robinson, *J. Chem. Soc.* **1935**, 1001.
[6] F. Seel and D. Wesemann, *Chem. Ber.* 86, 1107 (1953).
[7] Soderback, *loc. cit.*; M. Strada, *Gazz. chim. ital.* 64, 400 (1934).

the first (a) is the more logical. X-ray evidence points to a linear arrangement of the S—C—N atoms.[8]

A thioderivative of thiocyanogen with the formula $S_2(CN)_2$ is prepared from sulfur monochloride and silver cyanide:

$$S_2Cl_2 + 2AgCN \rightarrow 2AgCl + S_2(CN)_2$$

On thermal decomposition the compound yields $(CN)_2S$ and $(CN)_2S_3$.

A cold solution of thiocyanogen on treatment with nitrogen(II) oxide yields nitrosyl thiocyanate, $NO \cdot SCN$. Thiocyanogen adds hydrogen chloride to form two compounds, $(SCN)_2HCl$ and $(SCN)_22HCl$. Both compounds are prepared by passing dry hydrogen chloride into a cold $1M$ solution of thiocyanogen. Suggested anhydrous solvents for thiocyanogen are carbon disulfide, carbon tetrachloride, and ether. The dihydrochloride in aqueous solution hydrolyzes to $(SCN)_2H_2O$. Structures suggested for the monohydrochloride, dihydrochloride, and monohydrate are, respectively,[9]

$$N \equiv C—S—S—\overset{\overset{\displaystyle Cl}{|}}{C}=NH$$

$$HN = \overset{\overset{\displaystyle Cl}{|}}{C}—S—S—\overset{\overset{\displaystyle Cl}{|}}{C}=NH$$

and

$$N \equiv C—S—S—\underset{\underset{\displaystyle OH}{|}}{C}=NH \quad \text{or} \quad N \equiv C—S—S—\overset{\overset{\displaystyle O}{\|}}{C}—NH_2$$

Thiocyanate ion acts as a catalyst in the reaction between azides and iodine according to a study involving the measurement of nitrogen evolved under different conditions of pH, concentration of reactants, and temperature. A linear relation exists between the initial thiocyanate concentration and the total nitrogen evolved. The rate of nitrogen evolution is unimolecular with respect to azide concentration. The apparent activation energy for the reaction is 20.6 to 21.1 kcal. The conclusion reached is that thiocyanate ion catalyzes the consumption of azide by iodine and at the same time the oxidation of thiocyanate by iodine is catalyzed by azide ion.[10]

[8] Strada, *loc. cit.;* L. F. Audrieth and P. Walden, *Chem. Revs.* 5, 339 (1928).

[9] E. Soderback, *Ann.* 419, 207–322 (1919).

[10] P. Senise, *J. Phys. and Colloid. Chem.* 55, 1151 (1952).

Selenocyanogen, (SeCN)$_2$. This compound is prepared by methods analogous to those previously discussed for thiocyanogen; electrolysis of potassium selenocyanate in alcoholic solution, and oxidation of silver selenocyanate by iodine ($I_2 + 2AgSeCN \rightarrow 2AgI + (SeCN)_2$). When lead tetracetate is treated with potassium selenocyanate, lead tetraselenocyanate is formed. The latter salt is unstable and decomposes to give selenocyanogen.[11] Molecular weight determinations in benzene support the dimeric nature of the molecule, (SeCN)$_2$; however, in glacial acetic acid there appears to be considerable dissociation. The Raman frequencies of the salt KSeCN correspond to the vibration of —C≡N. It is concluded that the selenocyanate ion is Se—C≡N$^-$. This radical is isosteric with Br—C≡N and, since the latter is linear, it is reasonable to assume that the selenocyanate radical is linear.

Selenocyanagon is a yellow powder which turns red on standing. If kept dry and under pressure it is fairly stable. It reacts with water according to the following equation:

$$2(SeCN)_2 + 3HOH \rightarrow H_2SeO_3 + 3HSeCN + HCN$$

In carbon disulfide selenocyanogen forms $Se_3(CN)_2$ and $Se(CN)_2$.

Oxycyanogen, (OCN)$_2$. Potassium cyanate is oxidized by hydrogen peroxide in a neutral solution to form oxycyanogen:

$$2KOCN + H_2O_2 \rightarrow K_2CNO_2 + OCN + H_2O$$

Other oxidizing agents are suitable, such as copper(II) oxide and hypobromites. Nitrogen(IV) oxide is reduced by carbon at 150°C to form oxycyanogen. The compound is also prepared by a reaction represented by the following equation:

$$Ag_2O + 2CNBr \rightarrow 2AgBr + (OCN)_2$$

The properties of oxycyanogen are typical of any halogenoid. It liberates iodine from an iodide solution, reacts with metals, forms interhalogenoid and halogen halogenoid compounds.[12]

The NCO group is assumed to be linear in the calculations and evaluation of the parameter of HNCO. The C—O distance is 1.171 ± 0.01 A; the N—C distance is 1.207 ± 0.01 A; the N—H distance is 0.987 ± 0.01 A and the N—O distance is 2.378 ± 0.005 A. The angle H—N—C is $128°5' \pm 30'$.

[11] H. P. Kaufmann and F. Kogler, *Ber.* **59**, 178 (1926).
[12] L. Birckenbach and M. Linhard, *Ber.* **62B**, 2261 (1929).

Infrared spectral measurements of cyanuric acid, $(HNCO)_3$, agree with x-ray measurements in the ring structure but disagree in the periphery structure. The former (infrared measurements) indicate that the C—N bonds are all essentially identical, and from the C—N distances the ionic character of the bond is about 50 per cent. In contradiction to the x-ray evidence, it appears that all the C=O distances are nearly equal and not greater than 1.25 A. The small splitting of the carbonyl frequencies verifies this conclusion. The N—H$\cdots$O hydrogen bond distances are probably not all equal. The stronger bond appears to be formed in the case where the C=O and N$\cdots$O directions make an angle of about 124° with each other. The bonds parallel to the *b* axis must be lengthened corresponding to the shortening of the C=O distance. The N—H$\cdots$O distance is probably not less than 2.87 A.[13]

Silver isocyanate (or thiocyanate) reacts with the appropriate alkylchlorosilanes to yield such a pseudohalide as $C_6H_5CH_2Si(NCO)_3$. Other reactions involving the formation of isocyanates of silicon, phosphorus, germanium, and antimony are summarized as follows:[14]

$$SiCl_3(SH) + 4AgNCO \rightarrow Si(NCO)_4 + 2AgCl + Ag_2S + HCl$$

$$SiCl_2Br_2 + 4AgNCO \rightarrow Si(NCO)_4 + 2AgCl + 2AgBr$$

$$PI_3 + 3AgNCO \rightarrow P(NCO)_3 + 3AgI$$

$$3Ge(NCO)_4 + 4SbF_3 \rightarrow 3GeF_4 + 4Sb(NCO)_3$$

Alkali metal alkoxides react with urea in solution to form the alkali metal isocyanate as

$$MeONa + CO(NH_2)_2 \xrightarrow{\text{MeOH}} NaOCN + MeOH + NH_3$$

The reaction is favored by heat and pressure if the reaction temperature is higher than the boiling point of the solvent (MeOH in the above case).[15]

Azidocarbondisulfide, $(SCSN_3)_2$. The oxidation of an azidodithiocarbonate, $MSCSN_3$, by H_2O_2, KIO_3, K_2CrO_4, $HgCl_2$, $FeCl_3$, $KMnO_4$, MnO_2, Cl_2, Br_2, or I_2 gives azidocarbondisulfide, $(SCSN_3)_2$. The best yields are obtained by using iodine in a KI solution as the oxidizing agent. The metal azidodithiocarbonate is prepared from CS_2 and a metal azide such as NaN_3. Electrolytic oxidation of $KSCSN_3$ also yields the azidocarbondisulfide, $(SCSN_3)_2$.

The compound is a white unstable crystalline solid which is slightly soluble in water. On shock or impact, an explosion may occur, with the

[13] R. Newman and R. M. Badger, *J. Am. Chem. Soc.* **74**, 3545 (1952); E. H. Wiebenger and N. F. Noerman, *Z. Krist.* **99**, 217 (1938).

[14] H. H. Anderson, *J. Am. Chem. Soc.* **72**, 193 (1950).

[15] Ger. 812,251, Aug. 27, 1951.

formation of nitrogen, sulfur, and thiocyanogen:

$$(SCSN_3)_2 \rightarrow 2N_2 + 2S + (SCN)_2$$

Two tautomeric forms are suggested for the molecule, the first of which is probably the more likely:[16]

$$
N\equiv N=N-C-S-S-\overset{\overset{\displaystyle S}{\|}}{C}-N=N\equiv N
$$
$$
\underset{\|}{\overset{}{}}
$$

with the first carbon bearing $\overset{\|}{S}$

and

$$
N\equiv N=N-\overset{\overset{\displaystyle S}{\|}}{C}-\overset{}{S}-\overset{}{C}-N=N\equiv N
$$

Azidocarbondisulfide reacts slowly with dilute acids and rapidly with concentrated acids to liberate sulfur. There is no sulfur precipitation, however, on treatment with nitric acid. The azidocarbondisulfide resembles chlorine in its reactions with an alkali at a low temperature $(-10°C)$:

$$(SCSN_3)_2 + 2KOH \rightarrow KSCSN_3 + KOSCSN_3 + H_2O$$

When the above system is acidified, the azidocarbondisulfide is reformed:

$$KSCSN_3 + KOSCSN_3 + H_2SO_4 \rightarrow K_2SO_4 + (SCSN_3)_2 + H_2O$$

There is some evidence that the salt, $KOSCSN_3$, is converted to the chlorate analog of azidocarbondisulfide:

$$3KOSCSN_3 \rightarrow 2KSCSN_3 + KSCSN_3O_3 \text{ (analogous to } KClO_3)$$

The acid, $HSCSN_3$, is comparable to sulfuric acid in strength $(K = 2.14 \times 10^{-2})$, it is stronger than HF, HCN, or HN_3, but weaker than HCl, HBr, or HI.

Cyanogen, (CN)₂. Cyanogen is prepared by thermal decomposition of mercury(II) cyanide, the action of potassium cyanide on copper(II) salts, or by the decomposition of silver cyanide. The vapor density of $(CN)_2$ is 2.321 g/l at 19.4°C and 316.6 mm pressure. The boiling point is $-21.17°C$, and the melting point is $-27.9°C$. It is a poisonous colorless gas with a faint but distinctive odor. The structure is best represented by $N\equiv C-C\equiv N$ from parachor measurements and from its small dipole

[16] A. W. Browne, *J. Am. Chem. Soc.* **45**, 2541 (1923).

moment.[17] Its general chemical properties strikingly resemble those of the halogens. It decomposes in the presence of moisture and sunlight forming ammonium oxalate, ammonium formate, and urea. The silver salt is insoluble in water but dissolves in an excess of the cyanide ion.

The Azide Ion, N_3^-. The pseudohalogen, $(N_3)_2$, has not been isolated. The ion, however, bears a strong resemblance to the halide ions as well as to the halogens. The silver salts are insoluble, mixed halogenoids are readily prepared, and the azides show an absorption in the near ultraviolet region similar to the spectrum of iodine.[18] Hydrazoic acid, HN_3, is a typical halogenoid acid. Its dissociation is slightly greater than acetic acid as evidenced by an ionization constant of 2.8×10^{-5}. The azide radical combines with certain of the halogens to form halogen azides of the type XN_3, where X may be any of the halogens.

The structures for the azide ion and the N_3^- group in covalent azides are very different. In the latter type, three structures are suggested:

$$1. \quad \begin{array}{c} N \\ \| \quad N{-}R^{19} \\ N \end{array}$$

$$2. \quad R{-}N{\Rrightarrow}N \rightarrow N^{20}$$

and

$$3. \quad R{-}N \leftarrow N \equiv N^{21}$$

Structure (1) has some support in parachor and spectroscopic measurements, and structures (2) and (3) are better represented by the electronic arrangements

$$R{-}\overset{..}{N}{=}\overset{+}{N}{=}\overset{..}{N}:^- \quad \text{and} \quad R{-}{-}\overset{..}{N}{-}\overset{+}{N}{\equiv}N:$$

A third unstable structure $[R{-}\overset{+}{N}{\equiv}\overset{+}{N}{-}\overset{..}{N}:^=]$ probably has no contribution because of the adjacent positive charges. An unsymmetrical N_3^- group results with a smaller resonance energy and lower stability. The heavy metal azides are essentially covalent and unstable. The evidence points to a linear symmetrical arrangement for the ionic N_3^- group.

[17] Cook and Robinson, *loc. cit.* (Ref. 5).
[18] P. A. Levene and A. Rothen, *J. Chem. Phys.* **5**, 985 (1937).
[19] A. Hantzsch, *Ber.* **66B**, 1349 (1933).
[20] N. V. Sidgwick, *Trans. Faraday Soc.* **30**, 801 (1934).
[21] *Ibid.*

Resonating configurations are:

$$-:\ddot{N}{=}\overset{+}{N}{=}\ddot{N}:^- \quad =:\ddot{N}{-}\overset{+}{N}{\equiv}N: \quad \text{and} \quad :N{\equiv}\overset{+}{N}{-}\ddot{N}:^=$$

The configurations are of equal importance. The alkali azides are ionic and fairly stable.[22] It is interesting to note that the two compounds $NH_4^+N_3^-$ and $NH_4^+(F{-}H{-}F)^-$ are isomorphous.

Halogen-halogenoids. Halogens not only combine with one another to form interhalogens, but they also form compounds with the halogenoids.

1. *Fluorine azide, FN_3.* This compound is obtained by treating hydrazoic acid with fluorine in a stream of nitrogen. It is a greenish-yellow gas, liquefying at $-82°C$ and freezing at $-152°C$ to a greenish-yellow solid. On thermal decomposition of FN_3, nitrogen and a compound of the formula N_2F_2 are formed.

2. *Chlorine azide, ClN_3.* This compound may be prepared from silver azide and chlorine, or by the addition of acetic acid to a mixture of sodium azide and hypochlorous acid in aqueous solution:

$$NaN_3 + H^+ \rightarrow HN_3 + Na^+$$
$$HN_3 + HClO \rightarrow ClN_3 + H_2O$$

The resulting compound, ClN_3, boils at $-15°C$ and melts at approximately $-100°C$. It is slightly soluble in water and soluble in most organic solvents. Chlorine azide is highly explosive, decomposing at $400°C$ at 2 mm pressure to form chlorine and nitrogen.

With liquid ammonia two reactions are possible:

$$ClN_3 + 2NH_3 \rightarrow NH_2Cl + NH_4N_3$$
$$3ClN_3 + 8NH_3 \rightarrow N_2 + 3NH_4Cl + 3NH_4N_3$$

The latter reaction takes place with an excess of ammonia. Alkanes are chlorinated by chlorine azide:

$$C_5H_{12} + ClN_3 \rightarrow HN_3 + C_5H_{11}Cl$$

Active metals react violently to form their azides, chlorides, and nitrogen:

$$4ClN_3 + 6M \rightarrow 4MCl + 3N_2 + 2MN_3$$

The reaction may be controlled by using a nonaqueous solvent while phosphorus reacts with detonation even at $-78°C$. The violence may

[22] A. F. Wells, *op. cit.*, p. 404.

be due to the liberation of azine, the formation of an unstable phosphorus azide, or the formation of a complex unstable chloroazide. Chlorine azide reacts with silver azide to form a blue compound of the formula N_3AgCl, which decomposes below $0°C$:[23]

$$2ClN_3 + 2AgN_3 \xrightarrow{-78°C} 2N_3AgCl + 3N_2$$
$$2N_3AgCl \longrightarrow 2AgCl + 3N_2$$

3. *Bromine azide, BrN₃.* Bromine vapor reacts with sodium azide to give bromine azide:

$$Br_2(g) + NaN_3 \rightarrow BrN_3 + NaBr$$

The compound may also be produced by the action of bromine on either sodium or silver azide in an organic solvent (as ether or benzene):

$$Br_2 + MN_3 \rightarrow BrN_3 + MBr$$

Bromine azide is a mobile, volatile, orange-red liquid freezing to a dark red solid at $-45°C$. Its hydrolysis is represented as follows:

$$BrN_3 + H_2O \rightarrow HBrO + HN_3$$

4. *Iodine azide, IN₃.* Iodine azide is a light yellow solid formed by the action of iodine on mercury(I) azide, $Hg_2(N_3)_2$, in ether or benzene. Iodine azide is slightly soluble in water but decomposes in this medium rapidly even at $0°C$ to give I^-, IO_3^-, and N_3^-. Attempts to produce the dimer $(N_3)_2$ from IN_3 and AgN_3 result only in the evolution of nitrogen gas.

5. *The cyanogen halides, CNX.* The cyanogen halides, CNCl, CNBr, and ICN, are prepared from the desired halogen and an alkali cyanide:

$$X_2 + MCN \rightarrow CNX + MX$$

Ordinary methods fail to produce CNF. The reaction of CNCl with HgF_2, ZnF_2, and SbF_3 and with AgF do not yield CNF. By the use of BrF_3 with cyanogen halides and boric oxide, mixtures of nitrosonium and nitronium fluoborates are formed. Likewise no CNF is formed from the reaction of CNCl, HF, and BF_3. The preparation of cyanogen fluoride has been reported; however, only very small yields are obtained by the direct fluorination of cyanides with strong fluorinating agents of the type AgF. The point of attack seems to be the triple bond of the cyanide, since, in the large proportion of the products of the reaction, the carbon

[23] A. W. Browne *et al., J. Am. Chem. Soc.* **65**, 1696 (1943).

and nitrogen are separated. The Hoffman method for the preparation of CNF involves the sequence of reactions: $CF_3CO \cdot Cl \rightarrow CF_3CONH_2 \rightarrow CF_3N:CO \rightarrow CF_3NH_2 \rightarrow CNF$; however, the yield is negligible due to the surprisingly high stability of $CF_3N:CO$.[24]

All the cyanogen halides except CNF trimerize to form cyanuric trihalides. However, this tendency to polymerize may be related to the purity of the compound.

Table 9.2 gives data on the bond length, (r), of the CN and CX links in A, the atomic weight of $X, (A_x)$, the ionization potential of $X, (V)$, in electron volts, and force constant values f in 10^5 dynes/cm.[25]

Using the standard frequency-force constant relations for linear triatomic molecules[26] and known values (see Table 9.3) of force constants for CNF, the calculated frequencies for CNF are $\nu_1(\nu_{CN}) = 2294$ cm^{-1}

TABLE 9.2. DATA ON CNX COMPOUNDS

X =	H	F	Cl	Br	I
r_{CN}	1.157	—	1.163	1.160	1.159
r_{CX}	1.059	—	1.630	1.789	1.995
A_x	1.008	19.000	34.980	79.916	126.904
V	—	17.42	13.01	11.8	10.5
f_{CN}	18.07	—	17.61	17.80	17.94
f_{CX}	5.70	—	5.01	4.10	2.92

and $\nu_3(\nu_{CF}) = 1052$ cm^{-1}. Other thermodynamic data for CNF are reported at $298.16°K$: $-(F^0 - H_0^0)/T = 45.69$; $S^0 = 53.97$; $(H^0 - H_0^0)/T = 8.28$; and $C_p^0 = 10.18$.[27]

The freezing point of cyanogen chloride is $-6.90°C$, the molal freezing point lowering in water is $3.18°C$, and the heat of fusion is 2720 cal/mol. It reacts quantitatively with water in the presence of HCl:

$$CNCl + 2H_2O \rightarrow CO_2 + NH_4Cl$$

Without HCl the reaction is very slow.[28] Cyanogen chloride is very poisonous. It is formed in effluent sewage water during the chlorination of thiocyanates which are destroyed in normal treatment. Even a minute amount of CNCl is detrimental to marine life.

[24] H. J. Callomon et al., J. Chem. Soc. 1953, 3709.
[25] W. J. O. Thomas, J. Chem. Phys. 20, 920 (1952); 19, 1162 (1951).
[26] C. S. Wu, Vibrational Spectra and Structure of Polyatomic Molecules, Edwards Brothers, Inc., Ann Arbor, Mich., 1946.
[27] N. W. Luft, J. Chem. Phys. 21, 1900 (1953).
[28] D. E. Douglas and C. A. Winkler, Can. J. Research 25B, 381 (1947).

Cyanogen bromide reacts with sodium azide to give the interpseudo-halogen, cyanogen azide, $(CNN_3)_2$. In an ammoniacal solution, the latter compound undergoes a reaction represented by the following:

$$(CNN_3)_2 + 2NH_3 \rightarrow NCNC(NH_2)N_3 + NH_4N_3$$

Treatment with water gives cyanamic acid:

$$(CNN_3)_2 + 2H_2O \rightarrow CO_2 + 2HN_3 + H_2CN_2$$

The dissociation energies for CNCl, CNBr, and ICN from thermochemical calculations, based on a value of 100 kcal for C_2N_2, are 78, 68, and 58 kcal, respectively.[29]

There is some evidence that the iodine in iodocyanogen is positive in contrast to the negative nature of bromine and chlorine in cyanogen bromide and cyanogen chloride. The latter two, when boiled with potassium hydroxide, yield potassium bromide and potassium chloride, respectively:

$$\overset{+}{C}N \overset{-}{Br} + 2KOH \rightarrow KOCN + KBr + H_2O$$

$$\overset{+}{C}N \overset{-}{Cl} + 2KOH \rightarrow KOCN + KCl + H_2O$$

Iodocyanogen, on similar treatment, gives hypoiodite or iodate ion and the cyanide ion:

$$\overset{+}{I}CN + 2OH^- \rightarrow CN^- + IO^- + H_2O$$
$$3IO^- \rightarrow IO_3^- + 2I^-$$

The iodocyanogen or cyanogen iodide may behave as an electromer:

$$\overset{+}{I}\overset{-}{CN} \rightleftharpoons \overset{-}{I}\overset{+}{CN}$$

With hydrogen chloride, the iodocyanogen is converted to iodine monochloride:

$$ICN + HCl \rightarrow HCN + ICl$$

The reaction of ICN with water in dioxane and in aqueous solutions at 30 and 45°C is catalyzed by HCl. The products identified are ICl, I_2, NH_4Cl, and CO_2. The mechanism suggested for this reaction is as

[29] P. Goldfinger, *Bull. soc. chim. Belges* **56**, 282 (1947).

follows :[30]

$$ICN + HCl \rightleftarrows ICl + HCN$$
$$HCN + H_2O \rightleftarrows HCONH_2$$
$$HCONH_2 + H_2O \rightleftarrows HCO_2H + NH_3$$
$$NH_3 + HCl \rightleftarrows NH_4Cl$$
$$HCONH_2 + 2ICl + H_2O \rightleftarrows CO_2 + I_2 + NH_4Cl + HCl$$
$$2ICl + HCO_2H \rightleftarrows CO_2 + I_2 + 2HCl$$

Cyanuric Chloride, $C_3N_3Cl_3$. Cyanuric chloride was known as early as 1830. For many years, however, it was assumed to be an isomer of cyanogen chloride. Its versatility as an industrial chemical has only recently been recognized. The compound may be classed also as a *polypseudohalogen halide*. The triazine formula for cyanuric chloride is accepted with the chlorine atoms on carbon atoms as shown by the structural formula. Cyanuric acid and melamine must, then, be closely related to cyanuric chloride:

isocyanuric acid   cyanuric acid

cyanuric chloride   melamine

Cyanuric chloride may be prepared from chlorine, hydrocyanic acid, and hydrochloric acid by continuously chlorinating aqueous HCN in a reactor above which is superposed a wash column. Cyanogen chloride

[30] L. E. Bodnar and A. B. Van Cleave, *Can. J. Chem.* **31**, 923 (1953).

vapor may be catalytically polymerized to cyanuric chloride.   The latter is purified by passing the polymer over or through porous activated carbon.   Heavy metals are so removed.[31]

A large amount of physical data is available.[32]   Pure cyanuric chloride is a colorless, crystalline solid with a pungent odor.   The specific gravity is 1.32 and the melting point is 145.75 ± 0.05°C.   Crystallographic properties are summarized in Table 9.4.

The heats of formation ($-\Delta H_p$) at constant volume and constant pressure are 107 kcal/mol and 108 kcal/mol respectively.   The heats of combustion ($-\Delta H_c$) at constant volume and pressure are 294 kcal/mol and 293 kcal/mol, respectively.   The heat of vaporization (ΔH_v) is 11.2 kcal/mol at 100 mm Hg.   The heat of sublimation ($-\Delta H_s$) and heat of fusion (ΔH_f) are 17.3 kcal/mol and 5.4 kcal/mol, respectively.

TABLE 9.4.   CRYSTALLOGRAPHIC PROPERTIES OF CYANURIC CHLORIDE

Crystal system	Monoclinic
Axial elements	$a:b:c = 1.0176:1:1.5010$ $\beta = 83°50'$
Habit	Granular
Principal refractive indices	$N_X = 1.440$
	$N_Y = 1.740$
	$N_Z = 1.745$
Birefringence	$N_Z - N_X = 0.305$
Optic sign	Negative
Optic angles	$2E = 27°; 2V = 15°$

The infrared absorption spectrum of cyanuric chloride in mineral oil (Nujol) has been measured in the range 700–3800 cm^{-1}.   Certain of the frequencies observed are in the range expected of a benzene analog.   The ultraviolet spectra have been observed in methyl alcohol and cyclohexane.[33]   In the latter solvent a slight peak is observed at 2600 A. This band is believed to be due to a single-triplet transition, rather than analogous to the 2600 A absorption system of benzene.

No depolymerization occurs when cyanuric chloride is heated to 190°C.[34]   The compound is hydrolyzed readily by water vapor to various hydroxy triazines and hydrochloric acid.   At 0°C no hydrolysis takes place for some 12 hours.   At higher temperatures the hydrolysis is much more rapid.   When heated with 10 per cent aqueous sodium hydroxide solution at 100°C, the compound is hydrolyzed to 2-chloro-4,6-dihydroxy-s-triazine.   The third chlorine is not replaced below about 125°C.

[31] Brit. 667,825, Mar. 5, 1952; Brit. 674,813, July 2, 1952.
[32] New Product Bulletin, Vol. I, Revised Ed., 1952, American Cyanamide Co., New York.
[33] G. W. Costa, R. C. Hirt, and D. J. Salley, J. Chem. Phys .18, 434 (1950).
[34] H. E. Fierz-David and M. Matter, J. Soc. Dyers Colourists 53, 424 (1937).

TABLE 9.5. SOLUBILITY OF CYANURIC CHLORIDE AT 25°C

Solvent	Solubility (g/100 g Solvent)
Acetone	25
Acrylonitrile	19
Benzene	19
Carbon tetrachloride	7.5
Chloroform	20
Dioxane	55
Nitrobenzene	18

Cyanuric chloride is soluble in acetonitrile, ether, acetone, carbon tetrachloride, heptane, and acetic acid. It is practically insoluble in cold water but reacts with water at an appreciable rate above 10°C. Table 9.5 includes some solubility data for cyanuric chloride.

Cyanuric chloride may be considered as a nitrogen analog of acid chlorides, $\overset{O}{\underset{\diagdown}{\overset{\diagup}{C}}}$—Cl. As with acid chlorides, the rate of reaction of cyanuric chloride depends upon various factors such as solubility, temperature of reaction, and the nucelophilic compound taking part in the reaction. In addition, the reactivity of chlorotriazines is also dependent upon substituents on the triazine nucleus, just as the reactivity of acid chlorides is dependent upon the alkyl or aryl substituents:[35]

[35] American Cyanamide Co. Bull., *op. cit.*, p. 31.

Concentrated sulfuric acid ruptures the cyanuric chloride ring at 150°C. Complete hydrolysis takes place at this temperature as represented by the equation

$$C_3N_3Cl_3 + 6H_2O \xrightarrow[150°C]{H_2SO_4} 3HCl + 3CO_2 + 3NH_3$$

It has been reported that nitric and sulfuric acids hydrolyze cyanuric chloride to cyanuric acid at ordinary temperatures.[36]   Cyanuric chloride when refluxed with glacial acetic acid is transformed into cyanuric acid. Concentrated hydrogen iodide solution (67 per cent) converts cyanuric chloride to 2-chloro-4,6-diiodo-s-triazine.   Potassium iodide (in acetone), on the other hand, replaces but a single chloro group to form 2,4-dichloro-6-iodo-s-triazine.

Aqueous ammonia and cyanuric chloride react at 100°C under pressure to form melamine:

$$C_3N_3Cl_3 + 6NH_3 \rightarrow C_3N_3(NH_2)_3 + 3NH_4Cl$$

Aliphatic and aromatic amines react to form substituted melamines:

$$C_3N_3Cl_3 + 6RNH_2 \rightarrow C_3N_3(NHR)_3 + 3RNH_2 \cdot HCl$$

With the potassium salt of monosubstituted cyanamides, mono-, di-, and tricyanomelamines are formed:

$$C_3N_3Cl_3 + 3KN{\overset{\displaystyle R}{\underset{\displaystyle CN}{\diagdown\diagup}}} \rightarrow C_3N_3(RNCN)_3 + 3KCl$$

Potassium hydrosulfide reacts with cyanuric chloride to form the monopotassium salt of trithiocyanuric acid in good yields:

$$C_3H_3Cl_3 + 4KSH \rightarrow C_3N_3(SH)_2(SK) + 3KCl + H_2S$$

Sodium azide reacts in a stepwise fashion to form cyanuric mono-, di-, and triazide.   The latter is a powerful explosive:

$$C_3N_3Cl_3 + 3NaN_3 \rightarrow C_3N_3(N_3)_3 + 3NaCl$$

In general, cyanuric chloride undergoes Grignard, Würtz-Fittig, and Friedel-Craft reactions in the same fashion as benzene and its derivatives.

A wide variety of applications for cyanuric chloride (real and potential) present themselves.   The versatility of the triazine ring in dye-

[36] P. Klason, J. prakt. Chem. 34, 152 (1886).

stuff synthesis is well known. The three chlorine atoms on the ring permit the condensation of three different molecules. Three groups of dyes are derived from cyanuric chloride—azos, brighteners, and vats. Other applications are found in the production of mothproofing compositions, insecticides, surface-active agents, pharmaceuticals, plasticizing agents, tanning agents, resins and plastics, and explosives. In the latter instance, cyanuric triazide has certain advantages over mercury fulminate, however, difficulties are encountered in mass handling of the former.

Cyanuric chloride exhibits an intermediate order of toxicity. Internally it has a corrosive effect on the gastrointestinal tract.

Oxycyanogen and Thiocyanogen Halides. The oxycyanogen compounds may be prepared by the action of halogens on silver cyanate:

$$X_2 + AgOCN \rightarrow AgX + XOCN$$

Thiocyanogen halides are prepared from lead thiocyanate and the appropriate halogen:

$$2X_2 + Pb(SCN)_2 \rightarrow (XSCN)_2 + PbX_2$$

All the oxycyanogen halides form dimers: X_2N—$\overset{\overset{O}{\|}}{C}$—$N{=}C{=}O$. The halogen atom is assumed to possess a positive charge, which reverts to the halide ion when the oxycyano- or thiocyanohalides function as oxidizing agents.

INTERHALOGENOIDS (INTERPSEUDOHALOGENS)

These compounds are the halogenoid analogs of the interhalogens.

Cyanogen Azidodithiocarbonate, CN·SCSN₃. This substance is prepared by the action of mercury(II) cyanide on the pseudohalogen, azidocarbondisulfide, $(SCSN_3)_2$:

$$Hg(CN)_2 + 2(SCSN_3)_2 \rightarrow Hg(SCSN_3)_2 + 2CN \cdot SCSN_3$$

A second method avoids the difficult process of freeing the desired product from mercury(II) azidodithiocarbonate. The following equation indicates this preparation:

$$CNBr + KSCSN_3 \rightarrow KBr + CN \cdot SCSN_3$$

Cyanogen azidodithiocarbonate is a white crystalline solid, soluble in water at 0°C to the extent of about 1.5 g per liter. It is more soluble in organic solvents. It is more stable than azidocarbondisulfide and is less sensitive to mechanical shock. Heating it to 65–70°C in a restricted space, however, leads to an explosion. On long standing, cyanogen azidodithiocarbonate undergoes gradual decomposition even at room temperature according to the following equations:

$$CN \cdot SCSN_3 \rightarrow N_2 + S + CN \cdot SCN$$
$$x(CN \cdot SCN) \rightarrow (CN \cdot SCN)_x$$
$$CN \cdot SCSN_3 \rightarrow N_2 + 2SCN$$
$$x(SCN) \rightarrow (SCN)_x$$

Hydrolysis may proceed according to one or another of the two reactions represented by the equations:

$$CN \cdot SCSN_3 + 2KOH \rightarrow KSCSN_3 + KOCN + H_2O$$

or

$$CN \cdot SCSN_3 + 2KOH \rightarrow KCN + KOSCSN_3 + H_2O$$

The potassium azidooxydithiocarbonate probably decomposes with the formation of a chlorate analog of azidocarbondisulfide. Ammonolysis proceeds according to the following equation:

$$CN \cdot SCSN_3 + 2NH_3 \rightarrow NH_4SCSN_3 + H_2NCN$$

Cyanogen azidodithiocarbonate dissolves in aqueous solutions of potassium azidodithiocarbonate with the probable initial formation of a polyhalogenoid, $KSCSN_3 \cdot CNSCSN_3$ or $KCN \cdot (SCSN_3)_2$ corresponding to the polyhalide anionic complexes.[37]

Cyanogen azidodithiocarbonate is considered to possess a structure similar to that of an interhalogen:

$$N\equiv C-S-\underset{\underset{\displaystyle S}{\|}}{C}-N=N\equiv N$$

Cyanoazide, CNN_3. Cyanoazide is prepared by the reaction between cyanogen bromide and sodium azide:

$$CNBr + NaN_3 \rightarrow NaBr + CNN_3$$

It is a volatile, crystalline solid melting at 36°C. The general reactions of cyanoazide are those of a dimer:

$$2CN \cdot N_3 \rightleftarrows N\equiv C-N=C(N_3)_2$$

[37] L. F. Audrieth *et al.*, *J. Am. Chem. Soc.* **52**, 2799 (1930).

Cyanogen Thiocyanate, CN·SCN. The substance is obtained by the interaction of mercury(II) cyanide and thiocyanogen:

$$2(SCN)_2 + Hg(CN)_2 \rightarrow Hg(SCN)_2 + 2CN \cdot SCN$$

It may be prepared in smaller yields by the action of an alkali thiocyanate and cyanogen bromide. Cyanogen thiocyanate is a crystalline, volatile solid melting at 61°C.

Cyanoselenocyanogen, CN·SeCN. This compound is a decomposition product of selenocyanogen, $(SeCN)_2$. Its properties are similar to those of cyanogen thiocyanate, CN·SCN.

A large number of other compounds may be thought of as halogenoids and interhalogenoids. Sulfuryl azide, $SO_2(N_3)_2$,[38] and carbonyl azide, $CO(N_3)_2$,[39] are analogous to SO_2Cl_2 and $COCl_2$, respectively.

In certain respects, nitrogen tetroxide is an inorganic radical similar to the halogenoids. Its formation from nitrites, and the existence of compounds like nitroform, $(NO_2)_3CH$, and nitroxyl chloride, NO_2Cl, support the analogy.[40]

---

[38] T. Curtius and F. Schmidt, *Ber.* **55**, 1571 (1922).
[39] T. Curtius and K. Heidenreich, *Ber.* **27**, 2684 (1894).
[40] P. Walden and L. F. Audrieth, *Chem. Rev.* **5**, 355 (1928).

INDEX

Acidic fluorine chemicals, health hazards of, 18

Acids: bromic, 169; bromous, 169; chloric, 160–164; chlorous, 157–160; cyanuric, 228; hydrozoic, 91; hydrobromic, 119; hydrochloric, 115; hydrofluoric, 105; hydroiodic, 122; hypobromous 168; hypochlorous, 152–157; hypoiodous, 171; iodic, 172; metaperiodic, 174; nitric, 53; perchloric, 164; periodic, 173–178; sulfamic, 68; sulfuric, 85

Actinium series, relation to astatine, 96

Alkali metals, reaction of with fluorine, 22

Alkanes, reaction with chlorine, 66

Alkyl chalcogenide, fluorination of, 41

Allison, 95

Aluminum: action of fluorine on, 16; evaporation of astatine from 97; fluocomplexes, entropies of, 27; reaction of with fluorine, 22

Amorphous iodine, 80

Amphibole, 10

Antimony, reaction with fluorine, 22

Antiknock fuel, 71

Antimony-fluorine compounds, 36

Aryl-iodine complexes, 85

Asbestos, reaction with fluorine, 23

Astatine, 95–99

analytical studies of, 98; bromine oxidation of, 99; chemical properties of, 97; discovery of, 95; isotopes, table of, 7–8; metallic, disproportionation of, 97; migration of, 98; oxidation of 98; oxycompounds of, 99; physical properties, table of, I.1; preparation from bismuth, 97; production of, 95–97; reduction of, 99; volatility of, 97; volatility of from surfaces, 98

Astatine solutions: critical deposition potentials, table of, 98; extraction by CCl_4, 99

Azide ion, 231; resonance of, 232; structure of, 231

Azidocarbondisulfide, 229

Balard, 70

Benzene-iodine, complex nature of, 86; thermodynamic properties, table of, 87

Berthollet, 47

Bistrifluoromethyldisulfide, 32

Bistrifluoromethyliodophosphine, 34

Bleaching powder, 48, 155

Blowing-out process, 80

Bromates, 170

Bromic acid, 169

Bromine, 70–77

absorption on graphite, 75; as a solvent, 74; chemical properties of, 75–77; concentration of, 72; density of, 74; dissociation constants of, 74; electrolytic preparation of, 73; history of, 70; isotopes of, 75; isotopes, table of, 4–6; laboratory preparation of, 73; occurrence of, 70; oxides of, 145–147; oxyacids of, 168–171; oxysalts of, 168–171; physical properties of, 74; physical properties of, table of, I.1; physiological properties of, 75; positive ion of, 180; preparation of, 70–74; purification of, 73; reactions with hydrogen, 75; reactions with nonmetals, 76; spectra of, 74; vapor density of, 74

Bromine—chlorine system, 194–195

Bromine azide, 233

Bromine monochloride, 193

Bromine monofluoride, 196

Bromine(I) oxide, 145

Bromine(IV) oxide, 146

243